THE GYPSY FAMILY CIRCUS OF 1933

Stories from a Long-Gone Era

Gary G. Steele

Copyright 2019

Gary G. Steele

This is a work of historical fiction. Names, characters, or incidents are either based on the author's memory expressed in fictionalized form or are products of his imagination. Any resemblance to actual persons is coincidental.

Ordering Information: Special discounts are available on quantity purchases by corporations, associations, wholesalers, and others. For details, email the publisher at garysteelecircus@gmail.com.
www.garysteelecircus.com
Printed in the United States of America
First Edition
Library of Congress Control Number: 2018914513

Publisher's Cataloging-in-Publication data: Steele, Gary G.
Title: The Gypsy Family Circus or 1933: Stories of a Long-Gone Era / Gary G. Steele. Description: 1. Historical Fiction, 2. Ethnic Fiction, 3. Gypsy Literature, 4. Roma Literature, 5. Circus Fiction, 6. Great Depression Fiction

ISBN-13: 978-1-7335146-0-6 (Paperback)

ISBN-13: 978-1-7335146-1-3 (Ebook)

1 3 5 7 9 10 8 6 4 2

www.garysteelecircus.com

Printed in the United States of America
First Edition
Library of Congress Control Number: 2018914513

Dedication

*For Jo, with all my heart, the joy of my life and
the love of my life over the
decades. Bora chums, Darling.*

*And thanks to mandi's Romanichal fokie, jivin' an' mourraed,
my English Gypsy people, living and dead, for the stories and
wisdom you handed down and the DNA and heritage of which
I am so proud. Nais tuk, all you Rawnies an' Ryes.*

*With gratitude to friends and family who have taken time and
expertise to read drafts and make comments. This work is better and
reaches its goals more clearly thanks to your insights and generosity.*

TABLE OF CONTENTS

RUMNIS LANGUAGE GLOSSARY

AUTHOR'S NOTE

This work is historical fiction intended to have high historical accuracy, but for a range of reasons, some modifications have been necessary. They warrant an explanation.

The currently acceptable names for ethnic groups are mostly not used in the dialogues of the characters. While the most offensive terms are omitted, other terms have been retained. The terms "African American" and "Native American" were not yet in use in the 1930s. "Roma," as a politically correct term for Gypsies in any country, had not been invented.

Traditional gender roles and stereotypes show up frequently, as do instances in which characters go beyond the stereotypes. There is no intent to reinforce traditional gender roles or stereotypes. What is portrayed is life as it frequently was in the United States in the 1930s.

There is little reference to tobacco use, but in reality many adults smoked a pack or more of cigarettes per day or rolled their own. Tobacco was ubiquitous and cheap. There was little or no consciousness of its lethality. The author chose to minimize reference to a practice that has sickened and killed various family members.

First aid, medical practices, and midwifery have vastly improved over the years. What were common practices then may have actually been harmful. They are included as factual at the time. They are not intended as recommendations.

No reference is made to wearing helmets for horseback riding. It was not a practice in the 1930s; however, the author does not intend to make a recommendation against helmets. Anything that increases the safety of a sport is desirable.

School truancy as described in this work would now be illegal and may have been illegal at the time. There is no intention of describing truancy as desirable but rather simply factual. In the same vein, children working as circus performers could now be seen as against child labor laws in some states. It might even be seen as child abuse.

Currently there is a spectrum of opinions on animal welfare. Some people believe that no animals should be kept, trained, or presented and no meat should be eaten. Some people believe that reasonable and humane treatment of animals is legitimate and even desirable. In this work, the author intends to reflect the treatment of animals as done by a particular group of people at the time.

Interested readers should note that at the end of this work there is a glossary of *Rumnis* words used in this work and a basic explanation of the Gypsy language.

1. THE STORY TELLER

Once upon a time, many, many years ago, back when Hudsons and Studebakers still roamed the surface of the earth and Jeeps were still just cheap little military vehicles, there was a boy who was raised on a circus. He was a show kid, a child performer. It was a good life, a very good life. I know a lot about that boy because I was that boy.

We showed in most states east of the Rockies, across Canada, even to Alaska, and once on a long tour of Cuba. In the spring of 1943, my parents left a town in Florida to repair and pick up some circus equipment in a town in Ohio and continue on to a town in New Jersey where the circus opened on May 1st. I was born in the town in Ohio, the first child in the family ever born in a hospital.

There was a treasure chest of stories I heard. An early one I remember was how bad the drive from Ohio through the panhandle of West Virginia and across Pennsylvania into Jersey was. In those days there were no four-lane interstate highways across the Appalachians and the Alleghenies. The trip consisted of endless gear shifting going up mountains and braking going down on windy two-lane roads, too often with a small town and a cluster of traffic lights in the valley. The Pennsylvania state speed limit was 45 miles per hour, but that was a joke. A driver was fortunate to get up to 30 or 35 miles per hour. The trip across Pennsylvania took three days.

We had a family secret, a deep, dark, terrible secret. We were Gypsies, members of that tiny and maligned ethnic minority. There was so much prejudice in that day against races, ethnicities, religions, and orientations that it would cost us business if anyone had known. People held stereotypical ideas about us. They said we stole things, kidnapped babies, were dirty, and so on. Revealing our identity was a risk we could not take.

Mama was the granddaughter of English Gypsies who came to this country in 1863. They had always traveled on a circus or some other traveling attraction, such as a route of fairs or markets or horse races. Gypsies have come from many countries to the US, since there are Gypsies in so many places. But all our roots go back a thousand years to what is now India and Pakistan. We left there and have been wandering over dozens of countries ever since. Scientists have proven our Asian origin through DNA. Linguists have shown that the broken, pidgin-like language that we still speak has its origin in Sanskrit, just as modern Hindi and Urdu do.

My mother was born to a mother who was traveling,

who was born to a mother who was traveling, and so on. I suppose this explains how she nursed a newborn, dealt with dirty diapers, and got some sleep on such a cross-country trip to open the new season as a star performer with the circus in New Jersey.

Life as a circus child was so educational. Every day there were applied lessons in U.S. geography, road signs, map reading, money counting, and dealing with people in the towns we showed, not to mention living on a daily basis in a diverse community with people from many backgrounds and ethnicities. There was also the care, feeding, and training of horses, dogs, elephants, and so on. Of course I helped to present trained animals from a very early age. By adolescence, I had four or five spots in every circus performance. These were the years after World War II, and the country was booming. The circus could be at its best. Men were back from the war to be in their acts again. New cars, trucks, and tents could be bought, and people could pay higher admission prices.

Now, about story telling, Gypsies are inveterate storytellers, and I heard many stories about circus struggles during the years of World War II as I was growing up. They were fascinating. With every retelling new details would emerge. I loved that they all could start with, "When you were just a little bitty kid..." Yet even more than the war years, I loved to hear about how the circus and the family made it through the Great Depression of the 1930s. This was one of the saddest periods in American history. Farms were sold for almost nothing, and factories and mills cut way back or closed completely. Unemployment was twenty-five percent nationwide and higher in some areas. Armies of poor tramps and hobos wandered the roads not knowing when their next meal would be. They were just trying to stay alive. Nobody knew when it would end.

And yet, people loved entertainment. They went to movies when they could scrape the spare change together. When a traveling circus came to town, even if it was not quite as shiny and glamorous as it had been in the '20s, people wanted to see it. They wanted escape from the routine and the shortages of their daily lives. It was only realistic for shows to lower admission prices, and in some towns attendance was even better than before the Depression started.

So I am going to tell you the best circus stories in the era of the Great Depression. They are from the decade before I was born. I heard them as child at night sitting around a fire or on a lap, barely staying awake. They are really good stories. I have woven many of them together and combined different characters. After all these years, I still love those characters. Many of them are my family or my ancestors. I know that the audience reading these stories did not grow up Gypsy or on a circus, so I have put in details so that anybody can follow along, even somebody who never rode jumping horses or put up a bigtop. People love a good story.

I have been very *bocky* – very lucky, with a rich life. The stories I heard in the old days taught me so much. Almost any problem can be tackled. Find different angles to attack it. Creativity gets you a very long way.

Be alert, but if you treat people respectfully, they will usually treat you fine. The strength of the family can move mountains.

But I better get busy telling the stories. I am an old man now, with not too many storytelling days left. I better use that Gypsy storytelling gene I hope I inherited. It would be a shame if these stories and the people in them were lost.

So gather around, kids, sit by the fire, and I will begin. *Besh doy* by the *yarg, chavies. Shun* what *mandi's a-pukkerin'*. Listen to what I am telling you. And if I slip into *Rumnis*, our old Gypsy language, I will try to remember to throw in the English meaning, too.

2. THE CAST OF BREWER BROTHERS CIRCUS

Grandpa GR and Grandma Camie Brewer were the heads of the Brewer Brothers Circus clan. His real name was Gilderoy. One of his jobs was serving as a "fixer." This meant he smoothed things out when some kind of "beef" ever came up with the show sponsors, the local law, or any of the townspeople. And of course he served on the informal but very effective Brewer family counsel that ran the show. He was also a horse trader, and he kept a string of horses, buying and selling as he and Camie went along with the circus route. Madam Camille, the name she used with the public, was a professional fortuneteller, or *dukkermingra*. Her *dukkerin'* or fortunetelling tent was put up beside her trailer and GR's horse truck on the midway of the circus. GR and Camie were both born in England and came to the U.S. as young children. They had no formal education, but they were astute business people who could read contracts and handle business arithmetic competently. Worth mentioning is that in the 1930s most people had limited education, with many not finishing grade school.

Woody Brewer was the older son of GR and Camie. He and his wife Amy were flexible performers in the show as well as good managers. One of Amy's other roles was tracking the money, monitoring the income and outgo, the short-term and long-term accounting for the circus. Woody had lots of jobs, but one of the most important was working with the local circus sponsors each day, such as the Elks, the fire department, the police department, the Moose, the Shriners, the VFW, the Knights of Columbus, American Legion, or the Odd Fellows. Woody's warm manner and quick mind minimized problems and maximized the chances of coming back to show in the town again next year. Woody and Amy had three children. Gilly was the oldest. Mattie was next, and little Bart was the youngest. Like their parents, all three were performers, and all three had lots of chores to do around the show. They were good kids, *kushti chavies*, with lots of brains.

Their oldest son, Gilly, had done something that nobody in the family had ever done before. He was the first one to get formal schooling. At the place where the show usually spent the winter, his parents sent him to the local school. He had done quite well, and his younger relatives followed in his footsteps. Their school year started quite late, usually late October, when the show got in off the road; and it ended early, when the show would go out on May 1st for the new season. But the seven Brewer kids managed to be fine students.

Gilly was now in the summer before his senior year of high school, and the principal had told him that his grades were good enough for him to go to college if he did well in his last year. Gilly did not know what that really meant, nor did anybody in his family. They just felt it was a great honor. But Gilly felt that he would have to make a decision about staying in the traditional Gypsy life or leaving it to move over into the world of the *Gaudjas*, the non-Gypsies. This was a decision that weighed on his mind. He was torn.

Gilly had an uncle on the show, Uncle Lucky. Lucky Brewer was Woody's younger Brother. His wife was Tillie. Of course Lucky and Tillie were performers, too, in addition to everything they handled to make the circus run well. Lucky and Tillie could work almost interchangeably with Woody and Amy. At the drop of a hat, they could go over and sell tickets, meet with sponsors, switch acts, or drive a different truck. They had four kids, four young performers in the show. Jesse was the oldest, followed by Mearlie, Louise, usually called Lou, and little Fred. The cousins were all close, but they became a little competitive when one or the other got a bigger spot in an act or learned some new trick.

The Brewers could never admit to being Gypsies, or *Romanichals*, as they called themselves. It was too dangerous for their business and their livelihood. The prejudice was too strong. If a few long-term acquaintances on the show suspected anything, they kept it to themselves. If the Brewers were overheard speaking *Rumnis*, the Gypsy language, and somebody had the courage to ask, they would simply say, "Yes, we talk the old English Cockney slang sometimes. It can be hard to understand." *Rumnis* is a sort of hybrid language, a cross between English and an ancient Gypsy language. It uses English word order and word endings, but it has a lot of its own vocabulary. When asked if they were Gypsy because their mother was a fortuneteller, they would reply something like, "Oh, no, we are English. You must be thinking of my mother's fortunetelling act. She is very good at it. People love it. You should try. But we are English."

The next largest group on the show was Chief Red Hawk Sugarstone and his band of Osage Indians. They were a major attraction. They traveled in an old school bus that had been repainted numerous times and had had several engines. They put up teepees to sleep in and cooked over an open fire when they did not like the food served in the circus cookhouse. Their very presence was endlessly fascinating to people in the towns. The Sugarstones had less privacy than anyone else on the show. Townspeople watched their every move. When they entered the center ring in full regalia to do an exhibition of traditional Indian dancing, the audience gave them rapt attention. The Sugarstones knew that they were making a living by selling all the old ideas that white people believed about Indians, but it seemed to be the best option they had, better than living on the reservation where opportunities were so limited.

The Marvelous Marveli Family had many generations

17

of circus blood in their veins. Nicolo and Rosa had come to the States eight years earlier from Italy, and their three kids were U.S. born. Nicolo's parents had come with them along with his two sisters and Rosa's mother and brother. The Marvelis were very versatile with aerial acts, juggling, and comedy routines.

The Suarez Troup was announced as being from Madrid, Spain, but when the Spanish Civil War was at its worst, Woody Brewer decided to say they were "directly from Buenos Aires, Argentina." They were really from Monterrey, Mexico, but with the prejudice of the time, it was better for them not to be Mexican. Their main act was the bareback riding act, but they did other numbers, too, and filled in wherever they could. If other Spanish-speaking people came to see the show, they usually did not comment on the Mexican accent of the Suarez family. They understood how the Suarez family might not be accepted as performers if prejudiced people thought that they were Mexican.

Uncle Harry and Aunt Hattie, as the couple were known, were the elephant people. They didn't do much else, since elephants need a lot of attention and good help was not always available. Elephants eat almost constantly and get really grumpy when they are not putting something in their mouths.

Uncle Choctaw was the show electrician, a title that did not begin to explain his real portfolio. He was a factotum. He kept a working inventory of light cords, hoses, ropes, boards, and bolts. He could do almost any kind of basic repair. With him was Aunt Jenny. Like the other women on the show, she could do many things, but her two specialties were making and mending circus wardrobe and conducting an informal school for the circus kids. The kids came as much because they wanted to, not just because of parental order. A dozen children of various ages would sit at her feet for a couple hours each day for circus-specific lessons. The older children helped the younger ones with circus math, such as the cost to feed five horses for a week when they ate a bale of hay a day and the cost was fifteen cents a bale. Map reading and road sign reading were very important lessons. When local newspapers were available, the kids learned to decipher the stories and give their views on what the reporters were trying to say. Everybody said that Aunt Jenny must have been a schoolmarm once, but she would never admit to it, one way or the other.

Pierre de la Croix and his New Orleans Show Band provided the musical accompaniment for the acts. Pierre's sons Aaron and Art rounded out the band. Pierre played the electric organ, one of the prized possessions of the show. His boys alternated from drums to trumpet to sax or even guitar. They were not really from New Orleans but rather from the nearby town of Les Allemands. Pierre's wife joined the show for periods of time when there was a good rail connection, and Aaron's wife visited, too. Art was still looking for a wife, or at least a girlfriend. They made a good living during the season. It was steady work with meals included. In the winter back home they could play dances for added income, but they made a lot less than before the Great Depression started. Though they were "bright skinned," in the parlance of the day, they were visibly "colored" and subject to Jim Crow restrictions. Within the community of the circus, they saw little discrimination. They joined other performers at tables in the cookhouse and used the same toilets. In Jim Crow states, whenever they were out in a town they had to "stay in their place," but they had learned to do that in Louisiana.

Poker and Pinky were the lead clowns on the show. Poker was from Massachusetts, and Pinky hailed from Connecticut. They had worked together for years. Poker dressed with a beat-up hat and ragged clothes and rubber head cap that made him look bald. His makeup was dark except for a wide white outline around his mouth, making a sad face. Years earlier, he had clearly imitated a hobo, but now it was not in good taste to imitate a poor hobo too closely. Pinky was the opposite -- happy and bouncy, with spangles and bright colors and a messy orange wig with a little hat perched on the side of his head. Together they had a large repertoire of gags and jokes to keep people laughing.

Jake was the canvas boss. He was in charge of seeing that the bigtop got put up and the bleacher seating got put in on time and that it all got down and hauled over the road. He had a number of long-term "roughnecks," or "working boys" on his crew. Some of them were colorful characters like Coke an' Aspirin, who put down several Cokes a day, each with a couple aspirin dropped in them; or Big Red, who really didn't live up to his name in any way. Jake supplemented the regular crew with locally recruited men who got a dollar or a couple meals for the day or who joined up for a few weeks. In the Depression, there were always men looking for work. The problem was that the men were often in poor shape and could hardly carry their end of a board. Sometimes they were actually weak from hunger. Out of pity, Jake would send the worst of these over to the cookhouse to see if Cookie needed somebody to clean chickens, peel potatoes or wash dishes for a plate of leftovers. Jake would complain to Woody and Lucky with comments like, "Damn! I can get more done with four well-fed farm boys with half a head on their shoulders than a dozen skinny hobos."

Napoleon is quoted as saying that an army marches on its stomach. Well, so does a circus, and Cookie ran the circus cookhouse with the help of Slim and a small crew. It had been many years since Slim was actually slim, but the name stuck. The cookhouse was really just a semi-truck with a wide awning attached, with side canvas added as needed to keep out sun or wind or rain, or sometimes to hide the diners from staring crowds or poor hungry hobos. Folding tables and chairs were put up beneath the awning. Sometimes the tables were set, and serving bowls were filled and waiting at each table. If time was short, however, food was served cafeteria style. A small flag was raised at the end of the awning when a meal was ready. If the flag had come down, the latecomer would go hungry unless there was a very suitable excuse. Coffee and tea were almost always available. Cookie was good at trading free passes to the circus at town bakeries for doughnuts and pie, or at roadside stands for watermelons, berries, sweet corn, or whatever was locally available to stretch the show's grocery budget.

There were about 70 people on the show, but in the 1930s a circus would be no circus without animals. There were three elephants, two leopards, 15 horses, thirty-some dogs, some ponies, and a few exotic animals including an ostrich, Lillian the llama, a little burro, and a ridiculous looking billy goat.

There were also a couple dozen cars, house trailers, pickups, and semi-trucks. But the modern reader must put aside any idea of contemporary vehicles. These vehicles had no automatic transmissions, power brakes, power steering, or power windows. Even windshield wipers were often manual, meaning the driver or passenger moved a little lever above the windshield back and forth to make the wiper blade work. Turn signals were manual. If the left arm of the driver was stuck straight out the window, it meant that a left turn was coming up. If the left arm of the driver was out the window and pointed straight up, a right turn was coming up. There was no air conditioning, but sometimes there was a little crank to move the bottom of the windshield out an inch to improve ventilation. There was only AM radio, and reception was often poor, especially towards evening.

The vehicles were dangerous, too, with no seat belts nor airbags, and no safety glass or dished safety steering wheels. In a collision, the driver could be impaled on the post of the steering wheel or crash through the windshield glass and suffer wounds, sometimes fatal ones, on the sharp fragments.

Flat tires were frequent, and many tires were repeatedly patched. The engines had to be topped up with oil regularly, and the radiators could boil over on long hills. Greasing was a routine operation. Vehicles lights were not dependable. Pollution control devices were unheard of. Smoke coming from exhaust pipes was considered normal.

The show folks did not see these deficiencies in the same way people would in this century. They were just happy to be motorized and could remember a few decades before when they would have moved by horses and wagons on a much smaller scale and traveled only ten miles a day. Of course, the big circuses went by train, had their own rail cars, went as far as a train could go overnight, and could only show towns big enough to have a long rail siding and a huge open field that people could come to. Trucks were more flexible for a show the size of Brewer Brothers.

In one respect, the highways of the 1930s were safer. There was less traffic, many fewer cars and trucks, and the road conditions made it impossible to drive very fast in most places. Yet the highways of the 1930s were very dangerous in other ways. Stripes were not painted along the edge of highways and sometimes not even down the middle. Road signs were smaller and infrequent for extended stretches. There were narrow bridges, one-lane bridges, bridges with weight limits for trucks, washed out bridges, and underpasses with height limits. Four-lane highways were rare. Potholes could make it necessary to creep along roads for miles. Driving was hard work.

But the show vehicles were a sight to behold. They were unmistakable. They were decorated with painted scenes of elephants, clowns, a leopard, a cowboy on a rearing horse, Indians chasing buffalo, or maybe a huge organ cactus with Western scenery in the background and a stagecoach going by, or a long-horn bull. Roman chariots also showed up, acrobats, a circus tent, etc., etc. Gold scrolling served as a border around these scenes, with a heading above proclaiming, "Circus Today" or "Follow Me To The Circus." "Brewer Brothers World Famous Circus" usually followed the heading. This painting was really an art form. Perhaps the most similar genre was the florid movie posters of the time. Each vehicle had a number painted prominently on an upper corner, such as "92" or "66." Necessarily, the numbers were double-digit ones, giving the impression that there must be dozens of vehicles for this huge circus. The numbers also had a practical purpose; they served as sort of shorthand for vehicle names. The show folks knew all the numbers of the vehicles, and everybody would understand a statement such as "88 and 74 are finally here, but where are 56 and 52?"

Don Wilson did the painting in the winter offseason. Don spent weeks on it every year. There was much discussion of which trucks and trailers needed to be updated, and what the update would be. If a singing cowboy was popular on the radio, some mild likeness of the man with a guitar on a horse might show up. If there had been some biblical epic movie, Egyptian pyramids would be thrown in. These trucks and the paintings on them are all gone now, rusted away in fields in Florida or Texas or someplace or sold for scrap metal. A few may have made it to circus museums in Baraboo or Sarasota. Many exist only in photographs. Circus fans have done good documentation of many shows and have great collections of old photographs digitalized.

The purpose of all this vehicle painting was advertisement, and it served its purpose well. Traffic cops were known to stop traffic to let show vehicles go by, and the occasional school bus driver would drive along side a show truck to let the kids look at the scene.

3. LADIES AND GENTLEMAN, AND CHILDREN OF ALL AGES!

"**D**oors!" That was the warning call from Amy Brewer to any show folks left in the tent before the doors opened and ticket takers started letting the public in. This meant that there could be no more practicing, repairing, or setting up props. Anyone in the tent had to be clean and nicely dressed. Everything needed to be ready for a performance to start.

Poker and Pinky, the lead clowns of the show, amused children and adults with a series of showy magic tricks and other jokes for the fifteen minutes before the show started. They moved around the tent, working the crowd, getting them in a good mood, warming them up for the performance. They could continue their warm up for quite a while, until all the ticket buyers where seated in the tent and Amy Brewer stuck her head in the front door and gave them the all clear sign, meaning that they could take a bow and leave the tent and the band could play a brief overture.

Pierre de la Croix led the band in a peppy rendition of a recent popular song with some theme about having a good time, or starting to feel good, or whatever would increase the audience anticipation of the show.

Near the end of the overture, Lucky Brewer would march into the center ring. He would be dressed in tails, white jodhpurs, long boots, and a top hat and look as if he were about to start the most important event in the whole town that day, and in reality, he usually was. As the music ended, he would blow long and loud on his whistle to mark the formal start of the show.

He would sweep his hat off and use it to gesture from side to side and from front to the back of the tent, covering the whole crowd. He would be smiling from ear to ear. His words came in a slow, measured rhythm. On a typical day, the introductory patter would go something like this:

Ladies and gentlemen, and children of all ages, Brewer Brothers World Famous Circus is delighted to present our performances today under the auspices and sponsorship of your wonderful North Rock Island, Illinois, Police Department, and in particular Police Chief Norman Gruttles and his fine platoon of law enforcement officers. You know what wonderful work these dedicated men do in your beautiful city of North Rock Island, and you can see why we are happy to provide a fund-raising opportunity for the benefit of your police department and the many good works that they perform. Please, take a second after the performance to drop by and thank these fine citizens and community leaders for what they are doing.

We know that you will greatly enjoy this afternoon's performance, ladies and gentlemen, and we have just a few requests of you. First of all, when you see one or more of our circus stars, and these stars could be from anyplace in our own great country of the U.S.A. or from anywhere in the whole world, do not hesitate, not for one second, to give them a loud and enthusiastic round of applause. Your applause will tell them that you love their work and artistry, and they will try just that much harder to please you.

Secondly, ladies and gentlemen, we ask that you keep a close hand on young children so that they do not run out of their seats at any time during the performance. They should not come onto the track around the three circus rings unless accompanied by a parent. We know that they will enjoy the show, and we want them to stay completely safe, too.

Lastly, by order of your local fire department and state and U.S. fire laws, smoking of cigars, cigarettes, or pipes is completely forbidden everywhere under the bigtop under penalty of severe fine. And if you are chewing tobacco, please be kind to your neighbors and spit only in a can or directly under the seats where you are sitting.

At this time, ladies and gentlemen, boys and girls, please all rise for our National Anthem.

Lucky would remove his hat again in a grand gesture and place it over his heart and look solemn. He would step to the side of the center ring as his nephew Gilly rode in on Yellowstone, a beautiful buckskin stallion with flowing white mane and tale. Gilly carried an American flag. The audience rose and stood at attention while the band played "The Star Spangled Banner."

"And now, ladies and gentlemen, it is my pleasure to present to you the 1933 Edition of Brewer Brothers World Famous Circus," Lucky proclaimed. And then he blew a long shrill toot on his whistle.

This was the signal for a Grand Entry Spectacle to start. It was a parade including nearly every performer and every animal with the show. It entered the tent through the "back door" behind the center ring and circled the tent on the track surrounding the three rings. The band played a rousing Sousa march. The parade was led by Gilly on Yellowstone, dressed in fancy cowboy wardrobe. Seven more riders followed him, all in Western gear. They carried flags, too, including the flag of the state where they were showing. The Marveli Family followed, marching in matching wardrobe, smiling and styling. The adults in the family wore large capes that they swung gracefully from side to side in a slow unison. Next was the Suarez Troop with their bareback horses. A man led each horse, and a woman sat on the back of each animal. The women rode with both legs to the left side.

Beautiful ostrich feather plumes adorned the heads of each animal, and the women wore ostrich feather plumes on their heads, too.

Chief Red Hawk Sugarstone and his Band of Osage Indians were next. Red Hawk, wearing a full eagle feather headdress, led the band, all parading in single file. The women and girls wore beaded buckskin dresses, with a single feather in their headbands. The men and boys wore breechcloths, armbands, neckbands, and anklets of bells. On the back of their heads and going down their backs were beaded ornaments with more feathers circling them. To the audience, the Sugarstones were a surprising part of the parade. Many had never seen "real Indians" in traditional dress, and they stared intently.

Next came five of the show kids, riding ponies and carrying flags, smaller versions of the large flags carried by the adults earlier in the parade. Their ponies had been on the pony ride on the midway just a few minutes before. There was a sixth pony, not ridden by a child, but led by a child. On the back of this pony was Spangles, the show's Dalmatian dog, standing up and wagging her tail.

The ponies were followed by what the people on the show called the "exotics." Pinky led the ostrich, and if there was a spare show kid around, he or she could be placed on the back of the ostrich, with a steadying hand as needed. Poker led Lillian, the llama. Other clowns led the donkey and the ridiculous looking billy goat.

There was a reason that the Uncle Harry and Aunt

Hattie came with the elephants last, and it wasn't just because the elephants made a good climax to the parade. It was because on occasion there were elephant droppings. Harry and Hattie always took Dolly, Blanche, and Jewel for a good walk before the show, but elephants eat a high fiber diet, and they are not always able to empty out completely when the trainers would like. These three elephants were pretty good, but elephants cannot really be perfect.

A clown followed the three elephants. He would be pushing a wheelbarrow loaded with a scoop shovel. His job was to pick up any elephant droppings, or on rare occasion, horse manure. Clowns who were given the job usually waved, laughed, and made it part of their routine. If the town were in an agricultural area, the audience would almost immediately see the humor in the wheelbarrow and shovel. In urban areas, where people were less familiar with animals, they might not understand at all.

At the end of the parade, the first eight riders converged into the center ring, arranged in four pairs, all facing the center of the ring.

At this point Lucky made his next announcement. "Now, ladies and gentlemen, celebrating an All-American dance, the square dance, we present to you an equine version you will never forget. Have you ever seen people do a square dance on horseback? Well, ladies and gentlemen, here it is, done by eight of Brewer Brothers Circus most skilled riders and most beautiful horses, the 'Quadrille on Horseback!'"

The band played a version of "Turkey in the Straw,"

and Lucky became a square dance caller, calling out various "dos-a-dos" and "a-la-main-lefts" to put the riders and their mounts through some basic square dance routines. The riders and in a different sense, the horses, knew the routine very well. Two lady riders on opposite sides of the ring rode to the center and circled each other waving, then the other two ladies did the same. One couple would ride across the ring to exchange places with the couple opposite them. Then the men would circle clockwise and the women circle counter-clockwise, weaving in and out and tipping their hats and greeting one another as they passed. The horses in this routine were really responsive. They knew the routine well and needed a minimum of direction with the bridles on their heads and the bits in their mouths. At the end, all four couples would exit the ring and pass around the track waving their hats and smiling. The "Quadrille on Horseback" was a fast-paced first act for the show.

Some of the riders immediately dismounted upon leaving the tent so that they could reenter the tent with their ropes to join the three rings of rope spinners.

Lucky announced, "And now, boys and girls, ladies and gentlemen, it is my great pleasure to present to you the greatest array of Trick and Fancy Rope Spinners ever assembled under the bigtop. You will not believe your eyes when you see the skill and speed of these wonderful artists. Right before you, right now, three rings of America's greatest Trick and Fancy Rope Spinners!"

More than a dozen performers, all dressed in Western

or Indian wardrobe, entered the rings with an assortment of ropes or lariats. They all began spinning ropes, something that the audience had heard about or maybe seen in movies, and a few had seen at rodeos. It was clear that there was no cheating here -- no ropes that had been stiffened. There were no circles of camouflaged wire. The performers all carried their ropes into the ring in small coils, and then opened them up to begin spinning.

In the 1930s, any act that had a Wild West theme or was related to Native Americans would be well received. People just loved cowboys and Indians. Indeed, the time was not all that far removed historically from the Great American Frontier. There were living men who had fought in Indian wars and couples who had been in land rushes and homesteaded. Cowboys were held in esteem, and young women were attracted to them. Rodeos were a staple of small town life in many states, and people loved to compete in barrel racing and bronco riding, and there were baby greased pig chases for the youngsters. Such was the popular lore that served as a backdrop for circus goers when the Trick and Fancy Rope Spinning act was announced.

In each ring, one of the performers was a child under the age of 12, and one was only eight. The child performers did not yet have the motor skills of the adults and could not do the harder tricks, but they could hold their own in this act, at least for the first few minutes.

Once the act started, Lucky Brewer continued with a rapid patter introducing each performer and naming the trick being done, "Starting in Ring #1, Miss Janet Barnes, rapidly switching the Spanish flat loop from her left to right hand; Mr. Harry Weaver, spinning a rope in each hand; Chief Red Hawk, showing the tricks that have won him prizes in powwows from Oklahoma to Idaho, and in the center ring, America's youngest trick and fancy roper, my daughter, eight-year old Little Miss Louise Brewer." By the time the introductions were finished, the performers were way beyond basic rope spinning. They were doing "the roper's dance," with one foot jumping in and out of the loop with each revolution of the rope, or they were even dancing with a rope in each hand and with the left foot dancing into one rope and the right foot into the other. Some had jumped into the rope they were spinning with no interruption to the spinning motion. They held the end of the rope in one hand just above their head or they passed the end from one hand to the other around their waist and continued a smooth motion so that the loop of the rope stayed flat and very parallel to the ground. Some would even kick a leg up and pass the end of the rope under the leg.

The spinning technique was in the fingers and wrist. The fingers constantly twirled the end of the rope and kept the ropes from becoming tangled, and the wrist powered the motion just fast enough to keep the loop from collapsing. With years of practice, the movements became second nature for all the standard tricks.

There were all kinds of colorful names or descriptions for the tricks. When a performer stood in the middle of the spinning rope and made the loop rise and fall from just off the ground to above his head, he was "flipping flapjacks." When a performer spun a rope in her teeth with a swivel at the end of the rope, while her hands waved in the air, she was "drying her fingernails."

The performers in each ring were almost constantly changing their positions, like dancers waltzing on a dance floor. This added more energy and movement to the act and allowed the spectators to have a better view of what was going on. One or both of the child performer's parents were always performing in the same ring with the youngster. When needed, in a low voice the parents offered encouragement, gave suggestions for improving technique, or cued the kids that it was time to go on to a new trick. In some performances, a child needed no comments, except maybe after the act something like "Good job again tonight," or "Do some more practicing with that longer rope, honey," or "Always keep smiling all the time in the ring!"

The second round of tricks in the act was harder. The children took bows and dropped out. Now the ropes were spun perpendicular to the ground rather than parallel. They were more like a bicycle wheel rolling in suspension above the ground. Indeed, two performers did line up with their ropes positioned as floating bicycle wheels and went around the edge of the ring. Others would roll their spinning ropes over their shoulders, alternating left and right, to do "backward ocean waves." The variation on these tricks was endless, and the spectators could barely absorb one trick before another started, and their eyes would skip from one ring to another in a vain effort to see everything.

Among the most attractive and difficult tricks was the "butterfly." The spinner spun the loop perpendicular to the ground and flipped it rapidly from the right side to the left, going back and forth, with an effortless motion. Once the name of the trick was announced, spectators smiled and nodded their heads. Yes, it looked like a butterfly.

Finally, the act would end with a series of "specialty tricks" in the center ring. Miss Amy Brewer would come in with a one-hundred foot rope and begin spinning it around her at a diameter of only about six feet, but gradually she would feed out more of the rope and increase the diameter and circumference till she could hardly hold the rope aloft anymore and it would cover almost the entire ring. This was known as the "cowgirl's wedding ring." Next Brady Barnes would spin eight ropes at one time, a world's record. He wore a belt with four short rods extending out. Small ropes on swivels were attached to each rod. With just the right hip motion, he would get all four of these ropes spinning in unison. Next his wife would hand him a short rod with a rope at each end. She had already started the two ropes spinning, and he kept the motion going in his right hand. Lastly, she gave him a final two ropes on a rod to spin in his left hand. If his concentration was right, he would have all eight little ropes spinning as he did a slow revolution so that everybody in the tent could see clearly.

Two of the men and one woman would do the very

challenging "Texas skip," a difficult variation of the "butterfly." They would spin the rope perpendicularly, moving it from right to left, and then they would jump back and forth through the spinning loop as it passed in each direction. They would do it so fast that their feet hardly seemed to touch the ground, and they would rotate all the while so that people everywhere in the tent could see the trick clearly.

The end of the act was done by Chief Red Hawk Sugarstone, the only man in the world known to be able to do the Texas skip on the back of a horse. Big Comanche was led in. This horse was a large, beautiful paint with unusual markings. There was only an Indian blanket over the horse, not a saddle. Big Comanche was so well trained that he would stand still in the middle of the ring with nobody holding his bridle. The horse had "eagle" feathers braided into his forelock and in a couple places on his side mane. He was an attraction himself. Chief Red Hawk had to remove his war bonnet for this trick. It would only get in the way as he skipped through the rope. He wore moccasins. Boots would be too hard on Comanche's back. He jumped onto the horse's back, then straddled it and stood up, stepping back to the horse's wide hips. There he would spin the upright loop and begin the Texas skip as deftly as if he were on solid ground. The audience would applaud long and enthusiastically. He would end with a bow and ride Big Comanche out of the ring.

And that was how each performance started in the summer of 1933.

4. PRINCESS TEEJANI

B eauty, danger, magic, surprise, and comedy -- such are the requisite ingredients, in one combination or another, for good circus acts. Any successful act must capture at least two of these. So it was that Amy Brewer captured her share in the "neck loop" act.

She entered the center ring in a gleaming gold satin cape and a white turban, from which peeked a fringe of blonde curls snipped from a wig, all the better to hide her long dark hair that was so visible in other acts she did. But this was her act, her solo.

Her husband Woody, now wearing a tuxedo, held her hand as she circled the ring at a stately stride, while the band played Ravel's *Bolero*. When she opened her cape, the interior lining of white and gold shone brightly. A small round red carpet lay in the center of the ring. She approached it, shed her espadrilles, and walked onto it in what appeared to be ballet slippers.

After an appropriate drum roll, the ringmaster announced, "'Princess Teejani' will now present an astounding performance, the likes of which no one in this audience has ever seen. Doctors and scientists cannot explain how the princess does these wonders and lives every time to do it again. All eyes are directed to the incredible performance of Princess Teejani."

At this point, Woody lifted the cape from her shoulders, and she stepped forward walking on her toes and reached for a loop at the end of a white rope that was descending on a pulley from high in the bigtop. The loop was like a wide leather belt, and it was lined with velvet. There were gasps as she took the loop, and with her head back at a nearly right angle, placed it so that the back of her neck rested firmly on it. She tightened the velvet loop by sliding a smaller leather safety strap down making the velvet loop come tight from the back of her neck to her forehead.

Unnoticed by many in the audience, she also grasped her hands on a small bar that extended from either side just above the velvet-lined loop. There were louder gasps as she rose from the ground as four men smoothly pulled on the rope with the pulley that drew her up. Gilly Brewer had a particular responsibility here. While he was the youngest of the four men pulling the rope and he had been doing it already for a couple years, the woman on the end of the rope was, after all, his mother. He was always steady and completely focused on the task at hand. His father Woody stood beneath Amy, ready to cushion her fall, if there was ever a need.

Once at a high level and when Woody blew a whistle that told the men to stop pulling and hold steady, Amy released the bar and extended her arms. She seemed to fly through the air in large circles by her neck. In the context of the time, this was especially amazing, even alarming, since criminals were routinely executed by hanging. Yet here at the circus was a graceful woman, hanging by her neck as she soared above the ground and assumed ballet-like poses.

What the spectators did not know was that Amy had learned this act from an aunt. For months Amy had done exercises to strengthen her neck and back muscles, and then she had conditioned herself with more months of practice in the neck loop while standing on her toes or barely off the ground. Over time, she increased the height from the ground and the suspension time. She also developed the arm strength to hold herself safely with her hands on the short bar above her head and to never let go of it when she was being pulled up or let down.

Even though Gilly and the other men pulling the rope were adept at moving in a smooth and steady way with no yanking or slipping, Amy's tight grip on the overhead bar and her head straight back in a tightened neck loop were the keys to her safety. Gilly was first in line among the men who worked the rope, and he watched every move his mother made, always alert for the slightest changes that might indicate any problem or danger.

After three or so aerial circles above the ring, Amy would drop her arms down and snap her fingers, then grasp the bar over her head again. This told Woody to blow the signal whistle, and the men would move up with the rope going through the pulley to the top of the tent. She would gradually descend. Woody was there to touch her lightly and help her face forward. He would whisper when she had only a foot to go before reaching the ground. This allowed her to bend her knees slightly for a gentle landing and stand up straight, remove the loop, do a beautiful bow and show a brilliant smile.

This trick alone would have been worthwhile as an act in the eyes of the audience. They would expect no more. But the act continued. She placed the loop around her head again and snapped her fingers and grasped the bar. Woody blew the whistle. The men pulled her straight up. This time she took hold of a larger bar near the top of the tent, one that was rigged to be stationary.

First she twisted her body far to the left so that her arms were ready to spring. Then with a muscular thrust, she twisted sharply to the right and let go of the stationary bar. Thanks to a large swivel sewn in the top of the loop, her whole body spun in rapid rotations until she extended her arms to stop herself. Then she gave the signal and descended. Woody caught her more firmly this time so that she would have a moment to overcome any dizziness before acknowledging the applause for this magnificent trick. This was the point that Woody always whispered, "I love you, Amy." And she replied, "I love you, too, Woody." This was part of a short, secret habit between the two of them, expressing their love. It said that they were the most important thing in the world to each other. The act and the audience were secondary.

The finale of the act started when Woody placed what seemed to be a fluffy gown of white lace around her shoulders. Amy ascended again into the air. When the whistle blew, she let go of the small bar above her head and pulled a cord that released several folds in the gown so that four more feet of lace fell below her feet. This gave a startling vision of an increase in size. In the same instant, she took hold of two wands that had been sewn into the sides of the gown and began waving them in large figure eights. The wands were attached to long swaths of lace, and the immediate impression was of an angel flying through the air. The audience could hardly believe their eyes. While this third trick did not call for additional acrobatic skills, it was a remarkable visual surprise. For the children and many adults, it gave magical delight.

Amy descended straight down after this trick so that she would land in the middle of the extra folds of lace and could step from the gown easily. Woody took her hand and presented "Princess Teejani" to the audience for a final bow.

At homes in the local town that night and the next day, many families discussed how the "Angel Lady" in the circus could fly around so beautifully by her neck and not be hurt. Everybody knew that criminals would die in an instant when hanged by their necks. But the Angel Lady must have some special magic.

5. HORSE THIEVES

In the 1930s, horses and mules had a hard time. They suffered. This was in part due to the Great Depression. There was less farm work to do with them. Farms were being sold at sheriff's auction every day. People who could once afford a saddle horse for pleasure riding no longer could. There was less money to buy feed for horses. In some places, a fat horse was identified as a rich man's horse. As money got tight, many people had to sell off their horses. That sale could be after a long period of time when every effort was made to keep them, even when there was little pasture, little hay in the barn, and not much money to feed the family, not to mention horses. At the same time, trucks were replacing milk wagons, lumber wagons, and other conveyances that horses or mules had pulled. They were not needed any more.

The horse market was glutted in many states. Lots of fine animals went for a pittance to agents who scooped them up and hauled them off to slaughterhouses. How these animals were treated on the way to slaughter depended on the heart and the pocketbook of the man buying up the horses. Some men just did not have much heart, and since "they were gonna die anyway," the poor animals were barely kept alive with water and little or nothing to eat till there was a full truckload of them to take to the slaughterhouse.

In the early weeks of the season, Brewer Brothers Circus ended up showing on a big grassy lot that over-looked a feedlot, a small parcel of land where animals were held till they would be sold. In this case, how-ever, it was a feedlot with not much feeding going on in it. Horses and mules were gathered there and kept till shipment to a factory where they would become dog food, glue, or whatever. Some of the adults on the show realized quickly what it was, and they didn't particularly want to explain it to the kids.

There was nearly nothing for the few animals in the feedlot to eat. The poor horses had cropped the grass down till there was hardly a blade left. In the manger down at the bottom of the hill by a gate there was no hay, and the nearby water trough looked completely empty, too. Three skinny horses and a mule stood around the manger and the water trough hopefully, waiting for the man in charge to care for them. When some children walked by, the horses came up to the fence and nickered pitifully, begging for grass. The children pulled handfuls of grass from the roadside and poked them through the fence, but they soon bored of pulling grass, and handfuls of grass from chil-dren could not really sustain the animals. People in the town knew that Old Man Mitchell was in charge of the horses, and his boss gave him money to feed and look after them till there were enough for the next shipment. But Old Man Mitchell had a serious drinking problem, and for days at a time the money went to pay bootleggers for moonshine. The horses did without.

One of the workingmen on the show noticed how bad the situation was, and out of pity he went down and turned on the windmill that pumped water from a well and filled the watering trough. At first the animals started to fight over the water as it came in, but they had little energy. And then they drank and drank, as if they than had not had a drink in days. When he took down a bale of the show's hay, he had to spread out the hay flakes in four separated places in the manger so that the hungry animals did not fight over them.

From the backyard of the circus, Mearlie Brewer, who always had her eye on any horses, noticed what looked like a little mare lying flat on her side in the shade of some scrubby trees in this feedlot. The mare didn't move. A couple hours later, Mearlie noticed that the mare was still there. "That's not right," she thought to himself.

Mearlie had inherited the Brewer trait of being a horse lover. She spent lots of time with the horses on the show. She brought them sugar cubes. She complained to the workingmen if she thought any of the stock had gone too long without feed or water, or if the awning should be put up to shade them. She tried not to be a pest about it, but she was a vigilant advocate for the wellbeing of these animals. Her family understood this and approved; indeed, they shared her feelings. For a child of her age, she had learned so much about horses, and the more she learned, the more she loved them. She just could not stand to see a horse, a mule, or a pony mistreated. There are modern day dog owners and cat owners who can understand these sentiments. They love their animals, and they will go to great lengths to care for them and easily spend money on them.

The little horse lying on her side for so long and not moving aroused Mearlie's curiosity. She climbed the fence and wandered over slowly to the horse. The little mare did not rouse as she approached. The mare could not even lift her head. And she was a very little mare, somewhere in size between a small horse and a large pony, a size that was not very common at all. Mearlie noticed how skinny she was, with hipbones protruding. Mearlie had not seen this very often, and she hated the sight. She slowly squatted down to get a better look. There were flies on the horse's eyes and nostrils, and she made no effort to get them off. Mearlie gently felt the horse's nose. It was warm or even hot to the touch. The eyes opened, but not with any recognition. It suddenly occurred to Mearlie that the horse was either very sick or had gotten so weak from lack of water that she could no longer even stand or eat. She had become extremely dehydrated and might not live more than a few hours.

In an instant Mearlie decided to do something. She ran back and climbed the fence and went to the horse truck. She got a bucket and filled it half full with water. She climbed over the fence with the water and carried it down to the horse. She dipped in her hand and tried to take a handful of water to the horse's parched mouth. At first, the animal was unresponsive, but after a second, she moved her lips and even parted them a little.

Mearlie scooped up another handful, and the horse seemed to want to absorb what was falling around her lips. Next the animal painfully lifted her head. Mearlie tipped the bucket so that the horse could get to the precious water without spilling it.

Then surprisingly, the horse drank, slowly at first, and then in great gulps. The bucket emptied fast. Mearlie had been right. The horse was badly dehydrated. But Mearlie did not know what to do next, beyond the obvious task of getting more water. She ran back toward the horse truck with the empty bucket.

Chief Red Hawk saw her and asked what she was up to. Mearlie explained, and Red Hawk asked, "Girl, are you sure you are doing the right thing? Are you just prolonging the poor animal's agony? Where is she going to get feed and water when the show leaves tomorrow? Who will take care of her then?" Mearlie did not like what she was being asked. She had no answers. She was just used to taking very good care of horses and other animals.

She paused a moment in deep reflection, and then she cried out, "Chief, we can't just let her die. She can live. We can save her. I know what we can do. We can steal her!"

"And girl, just how do you propose to do that? You just told me that the horse can't even walk. An' last I checked, horse theft is still illegal in all forty-eight states; it is a hangin' offense. Even if she could walk, what use do we have for her? Better talk to your folks about this before you cook up some hare-brained scheme. I don't want no part of it."

Mearlie filled the bucket half full again and climbed the fence. This time she was welcomed by the mare, which actually had her neck much farther up off the ground. She was ready to drink, even if not standing up. The bucket emptied again, and Mearlie ran up and refilled it, this time with a nearly full bucket.

The mare did not drink as quickly now. She was less desperate. Nevertheless, she finished the better part of the bucket. Well, Mearlie thought, water is one thing, but she obviously needs feed. Who knows how long she has been on her side here without a bite to eat?

Mearlie made still another trip and returned with a quarter-bucket of sweet feed, generously moistened so the mare could get it down more easily. It did not take the mare long to figure out that this was grain, very edible grain, and in a few minutes, she had eaten it all. Mearlie continued with water and feed, off and on, till it was time to get ready for the night show. All along, she had been hoping that someway or somehow, the little mare could get to her feet. But she didn't.

Mearlie took a flashlight to go check on the sick little mare when she had a free moment during the night show, but the mare was still there, flat on her side. She would raise her head as if to greet Mearlie, but even with encouragement, she did not rise. Mearlie was feeling desperate. She decided it was about time to tell her brother Jess and a trusted cousin Mattie so they could work on the problem together.

Jess and Mattie were at first unconvinced that anything could be done. They went through the same discussion that Mearlie had with Chief Red Hawk. "*Pourra bitta grai* is gonna *mourra* anyway. It's *dui nafla.* The poor little horse is gonna die anyway. It's too sick. Let it just die." But when Mearlie took them down to look at the mare, there was a change of heart. They agreed that something had to be done. Jess pointed out how skinny she was and how she didn't weigh that much more than a man did. This gave Mearlie the idea to pull her on to a piece of canvas and drag her out and just steal her. It was the only way to save her life.

The three agreed on the scheme, and Mearlie said she would get a piece of canvas from Uncle Choctaw or somebody, and they would see if they could pull the horse on to it, and then drag her out. In ten minutes, Mearlie was back with the canvas, and they had pulled the animal on to it. Now they had to see if they could drag the horse out. It was literally an uphill struggle, since there was an incline from the grove of scrawny trees to the circus lot. When they were about halfway there, they had quite a scare. Car headlights were showing down at the gate of the feedlot, and as the car turned, they shone up the hill to where the kids were dragging the horse. They all got down flat on the ground beside the horse, as flat as they possibly could. They were already out of breath from dragging the horse that far, but now their hearts were racing, and they could hardly breathe. They stayed still, not daring to say a word. Gradually, very gradually, the car moved on, and they were in total darkness again, except for the flashlight that Mearlie had. It was a false alarm.

It took another 10 minutes, pulling 20 feet at a time, till the kids ran into a solid brick wall of sorts. It was in the form of the barbed wire fence that separated the feedlot from the circus show grounds. They hadn't thought it all through. They were so close, and yet so far.

They tried lifting the bottom wire of the fence to see if somehow they could slide the horse and themselves under, but the bottom wire was far too tight. They looked at the top wires, with the barbs on them, and realized that the horse was too heavy to lift over anyway. It became obvious that they would have to cut the wire fence. This meant that the crime of horse theft was becoming more incriminating, with more indisputable evidence of their guilt. They were stumped.

Mearlie was the first to speak, "Chief Red Hawk is real smart, and he loves horses as much as we do. Maybe he will have an idea. We need to talk to him." Mearlie was smart, too, but she was young, and sometimes she had a way of being very direct and naïve.

"Chief, what is the best way to cut a wire fence if you want to steal a horse and get it out of a field?" The Indian had no idea what the child had in mind. He had forgotten Mearlie's earlier comment about the sick little mare. He just thought it was one of those silly questions kids sometimes ask. He decided to play along with question.

"Well, girl, there are three ways to cut a fence to get a stolen horse out. I would recommend only one of them, and that would be the Z slash. You see, anybody riding a fence line knows to look if the wire has been cut right by a fence post and then put back with the ends twisted tight by the post so that the fence stays in place and does not bow. And only an idiot would cut right in the middle of a fence section between two posts. When you try to twist the two ends of the wire back together it never works right, and you can tell it every time real easy. So if you want to steal a horse and get him through a fence, my only recommendation would be to do a Z slash."

"Oh, how do you do that, Chief?" Mearlie asked. By this time her cousins were listening with shocked faces. Here Mearlie had gone and told an adult what they were doing. Chief Red Hawk was a good friend, but they couldn't ask him to join in the plot or even not to tell on them.

"Well, young lady, it is actually real easy. You just get a pair of wire cutters or even a pair of pliers, and you go to the fence in a section between two fence posts. Then you don't cut either the top or bottom wire. You just cut the wires between top and bottom, but you do it one at a time, moving over one little square of fence each time you cut so that the slash is really at a slant, like a Z. Then you cut a little along the bottom. It is kind a' like a tear in your shirt. You have to get the horse through going under the top wire and over the bottom wire. It isn't that hard. When you finish, you just pull the cut places back together and twist them tight. Nobody hardly ever notices a fence cut like that. The cuts are not all up and down in a straight line. It's the best. Now, how many horses were you plannin' to steal tonight?"

"Oh, just one, Chief, and we already have her up to the fence." Mearlie said.

It was only then that Red Hawk understood that Mearlie was not playing a game. "What are you talkin' about? What horse?" he asked, in dismay.

Mearlie started to explain, but she could not get the story out clearly. Mattie and Jess gave a quick recap and summary. Then the Chief asked a question that stumped them. "Aside from going to jail, what exactly are you plannin' to do with this horse? You gonna sell it, hide it, ride off on it, what?" he asked. He was more serious than the kids had ever seen him before.

"But we have to save her," Mearlie said. "We can't just let her die. That is not what we do. We love horses, and we take great care of them, no matter what it takes."

"Yes, young lady, that is true, an' I love horses, too, always have. But what you want to do could get you in a heap of trouble. I can't have anything to do with it. Don't tell anybody what I told you. You see, the law aint good to Indians. They might just wanna give a white man a fine or something, but they wanna send an Indian back to the reservation or even put an Indian in prison to do hard time. That is just what it is like," Chief Red Hawk explained.

"But you gotta help us. We won't tell nobody. Just cut

the fence for us, or show me how, and help us drag her through. We won't tell nobody, honest!"

Red Hawk looked down at Mearlie and saw that she was starting to cry. He had his own love of horses, too, and he was on the verge of just saying he would cut the little mare's throat so she would not suffer anymore. He had put down horses before. It wasn't easy, but sometimes it was the best thing.

But with three kids looking up at him, kids he had known for years and kids who he knew really respected him, he knew cutting the mare's throat wasn't the best thing now. He agreed to go with them immediately, do the Z slash, help them drag the horse on the canvas behind the hay pile out of sight, and put the wire back right. He swore them again to secrecy and said they would have very bad Indian luck if they ever told.

It did take only about five minutes to cut the Z slash in the fence, drag the little mare through on the canvas, and complete the whole operation, or at least that key step in stealing the horse.

There were new concerns for the kids now. What if somebody came around the back of the hay pile? They would see a sick horse or pony on a big piece of canvas and know something was wrong. And it really was possible that somebody would come around the hay pile. Sometimes the workingmen would come and hide behind the hay pile while they took a leak, and sometimes they would entice a town girl to go back there with them to use it as a makeshift lovers' lane.

Mearlie had the best idea. They would just cover the horse with another piece of canvas and then put a cowboy hat where a man's head might be, and maybe have a pair of boots sticking out. It would look like somebody was just taking a nap or drunk or something. They got somebody's cowboy hat off the seat of a truck, and then Jess took off his own boots. In the half darkness, the "dummy" didn't look half bad. It would work for a while.

Then the three looked at each other. They were all thinking the same thing. They were going to be "in a heap of trouble" very soon. Mattie spoke first, "We gotta tell Grandpa. He knows how to handle situations. And if he knows first, maybe our folks won't get so *hona* with us, so mad." The other two did not reply. They all took off for Grandpa's horse truck and Grandma's fortunetelling tent, her *dukkerin' tan*. Jess was barefoot, but he ran over the hard ground at the same speed as the others.

"We're in a heap of *toug*, Grandpa, lots of trouble. You gotta help us, please! Our folks are gonna be *doosta hona* with us, so mad. We been *vaseta*. We *chored a grai!*" Mattie explained.

"Why, I never heard of such a thing. You *chored a grai?* Why on earth for? You know you can ride a horse of mine, a good one, any time you want. Honey, are you *pookering a hookabin,* tellin' a lie, as some kind of joke?" GR asked his grandkids.

"*Keker*, GR, I think they are telling *tatchi*, the truth. They aren't *pookerin' a hookab*in, and they are in a heap a *toug*. Let's *shoon* 'em and hear what the *chavies* have to say," Camie said. She had been standing nearby.

It took a while for the whole story to come out, and the grandparents realized with some alarm that at that moment there was a starved horse covered in canvas behind the hay pile. If the *muskers,* the cops, found out about this, there would be a lot of trouble. At the same time, the look on their grandchildren's faces, the sincerity, the concern they had, it made it hard for them not to be somehow proud of grandchildren who loved horses so much that they would work so hard and take such extreme measures. They just had to help the kids out.

"OK, *chavies*, kids, I believe you, and I can't believe what you have done, never heard of anything like it. But I do know why you did it, and I have to admit that at your age, I might have done the same thing, too," GR said.

"Now I am gonna walk over there real casual-like and check out this *poura bitta grai*. I can tell if she is really gonna *mourra* or if she has a chance. If she is gonna *mourra* anyway, well, that is the end of the story right there. We will put her down before we leave this lot for the next town. But if she might live, then we will somehow sneak her into the back of my horse truck and try to nurse her back to health," GR explained, trying to sound stern but really melting under the pressure of his grandchildren. Both he and Grandma Camie were laughing on the inside.

He and Camie were soon smothered in hugs and

kisses, *chums*, from the kids, even while GR repeated that if the horse looked like she was going to die, he would not put her in the truck. He would just put her down later that night, right where she was, probably with a knife to her throat. The children in their young lives had seen animals put down before, and though they understood why, they still felt pain. They lived partly in the sheltered world of a strong family, and partly in the real world, the world where pain and sorrow could come at any moment.

By the time GR got back from his casual walk to confirm that the horse had a chance of living, he had thought of a reason to take his horse truck around back by the hay pile. He would want to siphon some gallons of gas from one truck into his and to pick up a few bales of hay. That was plausible.

He also recruited the help of two of the most trusted workingmen, men who he knew would keep their mouths shut. They would help the kids drag the mare on the canvas up the gangplank of his horse truck into a safe hiding place. He would hang up a piece of canvas like a curtain far in the front of the truck and pull the horse there behind it. She would be kept separate from the other horses. She would not be seen in public. She was such a skinny mess that it would take weeks before she could put on enough weight not to be a disgrace to the show. She had to stay hidden.

The grandkids would have to do most of the work of watering and feeding her and cleaning. And they would have to sit down and tell their parents exactly what they had done. GR and Camie would be there, if they liked. It could be a family meeting, but it had to happen by the next day at the latest.

It took place the next day, before the matinee show. The six adults and three children sat down on the bleachers. The kids were so solemn that the two mothers, Tillie and Amy; and two fathers, Lucky and Woody, knew something was up. Their children were very creative, and somehow something had happened without their other children knowing about it or getting involved. It must be unusual. But if Grandpa and Grandma were in on it, it could not be awful.

The adults listened while the children explained, each one doing some of the talking. Because GR and Camie were there, they knew they had to be accurate and not leave anything out. It would seem that Mearlie was the ringleader, since she found the horse first and got the other two involved; so Mearlie was ready to take more blame.

The story took no more than ten minutes to tell, though it seemed like an hour to the kids. The four parents loved the funny, amazing story. They loved the fact that their children would go to such lengths to do what they thought was the right thing. They were very proud of their offspring. They tried to stay expressionless, perhaps reading one another's eyes to see if they were having similar thoughts about what the children were saying, though, at the same time, they had to think about what the punishment would be. It got harder and harder for Woody and Lucky to keep looking serious, and their wives were having the same problem. They stopped looking at one another. It would not do if they all started laughing.

When the story was over, there was a pause, and then Lucky spoke. He said, "You realize that what you did to save a horse could 'a' been terrible for the show. We all love horses, an' we want the best for them. But the *muskers* might 'a' got *hona* with us, the police could get mad at us. They always want to say that travelin' people are thieves. They could put somebody in the *sterobin* or give us a big fine. Some of the workin' men or performers might 'a' been jailed. You are not little kids anymore, an' you have to think of what is the good for everybody. Unless your *dadus* or *dais* has something to say now, you all should go out on the midway while we talk about what the punishment will be."

The kids looked down and went off out the front door of the tent to the midway. When Lucky made the comment about workingmen or performers getting jailed, the three kids all thought of Chief Red Hawk, and how it would be harder on an Indian. The help they got from Red Hawk was the one part of the story they left out. They had promised not to tell, and they had to keep the promise.

The children were barely out of sight before the adults were smiling and then barely controlling their giggles. Woody and Lucky broke into a laugh first, and they hugged each other and their wives. They were all beaming. When they tried to stop to talk, it wouldn't last, and the four would start laughing again. The parents had the same emotions that the grandparents had earlier. There was shock at how it could have turned out badly, and that it was a potential danger. Yet there was the admiration and pride. Their kids were so smart, so resourceful, and so *Romanichal*, it won over their hearts, even if they could not show it now.

A suitable punishment was quickly decided upon. It involved cleaning up *grai hinger*, horse manure, either from cleaning out the trucks or from behind the horses when they were tied to the side of the trucks. There were strict conditions. The workingmen could not help them, even the workingmen who were their best friends. Part of the punishment would last for two weeks, and part would last for the rest of the season.

Mearlie would have to clean up eight big buckets or one wheelbarrow full of *grai hinger* each day, and she would have to get an adult to do the count. The wheelbarrow could be done in two half wheelbarrows, since she was not strong enough to push a full wheelbarrow. Jess would have to clean up six buckets a day. Mattie would have to do four. That was the first part. The second part, the one that would last for the rest of the season, was that it would be completely their responsibility to look after the little mare they had saved. And they could not *chinger* about it, argue about it. Grandpa would never have to lift a finger to water her, feed her, or clean up after her. And as long as he said so, the little mare would have to be kept behind the canvas curtain so people would not see how skinny she was. When she got fat enough, Grandpa would take her out and just pretend he had bought her from somebody.

Lucky and Woody gave the special whistle that meant, "You should come back now," and the three kids returned.

Tillie spoke this time, "We want you kids to know that what you did was very wrong an' could have hurt the show a lot. You will get a punishment for it. We also want you to know that we love you very much an' that it is wonderful when you try to take care of animals an' work on problems so that you do what needs to be done. That is very good. What you didn't do this time was come an' ask us so we could tell you if it was OK or not. That is why you will be punished." She managed to look very serious as she explained their punishment and the conditions for it. Then she asked them to repeat back to her what the punishment was, so that everybody could be sure there was no misunderstanding. Then the parents motioned for the kids to come over for hugs and *bora chums*, big kisses, to reinforce the message that love is there all the time, even when there has been a problem.

As they watched, Camie and GR were feeling pride in their sons and the women they had married and how they were as parents. They exchanged a look that said volumes, and Camie, who was so good at staying calm, was almost tearing up. They must have been good parents themselves if a scene like this could take place, a loving, learning experience for their grandchildren.

The little mare was soon christened "Bones," and there was no problem with kids taking great care of her. Their brothers and sisters started helping out. Everybody loved Bones. In a month, she had put on enough weight to come out of the hiding place behind the canvas in Grandpa's horse truck and be outside tied with the other horses along the side. She made a good recovery, and she showed that she had a sweet nature, rather surprising in view of all she had been through.

The part of the punishment about cleaning up buckets of *grai hinger* was harder. Eventually, everybody on the show knew why these kids had to shovel horse manure. Mattie hated her punishment because it didn't seem ladylike. Jess just wanted to get it all done, but he was told if he did double the amount on one day, it did not mean he could have a day off the following day. Mearlie didn't mind as much, except that she was embarrassed that she could still not push a half-loaded wheelbarrow. Maybe next year she would be able to, but this year she just kept spilling loads if she put too much in the wheelbarrow.

GR kept it a secret that he really did not like Bones. He was tired of people asking him if that horse was a real horse or just a pony. Finally he made up the explanation that the mother was a pony and father a horse, and then people would smile and nod knowingly. Another problem with her size was that she could never be a show horse. She was too "in between." Maybe her mother was starved and couldn't give her enough milk. Maybe she was starved as a colt after she was weaned and was permanently stunted. Whatever the case, GR liked to see nice horseflesh, and Bones was not that.

But something happened to Bones. After she was wormed and after she put on real weight and filled out, her haunches did not stick out. She really shaped up nice. The kids decided to change her name, since you couldn't see her bones anymore. They had noticed that when there were wild strawberries at a show grounds, Bones just loved them and would do her best to eat as many she could, stretching her neck and halter in every direction and even getting down on her knees to reach under the truck to reach more berries. It was as if she was not given enough grain and hay. So she was renamed "Berries," and everybody agreed that this was a much nicer name and would bring her better luck in the future.

Berries never did become a show horse. The next season, she was just left in the pasture at the circus winter quarters. The kids pleaded for her not to be sold or given away as a pet, so there she was, just left in the pasture. The next March, though, there was a real surprise. She dropped a colt. It seemed like a miracle. There was no stallion around for miles, none except for the neighbor's workhorse stallion. There was just no denying that they must have somehow gotten together. The colt was pretty normal sized and had great coloring, a sort of medium dappled gray. The next year, Berries had another colt, a very good match for the first one. When the colts were eventually deemed old enough and nice looking enough, they went into training. They made a great pair. Berries continued her life as a brood mare, though the mystery of how she could get together with the neighbor's stallion each year was never solved. She had seven colts, three of which became show horses. And it was all because Mearlie had noticed that sick little mare on her side under the trees in the pen where horses were waiting to go the slaughterhouse.

6. MADAM CAMILLE'S CLIENTS

Madam Camille learned the profession of fortunetelling, or *dukkering*, as it was called in *Rumnis*, almost literally at her mother's knee, and her mother had learned it at her mother's knee, and so on back for countless generations. It was usually a profession among the women, but sometimes a man could do it, too, and he called himself "professor."

There were some unspoken guidelines to good *dukkering* that became almost automatic. Listen a lot. Have the clients do most of the talking. Have them make choices. Find out if what they said was the concern really was the concern. Never lie. Think about the future, since there might be an opportunity to come back to *dukker* here again. Have people leave with specific steps they could do to make the future they wanted come true.

It was understood that bad *dukkering* would bring *vaseta bok,* bad luck, for the *dukkermingra,* the fortune-teller, and her family. It was never a question of just getting money. Indeed, if Madam Camie had a weakness in her *dukkering,* it was that on occasion, she took too great an interest in her clients, placing less interest on bringing in money and more on the welfare of a poor client who was in bad circumstances. Her husband knew this and all her family did, but they never questioned it. After all, wouldn't they want to be helped by a wise woman if somehow they found themselves in a very bad way?

Even though she knew how to fit right in when the occasion called for it, Madam Camille was an outsider, a fact that gave her unusual insight and empathy. She was a foreigner, born in England. She was a traveling person, on a family circus. She was a Gypsy, of an ethnic minority that was little known or understood and toward which there was significant animosity. Better never to admit being Gypsy. And she was a woman, necessitating all the skills and subterfuges needed to succeed. Outsiders and underdogs always have to understand much more about the ways of the majority world than vice versa.

Madam Camille had largely two types of clients. There were those who wanted to have their "fortune told" because they were curious or wanted amusement or did it on a dare. Then there were those who were in some sort of an emergency or confronting some large problem or were desperate for whatever reason or combination of reasons. Within each of these two groups there was an infinite variety. It was not unknown for a person to drift from one category to the other.

Madam Camille had a fortunetelling tent that her husband put up at fairs and celebrations or other events, but her favorite place, her favorite circuit, was on Brewer Brothers Circus, where she and her husband could be close to their sons and daughters-in-law and seven of their grandchildren. They had so much to share with them.

The fortune-telling tent was really a large awning coming out from their travel trailer. In fact, it mostly hid the travel trailer, since it was usually walled in with a series of canvas curtains so a person could enter and leave discretely. Also, another curtain could divide the space further and make one or more waiting rooms. The fortunetelling room itself was furnished with a pretty oriental carpet laid down over a piece of canvas to protect it from the grass. There was also a small table, some comfortable wicker chairs, and perhaps a tea set, and maybe some vaguely religious symbol. A small Bible was placed discretely on the table to allay any fears that a believer might think that in some way Madam Camille was involved in evil magic or witchcraft.

Her husband, Grandpa GR Brewer, would hang up two well-painted canvas banners across the front of the *dukkering* tent. The banners delicately proclaimed with words and symbols, that a good person could get help here thanks to Madam's mystical powers. "Seer, Palmist, Life Guide" were some of the words on one panel. On another read, "Love, Family, Money, Future, Business, Health." The banners also had symbols worked in, such as a star and a crescent moon and the planet Saturn, and something that looked like rays of light coming over a mountain, something that somehow gave a sense of power and goodness without promising conventional religion.

The idea was to attract everyone without putting off anyone. GR often sat in front of the *dukkering tan*, the fortunetelling tent, enticing in the shy, lending an air of legitimacy, radiating kindness and confidence. Of course at the same time, he would be surveying the midway of the circus in front of the big tent, spotting any problems or opportunities. The problems might include some drunk or perhaps some law enforcement official who needed a quick welcome and a good impression of the circus people. And he was good at picking out any likely candidates to buy a horse from the string he kept lined up by the side of his truck. He always dressed like a businessman, but perhaps a more sophisticated and somewhat dapper one than was par in the towns.

One afternoon, well before the matinee show, a man in his early thirties walked by, hesitant at first, and then slightly braver. GR spoke to him politely, asking if he would like to have a little chat with Madam Camille to find out if he would benefit from a reading. He agreed, and GR escorted him around to the side entrance of the tent and asked him to have a seat until Madam could be available.

Camille knew perfectly how to confront the man's shyness and confusion. It was true that all *dukkermingras*, fortune tellers, had a different approach and a different style, but she was one of the best. She was amazing at this profession. She soon gathered the hands of the young man into hers and studied his palms as well as his face.

"Oh, my, young man, I see that you are such a hard worker! You are a strong man who works many hours, an' you have love in your life, people who love you. It could be three or four children."

"Why, yes, ma'am, you are right. This is amazin'!"

"But I can't tell if there are three or four, an' I am not sure why. What is your name, young man?"

"Well, ma'am, that is why I need to talk to you. I need to find out if I will be hung for pigamy. I don't want my kids to have to go to an orphanage. I have to raise 'em. Their mother left us. She just went off an' left us. It was five years ago. Oh, an' my name is Beryl."

"Oh, Beryl, son, that is just terrible! You are such a good father. You must be a wonderful father."

The young man softened and smiled, flattered by the compliment.

"Well, ma'am, I try. You see, they are terrific kids, an' they deserve a fine mother, but I can't give them one. An' I am afraid I will be arrested an' tried an' hung because I have a lady friend an' I do pigamy. Then my kids would be put in a orphanage. An' I can't have that!"

"Ah, how awful! You have a problem. But let's work on it. I can see that you have not really committed a terrible crime of any kind.

"Your wife left you an' the children, an' now you have a lady friend. An' you and your wife never divorced. An' now you are interested in this lady friend. Is that right?"

"Yes, ma'am. An' she is a good woman, but, you know, she an' I do the thing that, well, the thing a man an' a woman do together. An', uh, we use those things you use so that she will not have a baby, an' we are not married. So I am doin' pigamy."

"Young man, I think you mean bigamy. An' there is no bigamy, because you have not married your lady friend. That would be bigamy, because you an' your first wife are not yet divorced. Bigamy is being married to two women at the same time. An' you are not doing that."

"Really, I am not a pigamist? I mean a bigamist?"

"No, sir, you are not. An' I will not judge what you are doing. An' from what you say, you should keep using those things. Having a baby now would not be good for you or for her. But you have to tell me more, an' then we will see what your future could be."

"Well, she is a widow lady a mile or so down the road from where I farm. I love her an' her daughter. She loves me an' my three kids, an' our kids all get along great. My kids go by her house on the way to school. I want them to get as much schoolin' as they can. I didn't get much.

"Sometimes when it rains, the creek they have to cross on the road to get to school, it comes up, an' the kids can't get across. I have to carry 'em, or I get on the horse an' go get them across the creek an' then I pick up her daughter, too. Four kids an' me on a horse, that's quite a sight to see. They are hangin' off left an' right, front an' back.

"But Sylvia, that is her name, her an' me, we can't be married. So that is the big problem. That is why I need help. You have helped me already. I don't have to worry about going to prison or being hung for bigamy."

"Beryl, there are three of four things you must do. If you don't promise me you will do them, then we need to stop right here. Are you willing, Beryl?"

"Ma'am, tell me what they are, an' I will do my best. I am poor, but there are five people who love me."

"First, you need to go to the courthouse an' fill out some papers. They will call it something like a 'missing person report.' If a person is gone for so many years, like seven years or ten years, you can get them declared legally dead. I don't know how many years it is in this state. But if a person is legally dead, then the widower, that is you, is free to marry again."

"You mean that in seven years from now, I could marry?"

"No, it could be sooner than that. It starts from the time the person disappeared, not when you file. Do you remember that time, an' do you have friends who would sign a paper that the date is correct?"

"Sure, everybody on our road knows the time an'

date. People couldn't stop talkin' about it. This big-mouth guy she must 'a' been seein' in town, he pulled up to our house in a big car. I was out in the field workin', but I could see it from a distance. She walked right out with a suitcase an' a pillowcase full of things. She took all her fancy clothes an' left all her regular ones. She aint comin' back.

"My older boy, he knew what was happenin'. He begged her, an' then the littler ones started cryin', but she just left them an' got in that big car. Maybe she went to Omaha or some big city with him.

"I came runnin', but it was too late, or maybe it didn't matter. I just couldn't settle the kids down. I couldn't settle myself down. I thought if I gave them some lunch, they could get over it a little, but there was no lunch ready. There was hardly any food in the house. She was just so mean the way she did it.

"I sat with the kids on the steps for hours, an' that night we all slept in the big bed together. They were somehow afraid that I might leave, too. I swore to them, I would be with them forever. We slept like that all in one bed for a month or more. I tried cookin' what I could, but after doin' the fieldwork, there wasn't much time. We made a game of doin' the dirty clothes. They would fill two tubs a' water in the backyard. Then, while I was out doin' field work, they would put the dirty clothes in one tub to soak with a little soap. In the evenin' when I come back, I would scrub them some on the washboard, an' we would sing songs. Then they would get in an' march up an' down on the dirty clothes some more. Then we would put them in the other tub to rinse an' wring them out an' hang them on the fence to dry.

"It was really rough goin'. An' then one day Sylvia come by with her little girl an' brought us supper -- potatoes, some bacon, some carrots an' stuff. It was delicious. An' she made a berry pie. We never had pie before. She said if the kids picked the berries, she would bake one any time.

"Well, there was no pie left that night. There wasn't nothin' left. An' Sylvia started coming by once a week, an' on Friday the kids comin' home from school just stopped at her place, an' I would come up, an' we would eat together, whatever either of us had.

"Then one thing led to another, an' one night all the kids had fell asleep, an' Sylvia an' me.....it just sort of happened. So there you have it."

"Beryl, I want you to go the courthouse this week an' file those papers for a missing person report. Do you know somebody there who is smart an' good at helping people? Try that one first.

"An' then you need to see a lawyer, but I need to tell you how to do that."

"A lawyer? But how can a poor man like me pay for a lawyer?"

"You are smart, Beryl. You can do it. Do like I say. Tell him you want fifteen minutes of his time for a little consultation, a conversation, to see if there is some work he can do for you. The consultation needs to be short an' free. If he says no, just go to another lawyer. Don't let them sucker you in an' then charge you.

When you find one you like, an' it might take two or three, tell him that your wife ran off five years ago an' you have filed a missing person report an' you want to file for a divorce in absence."

"What does that mean, in absence? Does it mean you can get a divorce even is she isn't there? An' I thought a woman had to get the divorce. Can a man ask for the divorce, too? What would be the reason for the lawyer to give me a divorce?"

"The judge grants you the divorce, not the lawyer. The lawyer just takes care of the paper work an' has everything in order. An' the reason or grounds is that she abandoned you an' your family an' didn't come back for five years, an' you can prove it. But in your little consultation, you have to get the lawyer to say what it will cost. You have to get him to say it. If you don't, he might want to make up a big bill later. Not all lawyers are good men. Some are, an' some are, well, I am a lady an' there are words I won't say.

"Be careful that the lawyer does not beat around the bush an' just say that the price will depend. That is not good enough. You have to get a quote of what the biggest cost, the maximum cost, will be so that they can't add on extra charges at the end."

"Would a lawyer do that? I thought they were legal men."

"Yes, but that doesn't mean that they are all honest. You have to be sure they are honest with you. So you have to get an estimate, a maximum estimate. An' then you bargain a bit with them. If you grew up on a farm, you know how to bargain when you go to sell cows or pigs or crops. You just bargain for this, too. Just say, Mr. Jones, I am just a poor farmer an' times are hard. I want a divorce, but times are hard. I can give you half that much money, an' I will throw in some chickens or a calf, or do some work on your place."

"You mean you can talk like that with a lawyer? Who am I to talk like that with a law official?"

"Son, you are a private citizen an' a good man. They are not law officials. They are really businessmen. Their business is helping people with the law, an' they want business. An' you could be a customer. You wouldn't be the first poor farmer who came for help.

"Now, can you do that? Can you talk to them till you find one you like an' then bargain for what you can pay?"

"I sure know how to bargain. I know how to get my money's worth. I can try it with lawyers, too."

"OK, Beryl, go to the courthouse an' fill out a missing person report. Start talking to some lawyers, an' there is a third thing. It's only about twenty miles to the South Dakota state line. You know the town across the state line. Go there an' see if it is easier or shorter to get a person declared legally dead or to get a divorce in absence there, an' so on. If a person is legally dead in one state, they are legally dead in every state. If you are divorced in one state, you are divorced everywhere. Now can you do all this?"

"Oh, gee, it will be hard. I have never had such dealin's. But I have to. I want to marry Sylvia. Madam Camille, you have changed my life. I have a future now, an' my children do, too. I don't have to worry about prison or hangin' or orphanages for them. I can't wait to tell Sylvia."

"No, son, you don't have to worry, not if you can do what you have to do, an' you have done lots of other hard things. I have faith in you. My readings usually cost two dollars, but you are a poor man, an' like you said, times are really hard. So, son, I will charge you just a dollar, but only if you promise that sometime this month you will put a dollar in a secret place that only you an' Sylvia know about. It is to start a little savings account for you two for a rainy day. You can go now, an' give your kids a big hug for me, an' hug Sylvia, too."

GR noticed that the shy and troubled man who walked in the fortunetelling tent walked out a changed man. He was standing up straight, walking with a purpose, and maybe he had a bit of a smile on his face.

Next GR noted a group of three girls of high school age, clustered together and giggling. They were staring at the banners in front of the *dukkering* tent and whispering back and forth.

GR made an opening pitch to them, one that he had made many times before in one form or another. "Good afternoon, ladies. My, my, the boys in this town must be blind to let classy young ladies like you go alone to the circus! Why there should be a dozen boys just begging for the privilege of taking you! Well, Madam Camille would love to give you a reading, an' there is still plenty of time before the show begins. You owe it to yourselves to have a quick reading. You need to know what wonderful things will happen in your lives!"

The girls smiled and giggled some more at his comments, whispered together, and then suddenly one of them was pushed forward by the other two, and GR escorted her into the *dukkering tan* and told her that Madam Camille would be with her shortly for a reading. As GR left the tent, he called out in a mild voice, "*Trin vongered raklies*," so Camille would know that there were three girls in a group and they seemed to have money. She could plan the timing and charges accordingly.

Camille noticed how composed and confident the girl was who was seated before her, how she established direct eye contact and showed no nervousness. This was generally a sign that there was no serious problem and that the client was probably there on a lark.

"My, my, young lady, aren't you a pretty one! An' you have such good taste in how you dress an' fix your hair." This of course resulted in a big smile. "What is your name, my dear?"

"Sandra, my name is Sandra. An' this is the first time I have ever done anything like this. If I like it, my friends will come in, too."

"Oh, I see, Sandra. Well, let me take your hands. I believe I have a very clear reading for you. Let's see now. Oh, you have beautiful nails. They are indeed well kept, an' you have picked a very lovely shade of polish, not one of those cheap colors that some girls pick."

"Oh, yes, having perfect nails like this requires an awful lot of hard work on my part. It is not just automatic, but I love to look good," Sandra replied.

"Well, let me read your palms a bit. Some things are coming through clear. You are a leader." Camille paused between most sentences, so that thoughts could come to her more easily.

"Many girls in your school admire you an' follow you, an' the boys admire you, too. You have a lot of fun, but I am not sure that you work very hard at your schoolwork. You are intelligent, an' you could do well."

"Goodness, you are right!" Sandra exclaimed. "I am popular, an' I am smart, but I like to have fun an' I don't work all that hard. How could you tell?"

"Honey, it is my gift, an' I have been doing it for many years. Now, listen closely while I tell you something you should know. You might not like to hear it."

"Oh, what is it?" Sandra asked, with a puzzled look on her face.

"Honey, you are nice to all the popular kids an' the good-looking ones an' mostly the rich ones, but there are some you just ignore, like they are dirt. You barely look at them. You know their names. You know everybody's name. But you are very unkind to them because you do not even think they are worth noticing."

"Well, yes, you are right. They are not worth noticing.

None of my friends wastes any time on them. An' why should I? They aren't worth it," Sandra replied.

"Sandra, you are very young, an' there are so many things that you don't know. You have many gifts, but you aren't the young woman you could be. You have work to do."

"What do you mean? I thought this was supposed to be fun. I am probably the most popular girl at school, an' I will probably be homecoming queen. So, there!"

"What you say is true, honey, but it is not the whole story. There are many kinds of beauty, an' you could have all of them. An' kindness is a type of beauty that will never fade. You need that type of beauty, too. The Lord smiles an' blesses those of us who are kind, an' especially if we are kind to those who don't receive a lot of kindness. You see, they have good things, gifts, to give us, too. An' you don't want to miss those gifts. The gifts are like presents that don't have any wrapping. You can't see them. You give an' you get back, an' you don't count who gives more. You just give." There was a pause after Camille spoke.

"What are you saying? Am I supposed to be best friends with the girls who have patched dresses or who have holes in their shoes or that I should go out with ugly boys? I can't do that!"

"You are really quite intelligent, Sandra, an' you know how to get along with people. As I said, you are leader, or at least you could become one. All you have to do is start to say hello to these people an' maybe to smile at them. Notice them as people, as boys an' girls who have a place in the world, too. They are just as good as you are, only maybe in different ways. Be nice to everybody. Ignore nobody. Give out kindness every day. It will come back to you."

Sandra was almost confrontational. "But I don't want kindness from them. I don't need it. I want kindness, as you call it, from my friends. What are you sayin'?"

"Oh, my, my, Sandra. I will give you a very clear example. I knew a girl once whose name was Alice, an' Alice was even prettier than you are. She seemed to have everything. But behind her back, many of the kids her age called her Awful Alice or Alice the Snob. She saved her pretty smile only for the 'right' people. She treated others as if they were weeds beside the road.

"One day she borrowed her father's car to go to a football game. She was a team dancer, or what do you call them, cheerleaders?"

"Oh, I am a cheerleader, too," Sandra said.

"Well, she had a flat tire on the way to the game. An' she had no intention of changing the tire herself. She didn't really know how. She just stood beside the car an' waited for people to help. But, help did not come. All her friends were already at the game, an' the other kids found it easy to just ignore her the way she always ignored them. Even some kids who were walking by ignored her or said they had to hurry so they wouldn't be late for the game. It was over an hour before a farmer came along an' changed the tire. She missed most of the game, an' her teacher punished her because cheerleaders are supposed to be on time no matter what.

"Sandra, you live in a town where everybody knows everybody, an' there aren't many secrets. Someday you may open a shop or have a little business. But people will ignore you if you ignored them. They won't vote for you husband if he wants to go into politics. They won't even babysit your kids or paint your house. Awful Alice saw this sort of thing when she went to get her car fixed. The mechanic was always happy to put her at the end of the line, even behind people who came in after her. He didn't care if she didn't like it. There was no other garage in town anyway. An' he never gave her a price break, either."

"Some of the kids you ignore could later be a teacher for your children, or your next door neighbor, or even your dentist. But the reason to be nice an' to be kind is not because of what you expect to get back. That is just the obvious reason that any smart person understands. The reason to be good to everybody is because it is the right thing to do. It is what the Lord wants. Sure, people will admire you for it, but that is not the reason to do it. You do it even if nobody will ever know. You just make it your habit an' your way of life. You think about them. You don't think about yourself."

What Camille saw next did surprise her. There was a big tear running down Sandra's cheek, and her lip was quivering. And what Sandra said next was even more surprising.

"You mean I don't have to fight to stay in the good

kids' gang? I don't have to fight to be the best an' most popular? I can just forget about all the little rules we never talk about but that we use? It is so hard. You have to do it all the time. You have to try to be better than even your best friends."

"Sandra, you can do anything you choose to do. You have choices to make, an' you will have even more choices. If you start letting go of some of the little rules, as you call them, you will find that others might do the same. They will have more kindness, too. It doesn't matter if they don't, but they might. An' being genuinely nice to your close friends is a wonderful thing, too. They will love you all the more for it. Of course, again, that is not why you do it."

Then Camille paused again, for a long time, and she let Sandra think about all that they had said. It was always impossible to tell if a young girl like Sandra could really change, even a little, from a conversation in a tent with a fortuneteller before going to the circus, but Camille felt some confidence in Sandra. It was not exactly the same kind of confidence she saw in Sandra when she walked in, but it was confidence that Sandra could take more charge of her life and make some good choices.

And that encouraged Camille to take on another subject.

"Sandra, I am getting other messages for you about your future. Are you still interested?"

"Oh, yes, Ma'am. Please go on. Tell me!"

"Well, my dear, they have to do with love an' boyfriends. I believe you have a steady boyfriend, but I don't know what you really think about him. It is unclear."

"You must mean Jeffy. He is my boyfriend, an' he is OK."

"What do you mean, he is OK? Do you like him? Do you love him? Do you have things in common?"

"Oh, no. It is just that he is a big football player. All he really likes is sports, really, just sports an' kissin' me. An' he can't dance. An' he is not good in school. He can try, but he just can't get better grades. But I just need somebody to go out with."

"Well, you are going to have a baby with him. I see it right here," Camille explained, very seriously.

"No, that is impossible! I have never let him do anything. I even slapped him a couple times!"

"No, I see it right here. Next year, sometime before Christmas, you are going to have a beautiful little baby. Let's see, that means you get pregnant around next March, an' then you have to get married just as soon as you graduate from high school. An' you have a very pretty wedding, an' people can't tell if you are really showing or not. But then of course you show very soon afterwards, an' the whole town knows it was a shotgun wedding, but a very nice one. An' some of your friends have baby showers for you. But you have three more babies in three more years, beautiful babies, a couple boys an' a couple girls. My, my, you are busy. You beg your mother-in-law to come over an' watch the babies so that you can clean house an' do laundry, cook, do dishes. It never stops. Jeffy has to work all the time. He is hardly ever home to your little apartment."

"Oh, no, I don't want that," Sandra nearly screamed. "I don't even know how to cook. I don't want to get fat an' pregnant; well, maybe someday I do, but not for a long time. I don't want to marry Jeffy! Help me! What can I do?"

"Well, Sandra, you have to do it yourself. I can tell you what I see, but I can't help you more than that. If you don't want to marry Jeffy an' you don't want to have babies very soon, you have to make changes. They will be hard changes. You have to start getting the best grades in school that you can, an' you need to start now. With good grades, you have more choices. You can get different jobs. You can go to another town. You can even start business school or beauty school or maybe be a nurse."

"Oh, do you think I could do something like that?"

"That is something for you to work for, honey, if you want it. Talk to a teacher who you like. Getting very good grades is just one step, but a really important step.

"And you have to give up having one steady boyfriend like Jeffy. Be nice to him, but you need to break up an' see other boys, good boys. Be nice to Jeffy, because you will probably know him the rest of your life. Your kids an' his kids might play together, go to school together. You remember how important kindness is, niceness is.

"An' Sandra, I want to be clear with you. You say that Jeffy likes to kiss you. And I understand that. Maybe you like to kiss him, too. But Sandra, kissing has to stay above the neck, with no hands any place else, nothing else anyplace else. Just stay above the neck. An' when you slapped Jeffy, you were doing the right thing. Never wonder if you need to slap a boy, even a boy acting nice. If you even think you need to slap him, that means you need to slap him.

"Someday you will meet a boy, an' everything will be right, an' you will want to marry him an' someday have a baby with him. Don't be in any hurry.

"An' this is not as important, but it is important. Honey, you need to learn to cook, an' you need to learn now. Tell your mama an' daddy that you want to cook supper every Tuesday night, an' that you will clean up an' do the dishes, too. Just ask your mother or an aunt or somebody to give you some lessons. It is not as hard as you think. Then practice, an' learn more. Someday, you will want to have friends over for dinner, an' even if you have money an' have a maid, you have to work with her an' tell her how you want things cooked."

"Oh, we have a great maid! An' she could teach me. I love her. She has looked after me since I was a baby. An' she can really cook," Sandra explained.

"So, Sandra, you have a lot to do when you leave here. Tell me how you are going to do it an' when you are going to do it."

Sandra sat for a moment with a very thoughtful look

on her face. Camille waited patiently.

"Gee, the first thing I can do is relax an' just be nicer to people, to everybody, an' stop playing by all the rules about being popular. I have to try it. It will seem funny, but I can try it. An' relaxing feels good. Oh, an' of course I need to work on my grades and try for A an' B, and not just C an' B. I bet I could get two or three A's if I just tried. I want to be able to do whatever I want to do after high school next year. I will talk to Mr. March, our English teacher, about if I can go to college or whatever an' how to do it.

"The hard part will be Jeffy. He will get mad. He will tell me that he will sock any other boy who wants to take me out. He will be a problem."

"Jeffy doesn't own you. An' you never want to marry a boy who thinks he owns you." Camille was very stern.

"I sure don't! I can't live with somebody like that," Sandra agreed.

"Will you really be able to break up with him? Wouldn't it be easier just to stay with him an' then get married?"

"Never, I will never marry him. I will break up with him now. Maybe I won't be able to go out with other guys for a while, not until he gets a new girl friend, an' then he is her problem. An' other guys will be free to ask me out.

"But can I really learn to cook? The first time it will probably taste awful, and I will be ashamed. But if I am going to be a woman, I need to learn to cook. I am smart. I can do it. My nanny will help me," Sandra said.

"Well, darling, we have covered a lot in this reading. My, my! But now you have so much more to do! This is just a beginning." Camille wanted to be sure that the girl was really committed.

Camille looked at her face and couldn't tell if Sandra was crying or smiling or both. She told Sandra that she could just go visit the horses out back if she wanted to be alone for a little bit and then get back with her friends. And Sandra smiled broadly.

"Honey, I wish you all the luck in the world. The price for this reading will be five dollars, but what you have decided on will last you for the rest of your life. You are a remarkable young woman. I will be thinking of you and sending you strength for a long time," Madam Camille added.

Sandra reached in her purse and counted out five one-dollar bills, and then she rose and went out the back way that Camille pointed to. And the next girl was taking a seat on the wicker chair before the seat even cooled.

This second girl had the face of an angel; she just embodied sweetness. If there were a prize for sweetest-looking girl in the state, she would have won it hands down. And when she spoke, she was so sincere it was like honey dripped from her voice.

"I have never done anything like this before," she said, "and I have just one big question."

"Well, I am very happy to have you, my dear. Welcome. An' let's work on that question. But first tell me what your name is, an' let me look at you and your hands."

"My name is Jenny, ma'am. An' you don't do any evil work, do you, like a witch or somethin'?"

"Oh, Goodness, Jenny, who told you such a thing? A reading is to find out how to help good things happen to you." Madam Camille had fielded such comments many times, and it was important to put the focus back on the client quickly.

"Well, do you believe in the Lord God as our Savior?" Jenny continued.

"My dear, this reading is very serious, but it is about you, an' I have to tell you right now that if you do not believe in the power of faith an' the power of love, I don't believe I can do a reading for you." And at this time, Camille grabbed the little gold cross pendant that hung from her neck, partly as if to give her strength and partly as if to push it forward and confirm that belief was in her soul. "So tell me, an' be an honest girl, as if your life depended on it, do you believe in the power of faith an' the power of love?"

"Why, yes, ma'am, I do. I really do. I read my Bible every day, an' I try to lead a good life an' follow the Lord's way. So I believe in faith an' love. My daddy is a man of God, a preacher, an' I go to church twice on Sunday an' sometimes Wednesday or Friday. I really believe!" Jenny exclaimed.

"Oh, that is wonderful, my dear. An' it is such a relief. I thought you were a good child. But I had to hear you say it. The world needs more girls like you."

"Well, I have just one question about my future, an' it is a very big question. It is the only question that matters," Jenny said.

"What question is that, my dear?"

"Will I go to heaven or hell?" And as she asked the question, her face clouded, and what had been a cherubic expression became a painful one.

"Well, why on earth should you believe that you would go to hell, Jenny?"

"Well, Daddy says it is easy. Sometimes when he preaches, he tells stories about how easy it is if we do not follow the way of the Lord. Many people fall off the path, an' the Devil gets them, an' they suffer eternal damnation for all eternity, just like that."

"Darling, your daddy is absolutely right. It can happen, an' it must be awful. But you must tell me, are you doing something that would make you fall off the path to heaven?"

"Oh, no! But sometimes I worry a lot. It could happen, even to a good girl, or a good person. So I pray a lot, an' I read the Good Book a lot. But I still worry."

"An' do you do good acts, darling, good things for other people?" Madam Camille asked.

"Well, yes, sometimes I do, like our church's soup kitchen for the hungry hobos. Do you mean I should do more things like that?"

"You must follow your heart, my dear. But we are told that what we do tells where we are going. 'By their acts you shall know them.' An' there is another way to tell. One of the saints said that you can tell what a man is like by looking at his friends. Our friends are like a mirror of who we are. What are your friends like? Are they honest, loyal an' true? Do they care about you? Take a good look at them."

Jenny smiled again and said, "Oh, I have the most wonderful friends in the world! They couldn't be any better. They would do anything for me. They are even funny!"

"Now that is a very good sign! An' you do good acts. An' there is something else to think about. Do you love your mother an' your father?"

"Why, Ma'am, I love them to pieces, an' I will love them for a million years, always an' always, an' my little brothers, too. I will never stop lovin' them. I couldn't. An' they love me."

"You warm my heart when you say that, Jenny. An' do you love the Lord, an' does He love you?"

"What do you mean? Of course, I love the Lord God deeply an' I always will, an' when I pray I can feel that He loves me. My mother an' my father have taught me that way."

"So if the Lord loves you an' you love him, do you think that a loving Lord could let you fall off the path an' suffer for ever an' ever?" Madam Camille asked.

"Oh, when you say it like that, no! He loves me. He will give me strength. He would not let me fall an' suffer."

"So do you believe you are on the path to heaven or to hell?"

"Jenny's face burst into a huge smile. I am on the path to heaven! My soul will be saved. I won't go to hell. Oh, it feels wonderful! I am so thankful to the Lord, an' even to you, Ma'am."

"Jenny, you are on the path now, an' I believe you will stay on the path. There are things you must do, an' I feel sure you are going to do them."

"What are they, Ma'am? What are the things?"

"You must keep talking with your father an' with your mother. They need to know how you feel, an' they will give you more guidance. You need to keep reading your Bible. You need to do as many good acts as you feel you should. An' you should never be smug."

"What does smug mean?"

"Smug means that you think you are better because you feel saved an' that other people aren't as good as you. You are better than they are. Some people can be like that," Camille explained.

"Oh, I see. That would not be the way of the Lord."

"No, Jenny, it would not be. An', Jenny, the big question you had, we can only answer it for right now. The answer forever is up to you, but you are on the good path now. Everyday, you can think if you are on the path, an' you will be. But if you ever have any doubts, you can do something about it an' get back on the path!

"One of the secrets to staying on the path is not to worry just about yourself but about other people. What can you offer to help them? What kind of friend can you be? What good acts would be the right thing to do, now? If you love an' help other people, that will help you stay on the path."

"Oh, thank you. I see it better now. I understand," Jenny said, with her very sweet smile showing again.

"Jenny, a reading like this does not exactly have a price. It is not something you buy. But you do pay for it. You pay for it in two ways."

"What do you mean? What are the two ways? Do I have to pay twice?"

"You will give me four dollars right now. That is the easy part. But then you will pay by doing good acts for other people. Helping hungry hobos is a good act, but you can do good for any people, any day. Just do good acts quietly, an' that will be your real payment to me, but more important, payment to the Lord."

Jenny gave her the money, an' her hand was almost trembling. She could not speak. But she was very happy, an' Camille knew that the payment would go on for a very long time.

There was still a third girl in the trio, and she was a little afraid of being late for the circus performance now, but GR assured that she could go right on in to

Madam Camille's tent, and there would not be a big problem.

A girl who said her name was Billie Jean came in quickly and took the seat. She was smiling, but it was a skeptical smile. "The only reason I am here is because I told my two girlfriends that if they did it, I would do it, too. It was sort of a dare. An' now I don't know what to tell you."

"Well, Billie Jean, a dare is as good a reason as any to come in. An' you are very welcome. You seem to have very nice friends."

"Yes, they are terrific. We have a lot of fun, an' they help me fit in. I love them."

"Darling, what do you mean that they help you fit in? Why do you have to fit in?"

"Well, most of the kids in the high school are town kids, but I am from a farm a couple miles on the other side of town. A lot of farm kids don't go on to high school, but my parents wanted me to."

"An' why did they want that? Wasn't there work for you to do on the farm?"

"Sure, there is always work on a farm, but they wanted at least one person in the family, even if it was a girl, to go to high school, an' now I have only one more year."

"Was it hard for you?"

"Oh, the courses were not really hard. I am good at books and figures. I get very good grades, an' I am usually at the top of the class. That was not the hard part. The town kids are different, an' they have different things, an' sometimes they think farm kids are, you know, dumb. Well, I showed them. An' now nobody makes any wise remarks anymore, an' I have even had some of them out to the farm. An' Sandra an' Jenny have been great. They taught me about makeup, an' we even trade sweaters an' other clothes."

"So what are you going to do when you graduate next year, an' it looks like you are going to graduate with prizes. Congratulations!" said Camille.

"We will finally have somebody who went to high school in the family, an' even finished high school. An' there is so much to do on the farm. There are all kinds of projects, an' now I know figures very well, an' there is stuff from the county agriculture agent that I can ask my folks about."

"Honey, I mean longer than that."

"Oh, well my mother an' father say I would make some lucky farm boy the best farmer's wife around here, but they are just being nice. I would probably know more about farming than he would, an' he might not like that. You see, I know practical farming from experience, but I also have a head for kind of the scientific an' business side. So I don't know what I want to do.

"An' a lot of farms have foreclosed around here, an' the people have moved off. You can buy a farm cheap now. Sometimes the bank just wants you to take it over. Why, we even hire some of the people who had to leave their farms when we need help. One of them is a nice boy who is very nice to me, but I don't want to settle down, not yet."

"Billy Jean, I have an idea. But people might not understand it."

"What is that, ma'am? What is the idea?"

"If you want to, you could try a year of college an' see if you like it. What would you have to lose?"

"Me, go off to college? Nobody in my family has ever done that. What would people say? An' how would I pay for it?"

"Nobody in your family ever went to high school either, an' you did. An' if you really have good grades, you could get a scholarship an' work part time. What do you think?"

"Oh, my goodness. Is that possible? Am I smart enough? Can girls get scholarships? What would I study?"

"Honey, it is all up to you to find out. You seem to have a lot of brains, an' you should talk to a good teacher at your school to get started. There is a lot of work, but you are used to new things an' work."

"Could I study about animals an' crops? Will they let a girl do that?" Billy Jean asked.

"Sweetheart, I really don't know. But I have seen girls at colleges when we show in towns where they have one. The circus was in a town about forty miles back the road, an' there was a college there. Oh, that was

Central State College, something like that.

"Do you have an idea where to start, if you want to go there?" Camille asked.

"Sure, I will talk to our principal an' my favorite teacher. It will take some time with my parents. They don't know anything about such a thing. They won't believe it."

"It's all up to you, Billie Jean. Now give me four dollars, instead of five. I want you to take that one dollar an' put it in a special envelope so you start to have some money for all your college expenses. Will you do that?"

"Oh, Yes, ma'am. I will. Here are the four dollars. This was so great!"

The three girls were quiet as they bought their tickets and got in line to enter the bigtop. This was unusual for them. They were each lost in their own thoughts. This quietness lasted till the intermission, and when they went to get popcorn, their usual chattering started. They could hardly stay quiet during the second half of the performance. They talked all the way home. They sat on the front steps of Sandra's house and talked for another two hours. They started a conversation that would last off and on for over fifty years.

Sandra was the first to get married, but it wasn't to Jeffy. It was some years after high school, and it was to a man who worked in his family's business across the street from a store that she had opened in a nearby town. When Jenny married, it was to a man she first met when they were both counselors at a summer camp. He was the first man she ever held hands with, the only one she ever snuck out of her bedroom window to go on a late night walk with, and the only one she ever kissed. He agreed to go to church with her, and least some of the time. Billie Jean met her husband in a graduate course on soil science. She got an A in the course, but he wouldn't have gotten an A if she had not coached him.

Sandra, Jenny, and Billie Jean saw Madam Camie every few years when the show was back in town. Later, some of their teenaged children saw her though the mothers did not know this till after the fact.

The three women shared so many things, including their joy when their husbands got back from World War II, and then when all their sons got back from Korea. Just by coincidence, the three became grandmothers the same month.

Their recurring conversation over the decades had one theme that came up over and over. It boiled down to a few questions: "What do you really want to do? Can you really do it? And what do you have to do to get it done?"

Maybe the conversation first started because GR enticed them to get readings in the fortunetelling tent, or maybe it was Madam Camie who gave them some real hard questions to work with, or maybe they were smart women who wanted to take control of their lives. Probably it was a combination of these. Whatever it was, it worked.

7. WHICH WAY TO GO?

I t was a soggy day in Tupelo early in the season of 1933. It had been raining most of the morning, and the show trucks and trailers were somewhat circled around the space where the bigtop would go up, if the rain stopped. The cookhouse was up with its large awning, and many people were under it, sitting around tables and drinking coffee waiting to see what would happen. The horse truck had been unloaded, and the horses were tied under the awning there and staying reasonably dry. The elephants were happy to be grazing in the rain. They liked the sweet grass on the lot, and the rain was warm. Uncle Harry was nearby in a slicker and rain hat keeping an eye on them.

Gilly had helped his father and mother put up the awning on their trailer, and they were seated under it, drinking tea. Within the next hour or so, Amy and Woody would have to decide whether to call off the show or not, either just the matinee or maybe both shows. They would like to make the decision in conjunction with the members of the local sponsoring committee, the Elks Club of Tupelo. The joint decision would be put off as long as possible, but eventually the Brewers would have to tell the show folks to start putting up the tent in the rain or not to unload, take a break, and later drive on early to the next town. The day could be a total loss, but bad weather was one of the risks of a "mud show" like Brewer Brothers Circus. Trucks, circuses, rain, and mud just went together at times. Two men in the Elks Club were trying to get a couple loads of sawdust to be delivered by a lumber company to spread around what would become the midway and then in where the three rings would be. This would help somewhat.

Amy had already covered the floor of the trailer with old newspapers to control the mud. At the next town, if there was no rain there, the newspapers could just be rolled up and discarded, mud and all.

The rain became heavier, and in a couple places, there was water collecting overhead in dips near the edge of the awning they were sitting under. Periodically, Gilly or his father would stand up and use a folding chair to push the water out over the edge of the awning where it had been pooling so that it did not place too much of a strain on the awning ropes and stakes.

Gilly was thinking about if the show would go on or not, but he also had something else on his mind. "Dad, I just can't make up my mind. I don't know what to do," he said to his father, who was sitting on a padded folding chair, as was his mother. The parents knew that the thing on his mind was school.

"Well, Son, it is your decision. Your mother an' I will be happy with you whatever you decide to do. But we sure wish you would go back for this last year of high school an' finish. Nobody has ever gone to high school before. More than that, you are the first generation to go to school at all. We would be very proud of you," Woody responded.

"Oh, *keker*, *Dadus*, no, Dad. I will finish high school, an' I will do a good job. I always do fine. It is interesting, an' I like it. What I meant was that I can't make up my mind about going on to college. I might find a way to do that, you know. Mr. Willis, the school principal, he said I was good enough. But I don't know what it would mean for me an' for the family." Gilly said.

Gilly's mother Amy joined the conversation. She offered them more tea and then put the pot down on a little table.

"Son, explain what you are thinking, the part about what it would mean for you an' for the family," Amy said.

"Well, Mama, who am I, an' where will I live? Will I be a *Romanichal*, traveling as I was born, or will I go live in the *Gaudja* world? What will I do?" the boy asked. "An' I think you need me here on the show anyway. There are a lot of things I am good at, an' you have taken care of me an' raised me an' taught me so much; it would only be fair."

"Gilly, your job is not to take care of us. Your job is to have your own life, live the way you want to, do what you want to do. You don't owe us anything. You are a great son. You make us so happy. That is payback enough, a hundred times what you would ever owe us," Woody replied, looking up at his wife. If there was any doubt about it, the look on her face confirmed that she agreed with what he was saying.

There was silence among them for a bit. Gilly took sips of tea very slowly, kind of as an excuse to give him time to think.

"But can a *Romanichal* go off to college an' find some other way to live an' still be a *Romanichal*? Is that possible? It would be giving up on the old ways an' giving up on who we are," the boy said. "Isn't that wrong?"

"Wrong? What do you mean, wrong, Son? It is not a sin. Why you know of people in the family who don't travel anymore, an' they are still family. We see them when we go through their town, where they sell cars or do pavement work or *dukker* or whatever. They are *kera fokie*, house people, but they are still us, still *Romanichals*. Grandpa says that even happened back in England. It's not the end of the world," Woody offered.

"Really, you think of it that way? I haven't figured it out. It is so great to be on a show. I know so much about traveling, about how to make a living on the road. I can do just about anything. Why, as I get older, I could run a show like you an' Uncle Lucky an' Aunt Tillie do. I really believe I could," Gilly said.

"Gilly, we believe you could, too. Every year we see you do more an' more. You could do just as good a job as we do. Maybe you'd be even better. You got lots of brains. You are good with animals. You are good with people. You are one of the best young horsemen I have ever seen, an' I am not sayin' that just because you are my son. You can do just about anything. *Tachi, gara*, True, boy, you could do it. There is no doubt," his mother said.

"Son, you even drove a semi-truck sometimes this season, bringin' it in without a scratch every time, an' you don't even have a truck driver license yet," Woody added.

Then Gilly continued, "Well, you remember I had that long conversation with Mr. Willis, the principal at my high school. He said he just didn't know how we did it. Every year we come back a month late to school, maybe longer, an' we get back in school an' end up doing just fine, getting high grades, sometimes at the head of our class. He said he wished all the kids in the school were like that. The state is trying to make school attendance required by law up till you finish grade school, at least, an' he said someday they will make you go to high school, up to age sixteen or something like that. If we didn't do so good in school, he would report us for 'truancy.' That is when you don't send your kid to school. But he says all the Brewer kids are so smart an' work so hard that he can hardly call it truancy. An' we do lessons on the road with Aunt Jenny."

Gilly didn't bring up that Mr. Willis might have been tempted to be more flexible with the Brewer children starting school late every year and leaving early because of the generosity of the Brewer family. Every year near Christmas time the Brewers put on two short benefit performances absolutely free for the school. The performance was on the football field without a tent, and it included seven or eight acts. All the school had to do was sell tickets. The performances were the largest school fund-raising events year after year, netting hundreds of dollars or more.

Gilly continued the conversation. "Well, Mr. Willis got very serious with me. He said I was good enough to go to college an' I should try. He would help me with all the paperwork an' stuff. He made it sound like something I could do," Gilly explained. "I'd have to go off to Springfield an' stay there an' go to Central State College. It is the nearest school an' maybe the cheapest. I might work at some part-time job drivin' truck or sellin' stuff, an' I can see if there is some scholarship money to help out. But I would have to show up at the start of school in September an' stay through the end in May. I could be with the show only in June, July, an' August."

Amy and Woody knew that some kind of conversation like this was inevitable, but they didn't know that it would come so soon. Their son was only seventeen, going on eighteen. It was his version of the young man's "I want to strike out on my own" conversation. It could be that a boy wanted to join the navy and see the world, or go pan for gold, or go work as a ranch hand, but especially in this family, the idea of going off to college was even more unusual than going to sea or going prospecting.

Gilly had heard many times how his parents never went to school, not a day in their lives, how they had been taught by their mother and father or grandma and grandpa how to write and do basic arithmetic, and then they kept learning on their own. And now they could deal easily with banks and handle contracts with committees and buy trucks and so on. They did very well, hardly ever being cheated. This type of "home schooling" was more common in the 1930s, though the term "home schooling" had not been invented in the modern sense. Parents who had a little literacy did what they could for their children when they lived too far from a school, or they needed the kids for work on the farm, or sometimes they were of some minority and they feared their kids would be mistreated. Hundreds of thousands of African-American children lived in places where there just was no "colored school." Many physically and mentally handicapped children were not sent to school at all.

But here was a case in which within the span of a generation a boy whose parents had no formal schooling would try for higher education. It was hard to fathom. The parents wanted to help their son, but they had no idea of the mysterious endeavor he was considering.

Nobody spoke for a long time. Nobody knew what to say. Gilly checked to see if more hot water was needed for still another round of tea. In a way, though Amy was a calm woman, her heart was about to break because she knew that one day, a day not so far away, she would lose her son to the big wide world. This loss is hard on any mother, but Gypsy mothers have a very hard time letting go, if they ever do.

"Mr. Willis did a lot of talkin' to me. He said that I

could study science or business or numbers an' accounting," Gilly explained.

"But you are pretty good at business already, Son," Amy said.

"*Nais tuk, Dias,* Thanks, Mama, but this would be how to do big stuff, like profit margins an' expense control, an' the best ways to do it. It could even help to make more money on a show."

"What about the science?" his father asked. "What is that about?"

"It is pretty interesting. It is about plants an' animals. An' I get good grades in it already. If I was really good at it, I could maybe even be a veterinary or somethin' like that. They have to know all kinds of science," Gilly replied.

"But if I go to college, does that mean that Mattie an' little Bart do, too. Or if I don't go, can they still go? I have to think of them, too, an' even the cousins on the show," Gilly continued.

"No, Son, you get to choose, an' then they will get to choose. We want you all to finish high school, if you want to at all. An' it would be so nice to have a big brother like you to be an example. But you can't lead your life trying to show them what they can do. You do what you want to do," Amy explained.

There was another long silence again, which Gilly finally broke. "Mama, Dad, I just can't figure it out, what I wanna do. I wanna be two people. I wanna do both things. I can't be two people. *Mandi's dosta boki,*

I am so very lucky, to grow up in a travelin' life with you. I get to see everything an' do everything. I see those poor town kids. There is no work or no money comin' in for the family. An' there is nothin' to do in those towns, nothin' to do except maybe git into trouble of some kind or maybe git some poor girl pregnant. Then they really are trapped."

His parents nodded in agreement. It was so obvious that the way they earned their livelihood was good for their children, and in more ways than just putting food on the table. It was about the strength and texture of the family, working together on a day-to-day basis, even when bad things happened.

"But I can do most anything I want, an' I can't make up my mind. It's funny, but I feel stuck sometimes," Gilly said.

Woody spoke first. "Son, I felt stuck too when I was your age. What road did I want to take? Did I want to stay a usual *Romanichal*? Did I want to make some new version of the life? Grandpa an' Grandma were so great to us that I felt it would be wrong to leave them. It finally ended up that they told me to leave. They just told me. They told me to go away for a while an' come back when I wanted to. They *delled* me a *bitta vonger*, gave me a little money, an' told me to go away. They said to take care of myself an' *vater* the *vaseta jouvals* an' *livnias,* to be on the look out for bad women an' well, I won't say the other word in English. They said to send letters then come back some time."

Gilly felt more of a man, more of an adult, to hear his father speak to him about *livnias.* His age of innocence was passing or already past. Amy tried not to be emotional, but she was getting teary. She knew Woody was right. If you don't talk about things, that doesn't mean they will just go away.

"Well, *Dadus, Dias,* what if I did go to college next year, an' I met some *Gaudja raklie* that I liked?" he asked his parents. He thought he knew what they would say about a girl he liked who was not a Gypsy.

"There are some *kushti vortin'* ones out there, Son. There are good lookin' ones," his mother replied. "It wouldn't be the worst thing in the world. It's just that some day, if you want to *rummer* somebody, just make sure it's a good woman you marry, if she is a *Gaudja* or some kind of *Veshna* or whatever. If she is *rinkna,* pretty, that's fine. But make sure she is a good woman." It was understood that he could marry a white girl or some kind or a "foreign" girl. The idea that he would ever marry a *kawla,* a black girl, just never could come up, not in the 1930s.

"*Ava, gara,* we see you *vortin'* those *gava raklies.* Yes, boy, we see you lookin' at the town girls. You are a healthy young man, an' you are not blind. You even went to a birthday party of some kind that you got invited to a few towns back. You must have done some smooth talking to make friends that fast. You promised you would go and do some magic tricks at the party, I believe," his father said.

"Yes, but did you ask her to go, or did she ask you?" his mother said. "But that is really none of our business."

"An' *tutti,* you are *kushti vortin'* too, an' the *gava rak-*

lies are *vortin' tutti.* Just don't ever let it go to your head, when those town girls look at you because you are good lookin,' but it takes more than good looks to make a man.

"I never saw a *vasita vortin' Romanichal mush,* never saw a bad lookin' Gypsy man, but I have seen some I wouldn't want to marry. I waited an' found one like your dad," Amy said.

"And we all know *Romanichal jouvals,* Gypsy women, are the best, in every way, an' I *rummered* the best there is!" his father countered, rising from his chair to give his wife a kiss, a *choum.*

Amy reminded her son that he would see some *kushti Romanichal* girls when they went down to Texarkana that year. This was where so many of the families gathered around Thanksgiving in late November for a couple weeks. They all went to the old fairgrounds. It was a good stopping place coming down from the North to head to warmer spots in Texas or the Gulf Coast. There could be more than a hundred *fokie* there, not counting the little kids. There would be Boswells, Broadways, Bryers, Coopers, Grays, Joles, Lees, Lovells, Smiths, Sparrows, Stanleys, Trails, Wells, and Whartons, some from all the families that had come over from England in recent generations.

These families were related to one another many times over, like people in a little European village. They just kept marrying back into one another's families. Woody had once pointed out that his grandfather's grandmother Mearlie Cooper and Amy's grandfather's grandfather Nehemiah Cooper were brother and sister. The families became so tangled up together that nobody could completely figure out their connections. People discussing all the links in the kinship would sit around talking about the connections and eventually just laugh because they couldn't make it all clear.

Yes, Gilly definitely wanted to go to Texarkana that year, and everybody else did, too. It was a time they could admit to being a *Romanichal*. They wouldn't even be there if they weren't. They felt free to be who they were. Everybody just naturally *rokkered Rumnis* more. The young folks hung out together, rode horses together, or stayed up late at night around a fire. When children reached a certain age, parents in no way discouraged this socialization. They remembered their own younger days. Various marriages had resulted in young people seeing each other there in Texarkana over the years. Parents couldn't help but be happier when their children wanted to marry within their own clan.

The gathering in Texarkana had become different since the days of horses and wagons. Now most everybody had trucks and trailers. They could cook inside on gas stoves if they wanted to. They could go into town easily. They didn't have to put up sleeping or cooking tents and take them down unless they wanted to. Yet the good times and the relaxation remained. To be with one's own kind was very safe and very strengthening.

Yes, he was definitely looking forward to Texarkana. Would Steenie Smith be there? Steenie's father was a great fiddle player and Steenie had learned, too.

She could even do square dance calling so everybody would have a good time. How about Allie Mae Joles? She had long, thick braids and was a fine storyteller. And then there were the Sparrow sisters, Blanche and Diddie. The boys were always buzzing around them. Rosie Mae Stanley was a terrific rider. She used to make money putting her hair up under her hat and pretending she was a boy jockey. She won a lot of races and money that way. These were all young women in his age group whom his parents would be happy to see him marry. If he didn't marry one he liked, some other *gara* would. If he really liked one, and she really liked him, then it would be better to act fast.

It got so complicated. If he did *rummer* one of them, would she agree to having him go to Springfield and become a college boy? If he married a *Gaudja*, could she live the traveling circus life?

His parents pointed out that all he had to do now was to finish high school and fill out papers to go to college. Then if he got accepted, and the principal was pretty sure he would be, he could decide. And then, if he wanted to, he could just try it for a year, or just a few months.

It was a relief knowing that he could chose either way and would probably get along. It was a comfort to know he had another year to decide and that he could pick and his family would be happy for him, would be with him, would stand behind him. This was a decision that would weigh on his mind all during the season of 1933.

8. SHEILA'S SURPRISE

Sheila was quite a mare, in some ways one of the most uninteresting horses on the show, almost too steady to be interesting. She was tall and white, or mostly white with just a faint bit of bluish "ticking" showing through from her blue-grey skin. Sheila was a completely reliable jumper. In a way, she had a personality by not having a personality. Unlike lots of the other horses, she was almost completely unexpressive. But she was so steady, so reliable, and really so intelligent, that whenever a new rider needed to learn to ride jumpers, Sheila was the horse of choice. She couldn't be frightened, and she completely ignored fireworks, fire trucks, ambulances, and thunder, all noises that could upset other horses on the picket line and even leave a couple of them as trembling blobs.

Sheila was so big boned that when she was in foal she hardly showed at all. Some of the other mares in foal looked like they had swallowed a bale of hay, and the performers and workingmen on the show would make bets about how many days they had to go. But with Sheila there was no telling, except for just a few days before when her udder would suddenly swell with milk, and then in no time at all, she had a colt. It was so effortless that it didn't seem like labor.

Sheila caused confusion when she gave birth during the season of 1933. One night there was a light rain during the show, but that was a minor inconvenience. Sheila had worked in the jumping act as usual, with the other five jumping horses, completely unperturbed, though Natalie Marveli, her rider, had begged off having her do the twin high jump with Mounty. Sheila had objected to being held back. She liked routines, and in her unexpressive way it was as if she never wanted to be shown up by Mounty, the tallest horse on the show and the co-lead with her of this act. Mounty had supposedly been bought from the Royal Canadian Mounted Police, hence the name, because his height actually exceeded their standards. The two horses had been jumping together for nearly a decade. After the show closed that night, back at the side of the trucks where the horses were tied, Sheila suddenly lay down. She looked back over her shoulder with what could have passed for a curious expression on her face, as if to say, "Is it that again?" She had had five colts before, and two of them were grown and on the show. Suddenly the contractions began, and Smoky, one of the working boys, called over Red Hawk, Woody, Lucky, and some of the working boys.

"Well," said Smoky, "I hope we can depend on Sheila not to hold us up too much tonight. It'll be about fifty miles over to Milledgeville." Milledgeville was going to be a big Fourth of July show, and all the arrangements needed to be well in order. Smokey's wish came true, within fifteen minutes, out popped a colt, a little stud, and even the performers and working boys who had been around horses all their lives could not avoid joining in a chorus of "oohs" and "ahs." Indeed, the little colt was cute, white like his mother, with the short and spotlessly clean mane and curly tail that a newborn colt has.

So that night, loading the horse truck became the last thing on the agenda, and some of the other horses were curious or impatient about the delay, since after all, the little grain troughs in the trucks had been filled and were waiting for them, right where their heads would be tied. The aroma filled the air. The grain was always oats or sweet feed, and it was part of the reward for a good night's work as well as a time saver, since the horses could eat their grain as the trucks took off.

But this night, as whenever a colt was born, there were extra arrangements, such as putting a few more separation gates in the truck so that the new arrival would not get lost under the bellies of the big horses or, heaven forbid, get stepped on. Yet it was funny that big horses seemed to have some shared excitement and knowledge of the fragility of newcomer. Nobody could actually remember when a big horse had stepped on a sleeping colt. So maybe it was more of a human worry than a concern among the horses.

The confusion about Sheila's having a colt came a few hours later in Milledgeville when the horse truck was being unloaded. The truck was half unloaded when a different colt wobbled to the door, one that was clearly a filly and a slightly different color than the little stud born earlier.

Where did this colt come from? No other mares were in foal. What happened to the other colt? Why was this colt staggering out on her own? What on earth was going on? There were six men standing around dumbfounded. Four of them had flashlights that kept clearly illuminating the fact that this was a different colt. Word of the mystery spread, and soon half the show folks came over to see the marvel. Circus people are good at figuring things out, but in this instance, there were no quick hypotheses flying around.

Finally, Smokey went back up in the truck to bring out the remaining horses and then Sheila and her colt from behind the protective separation gate. Sheila came out in her usual stately way, with the little stud colt following.

Oh, one mare, two colts -- of course, it was twins, rare enough in horses, but not unheard of. Sheila was a big horse, and perhaps that meant a greater propensity for twins. And if any mare could handle having a colt in a moving truck, it would be one with the steady, imperturbable nature that Sheila had. But how had the little filly got out from behind the separation gates and come out so independently? Some things just never get explained, at least not right away.

By dawn, the twin colts were standing on either side of their mother, greedily nursing to fill their stomachs for the first time. This was perhaps the only way that the colts were alike. The stud colt had been born in Franklinville, and there were no Franklins or Franks on the show, so Franky became his moniker. Since it was Independence Day when the show got to Milledgeville, somebody said the little filly should be named Independence, which quickly became Indy.

She really lived up to her name. Most colts stayed within nuzzling distance of their mothers for the first couple days then slowly increased the distance they would stray. Franky was exactly like that, the way a colt is supposed to be. Indy, on the other hand was as independent as the proverbial "hog on ice." Within the first week, she was far out on her own, exploring her world, and making friends everywhere. Sheila mostly stayed calm and would occasionally call her colt, but Indy rarely came, unless she was hungry. A system evolved that everybody kept an eye on Indy, but sometimes what is everybody's responsibility becomes nobody's responsibility. Before she was a few months old, she went on one of her exploratory trips.

The show was in the mountainous coal country of Pennsylvania, and it had set up on one of the few flat spaces around the town, near a steep embankment below which was a railroad track, and below that was a steep cliff down to the Allemongohoy River, one of those many rivers that traverse Pennsylvania. For whatever reason, Indy thought the embankment needed to be looked into. She started down it and then discovered that she was starting to slide in the gravel and bits of coal that littered the embankment. She went down farther and farther and let out a distress call for her mother. She finally found a bit of temporary footing on the train tracks, but then she discovered that with her greatest efforts, she could not climb back up. She let out much louder distress calls, frantic ones.

Sheila heard the calls. She calmly and effortlessly pulled her head back and down with a sort of twist that released her head from the halter and halter rope that tied her to the truck. It was as if she had always known she could free herself but just saved the trick for a time when she would really need it. She trotted over to the embankment and gracefully began the descent to her distressed colt. Franky, still never far from his mother, followed close behind. Soon they were both sliding down to a narrow flat strip, the narrow flat strip of the train track. By this time, working-men were standing up at the top of the embankment, strategizing on how to rope the three animals and get them back up, if that could be done. But a sound they heard interrupted those plans.

A train whistle blasted, and the locomotive was soon visible, coming around a bend toward the three horses. Disaster seemed imminent, but despite the screeching whistle that the engineer was blowing to clear the track, Sheila stood her ground, turning calmly to the train and facing the engine head on, blocking the path to her colts. There was a standoff. The track was on a tight curve. Passengers could see up to the engine of the train, and even a bit in front of it. They were soon hanging out windows of the train cars to watch the spectacle, calling out, "Stop the train!" and "Save the baby horses!" The men at the top of the embankment now had ropes and were seeing if one of them could descend with a rope around his waist and more ropes in hand to catch the mare and colts.

Sheila seemed to have reanalyzed the situation and gradually turned around and headed up the tracks away from the train engine. She kept a slow pace that her colts could keep up with. This continued for over a mile, and she knew the colts were tiring. Then the final barrier came up. It was a railroad trestle over the river where the train crossed. The trestle had only rails and ties with gaping spaces between, making it impossible for horses to cross. The passengers were now rooting for the horses more than ever, and the engineer was losing all patience and blowing the whistle harder and harder, yet he really didn't want to push three horses over the cliff to their deaths.

Readers of a certain age will remember that steam engines of the first half of the Twentieth Century were equipped with a device known as a "cowcatcher." This device resembled a snowplow, or rather two snowplows meeting in the middle to create a large V. The purpose of the cowcatcher was to catch and push cows off the track and prevent damage to the engine or even possible derailments. It was not just for cows, of course, but deer, moose, tree limbs or other obstacles could usually be cleared. The engineer was keeping a distance of at least five or six feet between the cowcatcher and the mare.

This second standoff seemed to last an hour, but it could not have been that long. The engineer was torn between keeping his passenger train on time for the stops in Pittsburgh and Wheeling on the one hand. On the other hand, it would be very bad publicity for the Pennsylvania Railroad if dozens of passengers saw him use the cowcatcher to push a mare and two colts off the track and to their deaths in the river below.

Time was passing, and then a circus pickup truck showed up at the top of the embankment with several of the circus people in it. One was Chief Red Hawk, a Native American, a performer, and a horseman. With him was Natalie Marveli, also a performer and an accomplished horsewoman who rode Sheila in the Grand Entry and in the High-Jumping Horses Act. They had both come at great speed when they were told what had happened. Red Hawk was dressed in beaded buckskin with lots of fringe for the Indian Dance Act. Natalie was in her Grand Entry wardrobe, in which she dressed in a tutu and rode Sheila sideways and with no saddle. The wardrobe included a rhinestone tiara complemented by some ostrich feathers in her hair. To have something practical on her feet, she had grabbed a pair of cowboy boots to put on, making for an incongruous combination. Natalie dearly loved Sheila and her colts and wanted nothing to happen to them. Both people were quite skilled with ropes. Red Hawk was a great trick and fancy roper. Natalie did aerial numbers in the circus, and they required climbing up and down ropes hanging from the top of the tent twice a day.

Red Hawk rapidly tied two long ropes to the trailer hitch on the back of the pickup and then descended down the embankment on one of them. Natalie followed him down on the second rope, hand over hand.

The idea was that Red Hawk would put the rope around one of the colts. Then the pickup truck would pull the little animal up, though there was a danger of the animal falling down and being dragged up the cliff and injured. Or Red Hawk might have to put the rope on himself to take the colt into his arms and do his best to walk stiff-legged up the embankment, as if he were rappelling upwards, quite a challenging feat. Or he would make a half hitch with the rope around the middle of a colt just behind the front legs and then another half hitch around the neck. These two loops around the animal would be tied together at the shoulder so that the colt could not be hanged and would balance somewhat, if needed, and be gently pulled up along the side of the embankment.

For her part, Natalie would calm the mare and the remaining colt, as much as they could be calmed, and the engineer in the locomotive would probably quit blowing the whistle. It could be that the mare would follow up on her own. Sheila was a jumper, after all, and negotiating a steep embankment should be something she could handle. Or she might be unable to leave the second colt as the first one was pulled or carried up. The situation was uncertain. What would she do if torn between the two colts, one on the tracks and one rising on a rope up to the pickup truck? By this time, passengers were spellbound by the drama unfolding. They had got quite a show for the price of their train ticket. Some had even managed to get out of their passenger car and stand where they could see better.

When Red Hawk had gathered up the more cooperative colt, Franky, he started up the embankment. Sheila was, as the saying goes, between a rock and a hard place, with one colt going away and one staying with her. She made some preliminary steps up the bank, but Indy, who was by this time really afraid, maybe for the first time in her life, called out to her, and she came back down on the tracks. Red Hawk, colt in arms, was pulled up in jerky stages by the rope attached to the pickup. It pulled ahead in low gear, with the rear wheels skidding occasionally. As soon as Red Hawk and the colt reached the top, he handed over Franky to the other men waiting there and went back down again.

Natalie was holding Indy, trying to keep her calm and not have her fall down the cliff to the river on the other side of the train tracks. Sheila, as always, was calm. If her second colt was pulled up, wouldn't she logically follow? Red Hawk put the half hitches with the long rope around Indy as he had Franky. Indy, however, was not the calm armful that Franky had been. She did not want to cooperate. She did not want to be held in Red Hawk's arms. She expressed her rebellion by squirming out of his arms twice, and that was even before they had ascended even a few feet up the bank.

The solution was to drop down a second rope. The idea was for the Red Hawk to go up on one rope with Indy being guided up by him as she was pulled up on the other rope. It would require some complex coordination, but there didn't seem to be alternatives. If Red Hawk and Indy went up, then surely, Sheila would follow up on her own. Next it would be up to

Natalie to find footing in her cowboy boots at least high enough up on the embankment so that the train could get by. Then a final rope could be dropped down for her.

Indy and Red Hawk did make it up the bank on separate ropes, though it was a time- consuming process. Indy kept wanting to stand up, and she couldn't, and Red Hawk on his rope could not always be close enough to control her. It was rather comic, but there was danger involved. Nobody laughed.

The danger was not really from a rope breaking. It was that the little colt in her scampering around on the embankment at the end of a rope would stick a foot in a hole or otherwise break a leg. And, yes, horses were shot in those days, adult horses or colts with broken legs, or actually any large quadrupeds, such as cows or pigs, though the latter two would be slaughtered for their meat. It would be awful to lose a horse, any horse, even a colt.

Eventually, with the pickup pulling slowly and backing up a bit when needed, man and colt made it to the top. Sheila made it to the top before them, climbing nearby on her own, but sending occasional showers of rocks down the side to the train and to Natalie. The sight of her mother at the top encouraged Indy, but she still wanted to climb up and get there in her own rebellious way. Her little heart was filled with excitement, even terror, and she had no experience for any such situations.

Natalie was delighted when she finally saw all three horses at the top. Actually, it was more like Sheila's head and the colts' rear ends, since Sheila had on a new halter and was tied to the truck, and both colts were nursing ravenously. The train passengers were cheering. Red Hawk gave her a wave that said, "Come on up now." But there was one thing Natalie had to do before leaving. She stood between the tracks about fifteen feet in front of the cowcatcher. Clad as she was in her tutu, tiara, ostrich feathers and cowboy boots, she could not miss such an opportunity. She gave a majestic ballerina bow to the engine and the engineer, eliciting a round of applause from the passengers who could see her from around the bend. The engineer showed some good spirit at this point and gave the train whistle a playful double toot. As soon as Natalie was part way up on a rope, the train started to chug away, with passengers clapping wildly as it pulled by Natalie and the scene of the rescue.

If the story itself had ended, the telling of the story had only begun. Up at the top of the embankment, Natalie was startled to see a new scene of action and confusion. GR and Camie knew a publicity bonanza for Brewer Brothers' Circus when they saw it, and they had somehow managed a sort of remote radio hookup for the local MBS station. A radio announcer who was better known for announcing baseball games was busy telling the story of Sheila, the colts, Red Hawk, Natalie, the engineer, the passengers, etc. He was an enthusiastic, vivid narrator, happy to know that hundreds of people were glued to their home radios as he told this wonderful story. Two men who looked like reporters were already interviewing Red Hawk, who was now wearing the war bonnet GR and Camie had brought. GR and Camie were coordinating all the publicity details.

Into every other sentence, they were weaving the words "Brewer Brothers Circus" and names of the next four or five towns to be played. They had distributed publicity photos, including one with Natalie majestically riding Sheila over the high jump. A photographer had captured several action shots down on the railroad tracks on film, though with the dubious technology of the time, nobody knew how many of the shots could be of newspaper quality. Natalie was about to straighten her hair and see if she could find some makeup when Camie came over to tell her not to do too much. She needed to look the part of a brave rescuer. Camie advised her to smile a lot, pose for pictures, tell about her love of the animals, and say nothing at all about her background, but to mention Brewer Brothers' Circus as often as possible along with the names of the next several towns. Then she introduced Natalie to a couple reporters from newspapers in nearby cities.

In the 1930s, even mid-size towns and cities still had two, three, or even more newspapers. The newspapers competed fiercely. They had to sell papers, keep up circulation, and sell advertising space. The common phrase, "If it bleeds, it leads," was strictly applied. Newsboys screamed about murder, bank robberies, gangster shootouts and fires while they hawked papers. But if there was one thing that could on occasion supplant bloody and violent headlines, it was the "human interest story." This usually involved firemen rescuing a kitten that had crawled up a tree or a boy saving his little brother from drowning in a swimming hole.

Yet such topics paled compared to this story. Oh, my! There was an Indian, a pretty trapeze artist, a locomotive, and of course a mare with twin colts about to be swept down a cliff to certain death in a river. It was all very fascinating, and there were so many good ways to spin the story. And spin it they did. Those who read different papers could imagine that widely different things happened. Most reporters managed to string the story out into installments over three or more days, with more photos, updates on the colts, the route of the circus, Red Hawk the Indian spinning ropes, Natalie on horseback, etc.

A fact that really helped the newspapermen was all the passengers who had been on the train, who had hung out the windows along the curve to see or even gotten out by the tracks. They all had their version of the story to tell. The story got so big that four reporters actually got on the train in Pittsburg and rode it to Wheeling or beyond to get eyewitness interviews. The engineer was the biggest catch of all, and he was required by the Pennsylvania Railroad to give an exclusive to the AP.

The divergence of how the story was told was reflected in the range of headlines:

Heroic Engineer Averts Train Wreck and Saves Circus Animals

Indian Trick Roper Lassos Locomotive

Beautiful Trapeze Artist Rescues the Horses She Loves

With Just Inches to Spare, Engineer Stops Locomotive from Sending Mare and Colts to a Watery Death

Cowcatcher Fails to Catch Horses

Pennsylvania Railroad Passengers See Death Defying Circus Performance

And perhaps the most egregious:

Injun Fights Engine And Wins

All the publicity paid off quickly and handsomely for Brewer Brothers' Circuses. Five of the next six performances were "straw houses." This was a circus term for happily over-sold performances at which bales of straw were brought out and spread in front of the bleachers so that children could be invited down to have "special, up-close seats" on the straw and more of the friends and neighbors of the town could get in the bleachers and enjoy the performance. All the extra ticket sales were pure profit, pure joy for the owners and performers.

9. THIRTY WONDERFUL DOGS

The reason there were thirty wonderful performing dogs on Brewer Brothers Circus was a man whose name was Kirk Adams. Kirk was not originally a circus man. He was hard to categorize, but he had gifts to share with the world. He was a "cracker," or his background was cracker, in the original sense of the word, as a traditional or typical white from Florida or Georgia, without any pejorative connotation.

Kirk was also a bit of a Bohemian, a non-conformist, a free thinker. He did not finish high school, but he was widely read. He incongruously delved into philosophy, the history of religions, antiques, and the training of horses. He was a very kind man, kind to people and kind to animals.

As a youth, he had served in the US Cavalry. Then

he had held jobs in pulp paper mills in North Florida and on the docks at Jacksonville, but he wandered farther south along the Atlantic Coast, and he developed a particular affinity for Ormond Beach and Daytona Beach, where the beach was so wide that cars were permitted to drive on it at low tide and there were automobile races.

He had made some money clandestinely, but with full knowledge of the Volusia County Sheriff's Office. Kirk put together a deal with some Cubans he knew. The Cubans would come in by boat at night and bury cases of Cuban rum above the high tide line at a stretch of beach a few miles north of Ormond Beach. Kirk would go the next night and use some stiff number-nine wire to poke in the sand till he heard the clink of the wire hitting rum bottles. He would dig up the rum and bury the agreed upon amount of dollars where the rum had been.

This was at the height of Prohibition, and there was money to be made in the sale of bottles of quality rum. It was so much better, in the taste of many, than the less predictable quality of local moonshine. Kirk's steadiest customers included the sheriff's office, and he was happy to give them a discount price to help ensure their silence.

Kirk was wise enough to invest a sum of his money in land after the stock market crash. As an old mentor had told him, "Buy some land. They aint makin' no more of it." So at a sheriff's sale, Kirk ended up buying thirty-five acres that he had never laid eyes on. This was on the mainland across the Intercostal Waterway and a couple miles from the ocean. Nobody else put in a bid on the tract of land, and Kirk got it dirt-cheap.

For years, he never even visited it. He just paid a few dollars each year in taxes. Then a road was put through, and he could actually go see it. He made his first profit by selling an acre a year later. He got three times the price for the acre than he had paid for the whole tract a few years before. Land buying became his hobby, and it eventually contributed more to his net worth than any work he ever did.

One day he had business on Beach Street in Daytona, and he saw a girl coming out of a dry goods store with a man who looked like he could be her father. The girl had long black braids far down her back and a flowing colorful dress. She was dressed in a "high class" sort of way but not showy about it. The man was well dressed in a similar way. Kirk could not take his eyes off the girl.

She and the man got into a Maxwell sedan with broad whitewall tires. Kirk found himself following in his old Model T pickup. They went north on Beach Street, stayed on the west side of the Halifax, and ended up in Holly Hill. They turned in and stopped on a stretch of undeveloped land with lots of live oaks and Spanish moss. Kirk saw that there was a house trailer and three tents, one with the sides pulled up to let the breeze through. The smallest tent was white, and it was prominently placed nearer the road. There was a large canvas sign in front, more like a painting, with these words:

SPIRITUALIST - PALMIST - SEER

MADAM DOUANA SEES ALL, TELLS ALL

LIFE, LOVE, MONEY, HEALTH, HEART, FAMILY

OPEN FOR READINGS NOW

There was the image of a large palm of a hand between the first and second lines on the sign.

Kirk parked his pickup some distance back and walked up to the place where the car had turned in, trying to act very casual, not to stare at the girl as she got out of the Maxwell and took a seat near the tent with the sides tied back. There were other women there, and they all had a family resemblance. There were also two young boys.

Who were these people, and why were they camped like this? Were they Gypsies? How could he meet the girl?

Kirk thought up an excuse to walk up to these people. He was going to ask for help to find an address he was looking for and then to admire their tents and ask where they got them.

His throat was dry. He was nervous, but he had a slow polite way about him that was on his side. He asked about some address he made up. The man explained that he did not know about the addresses here. Most people seemed to get their mail right at the Holly Hill post office. These people with the tents were not from around here anyway. They were just passing through.

Then Kirk started asking about the tents. The man continued and explained that the tents were from Rouger Awning Company on North Young Street in Ormond. That was one of the reasons they came through here every year or two. Tommy Rouger's main business was sails for sailboats, but he could make any kind of awning or tent just the way you wanted it, redo it if you wanted, and give you a good price.

While the conversation was going on, Kirk dared to take a glance at the girl and smile at her. The man and the woman who appeared to be her mother knew that this young man was probably far more interested in their daughter than in tents and awnings; nevertheless, they were polite to him. He seemed well mannered.

When Kirk asked where they were traveling to, the man just replied that they traveled most of the year, staying where it was warmer in the winter. Then Kirk noticed that there were half a dozen horses and a few ponies tied to a picket line back in some trees and that there was a truck large enough to haul them in. This emboldened Kirk enough to ask if the man knew horses and if he dealt in horses.

"Why, yes, young man, I do. Are you in the market for a ridin' horse?" the man asked.

"No, sir, I haven't ridden much since my days in the cavalry. Guess I got enough ridin' in to suit me in the war, but I do admire horseflesh," Kirk replied.

This was a definite plus for Kirk in the eyes of the parents. He was offered a seat and some tea. He offered to help on the weekend when the family opened a horse and pony ride along a spot north on Highway A1A where a lot of tourists came by.

This was the beginning of his long association with the Brewer family, and a short-term marriage to one of them, the girl with the long braids whom he had first seen with her father that day on Beach Street. He joined up with the family as a workingman to look after horses and travel with them. He liked everything about them, the fact that they traveled, that they were Gypsies, as they eventually confirmed but which they told him to tell no one – on pain of instant dismissal – and that they were joining up with a circus owned by other family members.

Kirk made himself valuable on the circus. He could get along with any horse and any person. He never hesitated to get his hands dirty. His biggest work interest was watching people train animals. His personal interest was the girl, Didee. That fall, they were married.

The Brewers had horse training well in hand, but Kirk noticed that there was no dog act on the show. That winter when they were back in Holly Hill, Kirk began working on his first dog act, gathering up an assortment of strays, giveaways from people he knew, and rescues from the dog pound. Some he had to give back or take back to the dog pound. Part of Kirk's ethics was that he would never just turn a dog loose to survive on its own. That was too dangerous. It could starve or get run over or killed by other loose dogs. Worse yet, it could be captured and sold to a laboratory for experimental purposes, given some disease or tested with some drug. There were even stories of vivisections done on stray dogs that had been caught. It was far better for the little animal to be euthanized humanely at the pound.

He saw that dogs were like horses, or perhaps even more so. Different dogs had different temperaments and different abilities. The first tricks he trained them in were canine copies of the tricks and routines done by horses or elephants. Then he came up with some of his own.

Kirk knew intuitively that dogs were pack animals that liked hierarchy and routine. They wanted to belong and wanted to know what was expected of them. Most of them would do anything to please the leader of the pack, even if the leader was a human. They thrived on recognition and praise from the leader. They also wanted adventure and were happy when the pack was doing something together. Starting a training session or a performance was an exciting event for them. Perhaps it was like the pack going on a hunt back millennia ago.

Kirk was always looking for smart dogs that were expressive and unafraid. They had to be responsive. If they were, he would spend time with them and figure which sort of tricks came naturally to them and that they could learn easily. They would do almost anything for a human if they understood. They might start out walking on a narrow board propped up on a few bricks, but once they understood the human wanted this or that, and if the changes were gradual enough, they would soon climb up a little ladder and slide down a slide, or do any number of amazing things. Some dogs were so smart that they seemed to understand a trick by just watching another dog do it. Sometimes, something happened that was unplanned, something that could be a completely new trick.

But some dogs were not like that. It took only a few hours or sometimes a lot less to see that a dog just wasn't worth the time and energy to train. They were too easily intimidated, or perhaps they had been mistreated and could never trust a human, or maybe they lacked a sense of adventure or just plain intelligence.

Over the years, Kirk gained new insights into his dog training. Some breeds were harder to work with than others. One breed that was very good was the fox terrier. They were good performers. Some plain mongrels were good performers, too. With a couple hours of time together, Kirk got a good idea of how to teach the basic repertoire of tricks and then identify what special things the dog could learn.

Sometimes his dogs had litters of puppies, either because he wanted them to or because of an "accident." People often brought him dogs, to give him or to try to sell to him. Mostly, he just politely refused, offering various excuses. Only rarely did he see an animal he thought had potential.

Above all, training dogs took amazing amounts of patience. Some tricks took months to train. When one approach did not work, some other training approach had to be used. Kirk spent four or five hours per day training during most of the long, warm, Florida winter. He had a large fenced yard with lots of shade. He had chairs in several places. Some times there was a low table in front of a chair, and he would work with a dog on the table. There were dog cages and smaller pens on one side. He would work with one dog after another, giving each dog a lot of attention, training it to go from the known to the unknown, from something the dog knew to something he wanted the dog to learn.

The known might be something as simple as walking a short distance on the hind legs while Kirk gently held the front paws. Gradually, the distance would become longer, and the front paws would be put on a stick Kirk was holding and not his hands. The stick would gradually be higher and higher, till the dog was actually walking some steps on its hind feet with no support. From then on, it was usually a short time till the dog could just walk on the hind feet with no problem, except for one thing.

That thing was the dog's muscles. Different tricks required different muscles, and just like a human acrobat, the dog had to have time for the muscles to adjust, to strengthen. If the muscles got sore, that would be a set back. The dog would feel that the work was a sort of punishment.

Each little training session with each dog needed to be positive. The dog needed to want to come back for the next session. The dog's instinct had to be respected. It had to feel needed and praised and secure in the hierarchy of the pack. The small changes had to be clear. The dog had to understand what was expected.

Some tricks were relatively easy. Hind leg walks, waltzing, jumping through hoops – they were all simple. Jumping a rope was a little harder. It took longer, and the dog had to avoid being afraid of being hit by the rope. For most dogs, going down the slide was easy and even fun, once they overcame a little fear.

Front leg walks were hard. Most dogs could never do them. Back flips were also hard. They could take months. Usually, the dog had to like the equivalent of roughhousing. And the trick that Jack did, well, that was a natural, a happy once-in-a-lifetime trick. Jack was a little black and white Border collie cross. The trick had started out as the usual back flip, but Jack kept spinning, and then that seemed so good that it made more sense to leave it in. Jack liked it that way.

If you didn't love dogs, you could never do this type of dog training. It had to be gratifying. And for Kirk it was gratifying. Sometimes somebody would bring back a dog he had trained years before, and the dog would be anxious to come to him, to get praise and attention again.

By the end of that first winter, Kirk and Didee had their first dog act ready to present. Looking back on it years later, they laughed, commenting how basic it was and how it could have been so much better.

Their marriage did not last, but their friendship did. She eventually remarried, and it was to another *Romanichal*. Kirk found a woman who was willing to live with an eccentric like him and take a dog act, or actually twin dog acts, on circuses or on fair routes.

Over the years, Kirk trained hundreds of performing dogs. He was the only source of trained dogs for the Brewers. He always liked training dogs for them because they treated their animals so well and they knew to how work with them. His former wife and her new husband were friendly with him and his new wife. This relationship was very unorthodox for the day. They always visited when their paths crossed on the road and they saw each other's acts.

Kirk earned a reputation far and wide in the circus and entertainment world as an animal trainer, but there were people Kirk would not sell trained dogs to. That was because they could not learn how to get the dogs to perform. He was fond of saying that it could be harder to train people than it was to train dogs.

He always insisted on a week with a prospective buyer to see if the animal came to like the new owner and would be treated well, and if the buyer really understood and could communicate with the animal. If he was not satisfied, there was no deal. Sometimes he lost significant sums of money.

The Brewer kids usually got into their teens till they figured that Uncle Kirk was not a real uncle to them. He couldn't be. He wasn't a *Romanichal*, and he wasn't married to one. But they loved him just the same. They loved watching him train dogs, and they loved learning how to work dogs from him.

The fact that so many Brewers worked skillfully with dogs was the reason Kirk came up with the idea of having three dog acts, three rings of performing dogs.

Why have one dog act or two, if it was possible to fill all three rings with lots of dogs doing an entertaining routine?

The performing elephants were majestic, imposing, and exotic. The horses were beautiful, swift, and exciting. The leopards were frightening and unknown. The dogs were nothing like any of that. They were the smallest of the performing animals on Brewer Brothers' Circus and the most familiar. Almost all the spectators had a pet dog or knew dogs in their neighborhood. People saw dogs every day. The performing dogs really had to offer something different.

The three dog acts filled the three rings with ten dogs in each ring. The routines were full of action and surprises. Woody and his daughter Mattie worked in the first ring. His sister-in-law Tillie worked with her son Jess in the center ring, and her husband Lucky and their daughter Mearlie worked the third ring.

Using three little wagons solved the logistical problem of bringing thirty dogs into a bigtop in some orderly fashion. They were similar to children's play wagons, but about twice the size, big enough to haul ten dogs each with reasonable ease. Carpet was put in the beds of the wagon to keep the dogs from sliding as they rode. One wagon parked at the back of each ring served as the home base for the dogs performing in that ring. When they completed a trick, they automatically returned to their wagon.

The routines in each ring began with several dogs walking on their hind feet and forming a semicircle around Woody, Tillie, or Lucky. The dogs waltzed around on their hind feet whenever their trainer turned, all in reasonable synchrony with a peppy musical score played by Pierre's band. Next, four dogs in each ring would lie flat and roll over, doing the simplest trick in the act. But suddenly two of them would jump up and leap over the other two, then lie down and roll again and in turn be jumped over by the other two in a sort of weaving pattern.

The "walk-through" was next, with two dogs weaving in and out between the legs of the adult as he or she did a slow and rhythmic walk. This was followed by two or three of the dogs jumping through hoops brought out by the young performers helping present the act, followed by rope skipping, with one end of the rope held by the parent and the other by the son or daughter.

After each trick, the parent and son or daughter did a happy style with both arms extended wide and a big smile, facing one side of the tent and then the other, and finally pointing down to the performing dogs as if to say, "Aren't these wonderful little animals doing their best to put on a great show for you?"

Next a dog would come forward and simply lie down for the "pony ride," a trick in which a smaller dog would come and climb on the back of the first dog, with its four feet hanging over the sides of the larger dog. The larger dog would stand up and take the smaller dog for a little ride around the ring.

In the "London Bridge" trick, two dogs would rise on their hind feet and approach each other, putting their front feet on each other's chest. Three other dogs would circle under the arch they made.

The fast pace continued with a dog coming forward to walk on its front feet, a trick that most dogs could never master. And then another dog would come up on hind feet and embrace the first dog from behind, forming a kind of wheelbarrow that moved around the ring, a trick that never failed to bring forth happy laughter.

Fancy little barrels came out next, and two dogs jumped up on them and rolled them across the ring while others circled through open ends of the moving barrels.

Tillie and Woody had little dogs that could push a small cylinder of stiff wire, an imitation of the barrels that the bigger dogs had rolled, but this time halfway across the ring, a toy dash hound would come out and try to get through the cylinder, inevitably getting stuck and provoking more laughter.

Little slides, about four feet tall, resembling the slides on children's playgrounds, were brought out for the next trick, and nearly all the dogs came forward to climb up the little stairs and slide down the chutes, run around quickly and climb the stairs again for a second or third slide down. But in each ring one dog was a scene-stealer. This dog would turn around and slide down the slide backwards. In reality, it was easier to train a dog to slide backwards than forwards, but sliding backwards got the most laughter and applause.

At this point the music stopped, and the ringmaster announced a trick of special difficulty. Brewer Brothers' Circus was the only circus in America that in all three rings had dogs that could do backflips in the air simultaneously.

After a drumroll, a dog in each ring would come forward and upon command begin a series of high backflips that amazed the audience.

After the applause, the three dog acts became one dog act. All the dogs came to the center ring, and most of them took part in the spinning table trick. For this trick, barking was perfectly acceptable, and several animals at a time jumped up on a very low table that that had a large swivel under the middle of it. This allowed the table to revolve rapidly. It was skirted by fringe that flew out into the air as the table spun faster and faster as the dogs ran on it. The table was covered with rough canvas so that the animals could get some traction and not slip.

All the dogs wanted to stay on the table and run on it as the speed increased. They were competitive. Soon there were more and more on the table, and some would be bumped off and gamely rise to jump back on and find a place again. The barking became deafening. This was the dogs' favorite trick, and most of them had learned to do it in just a few days. The circus audience, however, had never seen anything like this, and they were caught between laughing and applauding. After a few minutes, the chaos had to be brought to a close, and the ringmaster announced that a special trick would close out the canine performance.

All the dogs except Jack were called out of the ring

and hauled away in their little wagons. Tillie brought Jack forward. Jack was wagging his tale vigorously, and sometimes his happy barking interrupted the announcement being made by the ringmaster.

"Ladies and gentlemen, we are proud to present the only dog in canine history who can simultaneously do a side twist and a back somersault in one movement. This is one for the books! Our star is Jack, presented by Ms. Tillie Brewer. Jack is a beautiful black and white Border collie, and when he performs, you will have to watch closely, or all you will see is a pretty ball of whirling black and white fur. Please note that Jack will rise over three feet into the air, and that he can perform this acrobatic marvel perfectly up to ten times without stopping.

"Ms. Brewer, are you ready to put Jack through his paces?"

Tillie would smile broadly and nod her head yes.

Once she gave the command, Jack would begin his acrobatic leaps, doing an aerial rollover and a backflip in one jump, and interspersing it all with yelps of glee. At first it was hard to see what this aerial trick was because the movement was so fast, but then people could discern that he was rolling side-to-side and head over heels with each leap. This trick required not only skill but also strength and energy, and Tillie actually had to stop him after about ten flips so that he did not exhaust himself.

When she stopped him, he would inevitably be disappointed, but his tongue would be hanging out and he would be panting rapidly.

This was a closing trick that showed that the dogs, too, could hold their own as performers and were just as intelligent and entertaining as the horses and elephants.

Yet the big mystery for the audience remained. How was it possible to bring such a group of dogs together and have them perform such tricks so happily? People just could not understand it.

Of course the explanation was Kirk Adams. Uncle Kirk ended up having a wonderful life, maybe because of his eccentric traits or maybe despite them. He became a vegetarian in an age when such a diet was so rare. He could identify many kinds of mushrooms and tell which were safe to eat. He started visiting antique shops in the towns where the show was, and he had quite an eye for underpriced treasures. He bought and resold them at considerable profit to dealers back in Holly Hill and Ormond. He collected old books, especially valuable first editions. He always considered the Brewer kids as nieces and nephews, and he treated them very kindly.

Not that many human beings find a way to make a living for most of their lives doing things they like. Probably more people should be as brave and nonconformist as Kirk Adams was.

10. TWO ELECTRICIANS

C hoctaw was a kindly man in his late fifties with little book learning but decades of practical experience. Everyone knew about some of his background, and nobody knew about the rest of it. He said his mother was from Canada, and that is why he spoke French. He said his parents had eleven children, and all of them were named for Indian tribes, with the girls getting names that sounded more feminine, like Sioux or Hopi, and the boys getting more masculine ones like Arapaho and Comanche. The joke was that his parents had to stop having kids because they could not think of any more Indian tribes.

His wife, or so he called her, was also kindly. She went by "Jenny," and all the kids and many of the adults called her Aunt Jenny and him Uncle Choctaw. If you ever asked him what his last name was, he would reply that folks just called him Choctaw or Chockie, though nobody ever did call him the latter. He and

Jenny signed the circus salary sheet each week with the name of Helmsley. And several years ago, when some of Aunt Jenny's family came around, they said their name was Helmsley. Thus it was discovered that he was for some reason using his wife's family name. But this being a circus, no comments were made and no questions were asked. Maybe he had been married before and maybe she had, too. And maybe they had formally divorced earlier spouses and maybe not. The man and woman had a past of some kind, and that really didn't matter if they were doing good work on the show now.

Uncle Chocktaw's official title might have been "Show Electrician," and such a title immediately conveyed respect and concern. Electricity was an essential service, but the danger of electrical shock was always present. In reality, he was a sort of factotum, and his portfolio included plumbing and water supply for the show (or where there was no water hookup at the site, getting a tank truck to bring water on the lot for the people and animals), basic mechanical maintenance and repairs (or getting a mechanic to come to the lot or the vehicle to a garage), and basic carpentry (or finding a carpenter who could build or fix what was needed). Of course, since times were so hard, it was always preferable for Choctaw to handle the job himself, even if the fix were only temporary.

Choctaw was also in charge of seeing that there was a crew to set up the *doniker*, when it was needed. *Doniker* was circus slang for toilet. Most places, like ballparks and fair grounds, already had permanent toilets so there was no need to put up the *doniker*. But sometimes there was a good town to show, and the lot was just some farmer's pasture on the edge of town, with no toilets in sight. Then a long, two-foot deep trench had to be dug, and the long skinny *doniker* tent had to be erected over it, with the back half of the tent right over the trench. Boards were then placed on a bench-like frame. For the ladies' side of the tent, the boards had four holes; two were considered a size appropriate for adults, and then a smaller one and a very small one for little girls. The men's side was different, with only three holes of various sizes, and then a completely open spot, which was intended to inspire men and boys to pee in so that the wood around the holes would not get wet. Each side had a little box with torn bits of newspaper in it to serve as toilet paper. There was a sort of double curtain for the entrances so that there would be no embarrassing moments when a person sitting down would be exposed to the world. There was even a snap inside to help assure a little privacy. Some lime was sprinkled down the holes after every show to control both odor and flies, especially in hot weather. The curtain on one side was marked "Ladies" and on the other side the curtain was marked "Men." Both sides also had a crescent moon drawn on them, which was in those days the universal icon for "outhouse." When the *doniker* was torn down, the trench was closed over with the dirt that had been dug out to make it. In a few weeks, there was little evidence of where the toilet had been erected except for the strip of very green grass.

There were endless jokes about the *doniker*, but everybody good-naturedly took turns putting it up and taking it down. It was unpleasant, but it was a necessity. By the standards of the day, it was a perfectly acceptable facility. After all, many people then had no indoor plumbing, or if they did, it was only a faucet and sink. Outhouses were still the norm in many places, and everybody was familiar with them.

As for the other half of this couple, Aunt Jenny, she was really good at making, altering, and fixing show wardrobe, and she often had a needle busy in her hands. She was also an accurate and rapid ticket seller and could handle any of the concessions, making and selling popcorn, snow cones, or cotton candy. She could keep the corn popper and ice shaver and cotton candy machine operating. She had lots of skills. There was not much she could not do.

Though she had no children of her own, she loved children, and she ran an informal but well-attended sort of summer school, with most of the show kids seated earnestly at her feet or on hay bales for two hours a day, practicing numbers, printing or writing, and reading stories. She much preferred to have the older kids read to one or two of the younger ones while she listened in and offered the gentlest and clearest of directions if any were needed. Since these were, after all, show kids, her lessons had a circus emphasis, with lots of map reading, U.S. geography, and arithmetic problems about how many pounds of sugar it would take to make cotton candy for a week if it usually took about five pounds a day or about what the cost of gas would be to get from one town to the next. People somehow avoided asking if she had been an actual schoolmarm, since that would have been kind of intrusive. If a kid was learning stuff, important stuff that not even town kids learned, then it was better just to be grateful and not pry. The circus business was a wonderful place where people could leave behind whatever past they had, reinvent themselves, and earn respect and a livelihood in a new life. Choctaw and Jenny had done just that.

This couple had a most interesting pet, a small African Gray parrot with an embarrassingly large repertoire of expressions. The parrot would imitate the sound of an engine starting up, a dog barking, or almost any animal calling for feed. At random times he spouted phrases such as:

Ladies and gentlemen and children of All Ages!

Get your red-hot popcorn right here!

Friday is payday.

I hate train tracks!

My Oh My, button your fly!

Time is money, honey!

Woody wants to see you.

Brought to you by Burma Shave

Where's the juice box?

The juice box was the waist high sort of transformer on little wheels into which anybody wanting electric power would plug in a light cord for a trailer, truck, the tent, the electric organ, the midway or whatever. Choctaw needed to be one of the first people on the lot each day to set up the juice box in a good location.

If there was no local electrical system to plug into, he had to fire up the noisy generator and make the juice box functional with it. The generator needed to be as far away as it could be, because of the noise, and people really liked the juice box as near as possible. Of course as Choctaw worked, people at the same time were asking where they could get water, or if he had patch material for a flat tire, or if there were any spare two-by-four boards in his truck. Choctaw did have a remarkable ability to field questions well and focus on his own tasks. He was a key person in literally getting the show up and going each day.

There was a bad scare in July when he keeled over at the juice box. There were screams, and people came running. Jenny left her sewing and the kids and was by his side, fearing that finally, despite all his skill and caution, he had got a shock. But how bad a shock? Would he be OK, or would it be the worst? Everybody was thinking the same thing but nobody said it. He was flat on his face, and there was some blood because he had fallen on his toolbox. "Don't touch him!" yelled his good friend Jake, the canvas boss. "He could still have juice goin' through him, and you could get it, too." Jake found a nearby board and knocked the juice box and all the cords a couple feet away with a good whack so that nothing was touching Choctaw. This disrupted the juice supply to most of the show, and more people came to see what the problem was. Choctaw still didn't seem to be breathing, and Jake and Jenny gently turned him over to see what could be done to revive him. Jennie's tears were dropping on him. Cries of "Give him air" and "Get him water" rang out. In those days, the techniques of first aid or resuscitation were unknown among most of the population.

Then Choctaw opened his eyes and blinked them in the sunlight. "What the hell?" he said. Then "Why do I have blood in my eyes?" and there were optimistic smiles all around. Jenny hugged him, getting some blood on her face. He absolutely didn't know what had happened.

Jake and one of his crew helped him back to a seat under a trailer awning and got the juice box operational again. They told him to take it easy for a bit. Jenny sat beside him with a glass of water in her hand and a studious look on her face. What did happen? It was like nothing that ever happened before, and it was not electrical shock.

Thirty minutes later, Choctaw was up walking around, a little slowly perhaps, and looking confused, but he was ambulatory and back at work. In a day he was fine. In a week, it was nearly forgotten, except with Jenny.

Then three weeks later, it happened again. He keeled over. Two days after that, it happened once again. This third time he fell down by a water tower—so it had nothing to do with electrical shock—and he was out for ten minutes or more. He was carried back to their trailer on an improvised stretcher made from bleacher boards, and Camie and GR stayed by his side till Woody brought a doctor from town, except that the doctor was actually a veterinary, since there was no medical doctor in the town, but the vet had by necessity garnered experience with the basics of the human body long ago. He examined Choctaw competently, asked a series of questions, etc. Then he asked Choctaw to walk around.

"Mr. Choctaw, it is hard to tell what really happened, and I understand this was not the first time. In some ways you look very normal, but your pulse rate is not really what it should be, and I have to tell you that your heartbeat is irregular, badly irregular, not beating as it should. From the way you walk, you may have had a minor stroke. It's hard to tell. For a man your age, you are in pretty good physical condition. That means you seem pretty healthy. You don't have to worry for right now. But I want you to slow down, way down, for at least a month. Spend most of your time sitting down. Don't carry anything heavy. Tell people what to do instead of doing it yourself.

"Mr. Choctaw, in less than a month, you need to see a real doctor, in a city, and be checked out. I know of men like you who lived to a ripe old age. I do have to say, though, that they were smart about it. They took care of themselves. And I know of some who didn't." The veterinary paused after this remark, to let it sink in. He made sure that Jenny and everybody standing around heard it, too. He had a fine grasp of the principle that sometimes how a patient's condition is communicated to him or her and the friends and relatives can be as important as the treatment.

"Mr. Brewer says that you hold an important position with the circus and a lot of people depend on you. Mr. Choctaw, those people could kill you. Then, I don't know who they would depend on. You would be gone. You would be dead. It is not easy to say this, but if it saves your life, ... no, it is up to you to save your life. If you can't work this out with your boss, quit this job. You won't last long on it anyway. Do you have questions?" He paused again. "Ms. Choctaw, do you have questions? Or should I say, 'Can you handle him?'"

Woody, Camie, GR, and Jenny all stood around, all shocked by the words, by the diagnosis. Then the vet excused himself to go off to some farms and castrate a bunch of calves, help an ailing sow, and see if a horse really needed to be put down.

A unanimous decision was made that Choctaw needed an assistant immediately, and a good assistant. This was a job nobody on the show could handle, since all were working at full capacity and beyond. Jenny said that she would do all she could in the meantime, but help was needed fast. They knew all the show folks would pitch in for a day or so to keep chaos from descending. But another man was needed. It would take somebody with a head on his shoulders who could follow orders and work fast.

Every day there were men who came around the circus, many just looking or just panhandling for food, and then some of them were actually asking for work. Many were hobos. They were victims of the Great Depression that started in 1929. They had no jobs, no homes, no family, and no future. There wasn't much that could be done for them, aside from offering a plate of food maybe, in exchange for a few hours' work. Some days they were just given food to help them keep on going. The men were ragged and weak, physically weak and weak in spirit. Some had at one time had families, jobs, and a certain rank in society, even if a low rank. Now they were anonymous. They were nothing. They were expendable. Charitable groups and churches tried to have regular soup kitchens for them, but there was never enough. Sometimes they were found dead along roadsides, in back alleys, or in barns where they had taken shelter and become too weak to walk out. They were buried as paupers. Such was the Great Depression.

The morning after Choctaw's third event, Camie and GR were sitting in front of their trailer with their inevitable cups of tea looking over what was to become the circus midway, noting what was done and what still had to be done, seeing what problems might need to be addressed and assessing the potential for the day to be profitable. A young man about twenty years old or so walked by, and then he walked by again. The second time he was braver. "Mornin' ma'am; Mornin', sir. Mind if I ask you where a boy might find some work around here and get a plate of something to eat? I can do most anything."

Camie spoke first, "Well, son, what kind of work are you good at?"

"Oh, ma'am. I am good with horses, trucks, an electricity, but I am hungry, so I'd be beholden for a chance to do anythin' for a little grub."

"Do you mean that, son?"

"Why, yes ma'am, I sure do. I am strong, an' people say I am smart. I will work long an' hard."

"OK, son, we can give you a plate of something to eat. First kill an' clean those three chickens tied to the back of the trailer. There is a bucket of hot water to soak them in an' pull the feathers. Cut up the pieces an' take them in this dishpan over to the truck where there are tables set up. Then scrub out those clothes that are soaking in that washtub, rinse them out in that other tub, wring them, an' hang them up. We'll have something for you to eat by then."

Then GR continued with the task list. "After that, son, I want you to clean out the horse truck there, clean up the manure behind the horses, an' take it in that wheelbarrow over to the manure pile by the elephants. Then wash that sorrel filly an' the little buckskin. Mind that filly, though. We have not had her long, an' she doesn't have any manners. You could make the acquaintance of one of her hind feet real fast if you get behind her. She is good at biting, too. Ever been around a horse like that before? How do you handle them?"

"Well, sir, as my folks used to say, handle them with respect. They usually aren't really bad horses. They are just ascared 'cause somebody treated them bad or maybe they were put in a pasture with mean horses or something. It's usually not their nature. Stay away from the hind feet. Talk to them nice an' gentle. Rake an' shovel from the side. Be a little smarter than they are. Watch their ears, too. You can tell a lot from their ears. Keep out of range so you don't get nipped. Grab the halter from the side an' keep their heads up. Sorry, I just love to talk about horses. But I can do whatever you tell me to do with your horses, sir."

"Sounds like you would be off to a good start. So after the horses, I want you to check over my truck. How would you do that?"

"Oh, maybe you just mean the oil, water, an' battery an' take a look at the tires. But I can run down the electrical, too, if you want, to see if there is anything loose or burned out bulbs, that sort of thing. Want me to check the plugs?"

"OK, young man, we'll see what you can do. Ask me questions when you need to."

The boy took care of the chickens in no time, asking for a butcher knife to get the job done. He gobbled the fried eggs and biscuit that Camie gave him, and continued on to washing the clothes, which took longer, but he was thorough. He showed experience in cleaning the straw and manure out of the truck and the manure outside behind the horses. But his experience really showed in how he washed the horses. He was gentle but got out all the dirt stains. He said the truck seemed all fine except for a loose clearance light on the left side and a burned out bulb on the right. There were some new bulbs in the glove box; so he replaced it.

He worked without complaining, asked only essential questions, remembered all he was asked to do, finished in less than three hours, then asked what else he could do.

"Dova gara's boutyin' kushti. And leste gins how to shoon. Maybe mandi'll dell leste to the veshna," GR said to Camie. ("That boy's working fine. And he knows how to listen. Maybe we'll give him to Choctaw." Actually, *veshna* meant "foreigner," and that was their word for

Choctaw, since his name was an Indian name.)

So, GR pulled out a piece of paper and wrote a cryptic message on it: "Good for a day or two?" He folded it over and wrote "Choctaw" on the outside.

"Young man, go over to the truck with the tables under the awning, an' tell them that GR an' Madam Camie said to give you a plate of something to eat an' a cup of coffee. Then ask where a man named Uncle Choctaw is an' take this paper to him. See what he says. Come back here when you are finished. If you do good work, you can sleep in this horse truck tonight, or under it if it is too hot inside."

"Well, thank you, sir, thank you, ma'am. I will do the best I can. I will try to do twice as good as I can. I am so happy to have food to eat!"

After the matinee show, the boy brought back the same paper and gave it to GR. Under GR's original words, Jenny had written, "OK for three days?" and Camie and GR knew that the kid was off to a good start.

Three days became a week, and then two weeks. But Camie didn't want anybody like this on the show that she didn't understand, didn't know the backstory of. She had to be sure the person was right for the show and there wouldn't be surprises later.

One afternoon she called the boy over and said, "Son, there are things you are not tellin' us, and things we are not askin'. An' you have a new chance here. You don't have to tell us what you don't want to. Uncle Choctaw an' Aunt Jenny are still satisfied with you.

But you are all alone. You are keepin' it bottled up inside. It is hard for a man to go on forever like that. What happened to you? Did you get a girl in trouble, steal something, do you have gambling debts?"

"Oh, no, Ms. Camie, I am not that kind of boy. I am really a good guy, but I did get into trouble."

"Son, you can tell me about it. If you really are good, you will stay. But we need to know. An' what you tell me is confidential. That means I don't tell anybody who doesn't need to know. Don't worry about that."

"Well, ma'am, it is a long story."

"That is OK. Let's go in my tent an' get a cup of tea. We can start today."

"I don't know where to start. You see, I never had any folks. My uncle an' his wife raised me, or at least he said he was my uncle. Some folks said he was really my dad 'cause we favored so much. They did take good care of me an' sent me to school, an' I had to work. I worked after school with my uncle in the hardware store owned by the Callums. Half the town was owned by the Callums. He also had me work in the garage across the street owned by Phil Callum an' in the blacksmith shop beside it owned by Bud Callum. So I really learned about a lot of stuff for a kid, an' I was good in school.

"I was always ridin' somebody's horse home from the blacksmith or drivin' somebody's truck or tractor back, even if I was too young. You learn a lot that way. I went to almost three years of high school an' got good marks. An' about electricity, well, it was about the time that they started runnin' juice out a' town to the farms down different roads. First one farmer would want to tap into the electricity an' have a light in the kitchen. An' then he wanted another light on the back porch an' maybe the front porch an' upstairs an' so on. Pretty soon, they would want juice in the whole house. I helped with a lot of work like that, could really do it myself, except it was a two-man job climbin' up an' down ladders an' everything while the other guy held the cable.

"An' then there was almost a scandal kind a' thing happened. People were laughing at Mr. Seymore. He said he wanted lights in his barn. They thought that was hilarious, but Mr. Seymore said it was no joke, an' electricity wasn't for the cows to see better.

"He just wanted to try an experiment. It seems he was absolutely tired of bringing kerosene lanterns into the barn to milk in the early mornin' an' havin' the hired man be careful not to tip them over an' start a fire. He wanted to see if he could flip on a switch an' light the barn an' milk the cows with no lanterns to worry about. Well, I bet it was no more than six months, an' ten other farmers wanted light in their barn, too."

"Son, this is interesting, an' I see how you learned so much for such a young boy, but something bad happened, didn't it?"

"Why, yes, ma'am. It did. How did you know? It was real bad. One night, my uncle an' me, we closed the hardware store an' took the money home to Mr. Callum to count an' close out. He wasn't home, but his wife was, an' she was dressed up real pretty, an' she was in a hurry for us to leave. She didn't even want to count the money. It happened so fast it was like lightnin'. This guy we didn't know came in. His face was covered. We thought he was goin' to rob us. Then he started shootin', an' Mr. Callum showed up, an' the guy shot him dead with one bullet. Ms. Callum was screamin', the guy with the gun took off on a horse, an' the neighbors came runnin', an' they got the sheriff.

"Poor Mr. Callum didn't have a chance. Funny, but the guy with the gun dropped it. There was a lot of confusion. Ms. Callum fainted or pretended like she did. Before you know it, she came to an' was tellin' the sheriff that we were doin' a hold up. We got thrown in jail. An' then they charged us with murder. It was awful."

"Yes, it was awful. It changed your life. It made you a criminal. How did that end up?" Camie asked.

"The Callums are powerful people in that town. An' the jury believed every word Ms. Callum said an' not a word we said. There was a lot of gossip, but the jury is not suppose' to listen to gossip. It took that jury only an hour to decide on a guilty verdict. My uncle got life, an' since I was just seventeen an' under his influence, the judge gave me just twenty years. I felt like I died that day, both for me an' for my uncle, the only dad I ever knew."

"Oh, son, it must have broken your heart. I see what has been burdenin' you. This is hard to hold inside." Camie was at her most sympathetic. The boy's face was ashen, except that his eyes were very red, and tears seemed to be forming.

"But Ms. Camie, that is not why I am here. You see I kinda got out, out a' prison, not on my own. But I can't go back, but I don't think they are lookin' for me. But I can't take no chances. An' I don't know what to do."

"Now wait a second, young man. Slow down. You aren't makin' a lot of sense here. I know this is hard on you, but you have to put it together clear. Take your time. I am listenin'."

"I am sorry. The important thing is, they probably think I am dead someplace."

"Dead? Well, son, what do you mean?" Camie asked.

"Just about a week ago, I was still in prison. It was when the Missouri River was doin' all that floodin'. You see, all the little rivers that go into it, they was bad flooded, too. An' I was in prison, an' they took a bunch of us prisoners out an' made us work fillin' sand bags to make a levee to protect this little town on the Massola River. I think they picked me because I tried to be a good prisoner an' had a good record. An' I didn't mind. None of us did. It was great to get out of the prison walls, even if it was for a flood. They worked us hard, real hard, an' there wasn't a lot to eat. But we got a little levee up about four foot high to help save the town, at least the main part of the town. An' we was reinforcin' it with another row of sand-bags to keep the river out.

"Well, all of a sudden, out of nowhere, this huge ol' tree came floatin' down the river, roots an' trunk an' branches an' all. It was a giant. It was somethin' to see. It was spinnin' aroun' an' aroun' real slow like. An'

157

then we realized an' the guards realized that it was headin' straight for our levee. The guards an' most of the prisoners ran back, but I was right up at the levee, an' so was another white boy. An' they had some colored prisoners workin' on the levee, too, only they didn't even take the leg chains off of 'em.

"The tree crashed right through the levee, an' me an' that other white boy got swept right out in the river. He was yellin' an' screamin', an' I think he was drownin', an' it got one of the colored boys, too. Only he had no chance at all with those chains on his legs. I think he went down pretty fast, poor boy.

"The guards was watchin', but they didn't know what to do exactly. I can swim pretty good, but I wasn't sure if that river would be too much for me. I waved my hands in the air some an' yelled a little, but it was hard to think. The guards could 'a' started shootin' if they wanted to. They sure wasn't goin' to try to rescue us. We was just some prisoners anyway.

"Before I could even think, that river took me a mile or two down, an' the guards couldn't see me no more, an' they had no way of knowin' if I was alive or dead, an' maybe they didn't care. The water was fast, an' it just kep' on takin' me an' takin' me, mile after mile. It could 'a' been a hour or a couple hours, an' I just kep' my head above water an' floated like. Then there was a different current. I got caught in some tree branches. It looked like an islan', a long islan' that the river was floodin' the trees an' everythin'. I pulled my prison shirt off to get out of the branches, but I still had those prison pants on. There was a way I could get down out of the branches an' get on the dry ground of the islan'. It took awhile, an' there was no way to tell if the whole islan' was gonna flood or what. The dry groun' was already all mud an' mushy.

"Then voices were callin' out to me, 'Help! Help!' I looked aroun', an' there was a woman with a boy an' a girl an' a couple horses. What were they doin' on this islan' in this flood? There was a big ol' dog, too. I was afraid of him. But the woman begged me to help. She said they had come over to this islan' to plant a garden like they did every year. They cleared an' plowed with the horses. Their farm was across the channel on the other bank. She said they wanted to plant a garden on the good groun' on this islan' before the rain came, an' you could walk across the water in the channel when they came two days ago, an' the horses came across easy. But then the water came up fast, like magic, an' they spent two nights in the rain, an' they couldn't swim, an' they didn't know how to get back. The woman an' the girl was both cryin'. They thought they was gonna die. So did the boy.

"They didn't say nothin' about my prison pants an' no shirt. They was too scared. I asked if they could ride, an' they all nodded their heads yes. They just couldn't ride across the deep water rushin' in the channel now to get back to their farm.

"I asked if I could hop on the bigger horse, an' they said yes, long as I didn't ride off. How was I gonna ride off? But the horse was a good one, powerful, an' he seemed like he had a good head on him. I rode him back an' forth a little, an' he was fine. He would even let me take him up to the channel.

Gary G. Steele

"I told the woman that I thought there was only one chance. I needed a good shillelagh to keep the horse goin', an' I would make two trips. I would take the boy across first, both of us on the big horse, with him holdin' on behind an' the dog in front of me. The dog would never swim it on his own, but if he got across, he could run to the farm where they lived an' maybe get help.

"I explained that I would have to go up to the head of the islan', an' when the horse got in the water with us on him, he would swim, but the fast water would make him go downstream a good bit, kinda like what happened to me. Then I would drop off the boy an' the dog some place on the bank across the channel when the horse could get footin' there.

"The woman said yes right away. She seemed like a lovin' kind of mother, happy to have one of her kids saved. But she wanted to be sure I wouldn't leave 'em, herself an' her little girl. I guess she finally saw that I had prison pants on. I said, ma'am, if I was like that, I would just take off on your horse an' try to save my own skin now.'

"I said after I dropped them off, next I would ride the horse up river on the other bank to where the islan' started across the channel, an' I would make the horse swim back across again, an' we would get swept downstream again, but I hoped not pas' the islan'. It would all be like a big Z.

"The horse would need a bit of a rest, but if it all worked out, on the second trip, I would ride the big horse across again, with the girl holdin' on behind me an' me leadin' the smaller horse with the woman on it. The smaller horse would be more likely to follow the big one, an' the big one might not be too afraid this time. An' it didn't matter that much where we came out on the bank, just as long as we got off the islan' an' to the bank.

"So we talked about this, an' even then, the river seemed to be comin' up more. An' there wasn't gonna be much more time. So I pulled the saddle off the big horse an' got on. You really didn't need a saddle. It would just be extra weight. The boy was brave, an' they lifted him up to hold on behin' me. The dog was wigglin' all over at first an' didn't want to sit across the horse in front of me, but the boy tried to talk to him an' pet him a little bit with his arm comin' from behin' my back. The dog settled down.

"The woman an' the girl kissed the boy, an' I headed off on the horse up to the tip of the islan'. It would be hard to use a shillelagh with the boy on the back an' the dog on the front, but it ended up I didn't need to much.

"That big horse kinda understood that we were all in it together. He rose up an' down a lot when we got into the water, an' he started swimmin', but he did what he had to do, even when that curren' was carryin' us along down the channel real fast. The boy held on for dear life an' the dog didn't move. I was ready to throw the dog off if I had to.

"That horse was powerful, an' he finally got footin' on the bank across the channel an' pulled us all up. I gave the boy my left arm so he could crawl down on the groun' an' then help get the dog. That dog took off right away for the farm or for someplace.

"The boy started yellin' at me, 'Please, mister, please, don't ride off an' leave us. Please, go back for my sister an' my mother, please!' I told him not to worry, an' he could stay alone here an' watch for us. An' now maybe his dad would come. His dad would know something was up when the dog showed up all alone an' barkin' his head off.

"So I rode the big horse up along the bank. It was easier with only me on him. I think he knew what was comin' next. When we got up across from the tip of the islan', I made him go back in the water again. He was tired, but his load was lighter now. We crossed in good time.

"I rode him up to where the woman an' girl was waitin' with the smaller horse. The woman was partly smilin' an' partly cryin', an' the little girl was jumpin' up an' down. They asked right away if the boy was OK, an' the dog.

"We had to let the big horse rest for a bit, an' I needed to try out the smaller horse to see if she would cross easy or if she was too afraid. If she was too afraid, we would have to leave her there to drown, an' I would have to make an extra trip. But she acted OK, an' she really wanted to follow the big horse an' stay with him. Animals can have a lotta brains when there is somethin' wrong goin' on.

"In about ten or fifteen minutes, the big horse seemed

rested, an' the woman lifted the girl up behind me on the big horse an' managed to crawl on the smaller horse herself. When we were ready, we headed up for the tip of the islan'. I tried to soun' all calm an' easy, but to tell you the truth, inside I wasn't. The boy, he was a good passenger, but how would these two be? The woman tried to look calm an' keep her daughter calm. She gave me the reins for the small horse so I could lead her while I rode the big horse, an' then it was all up to me.

"We got in the water in a little different place, an' the mud must 'a' been deeper, deep enough for the horses to struggle with their feet in the mud till they got out to swim. The little mare had a wild look in her eyes, but she was not gonna' let that other horse leave without her. We did make it to the other bank, or I wouldn't be sittin' here now. The boy was there, jumpin' up an' down. They all hugged, they even hugged me 'cause they said I saved 'em. But I was no hero. It was just what you needed to do. We led the horses to where their farm was. I said I had to stay in the barn. We never talked about me bein' a prisoner exactly, but they knew it, or at least the woman did.

"They went in the house, but it wasn't till nearly dark that the man came home. They told me later that he had been away for a couple days with the wagon gettin' supplies an' had no way of knowin' what they had been through. They must 'a' talked for a couple hours, an' they cooked some kind of food. I could smell it. An' I just waited there in the barn, wonderin' what I was gonna do next but hopin' they could give me some kind of help.

"The man an' woman came out to the barn after dark. He was carryin' a lantern, an' she had plate with somethin' to eat for me. He started talkin' first. He said they had to get me outta there fast. The guards from the prison might be comin' with dogs to track me down. If they foun' me aroun', these folks would be in bad trouble for helpin' an escaped prisoner. They had to get me outta there right away. They let me eat while they talked. I was so hungry.

"The woman said that she had some of her brother's clothes to give me, about the same size, an' a pair of shoes an' some food an' three dollars. The man said it wasn't gonna be that easy, because they had to make sure the bloodhounds didn't pick up my scent. He told me that I would have to go out behin' the barn where there was a forge, the kin' you make work with a crank. He asked me if I had made any stink yet or peed anyplace aroun' there, an' I told him no. He said the boy would start a fire in the forge an' crank it to make the fire good an' hot. I would have to take off all my prison clothes, everything I was wearin', an' burn 'em up completely in that forge. They had to be turned into ash. That included everything, even my prison shoes. Then I would have to put coal oil all over me, everywhere, head to toe, every part, even rub it in my hair.

"I asked if that was all really necessary, if the bloodhounds was that good. He said that that some of those dogs could tell you three days later what cow a cowpie in the pasture came from, an' he wasn't takin' any chances.

"After I was covered in coal oil, he would let me get in the back of the wagon an' sit on a bit of straw. He would drive me to where the road crossed a creek, an' I would get out in the creek an' wash myself off with lye soap. Then I could put on the clothes an' the shoes they gave me an' go on. But later, he really took me a mile or two up the road to help me confuse the dogs more. It was still night. He let me out at a special place, an' he told me to go up river, not down river. They would never expect that. In about three miles, there was a railroad line with two or three freight trains a night an' a little sidin'. He said I should git onto a train an' stay on it till I got out of Missouri an' even the corner of Kansas the train crossed an' into Nebraska. He said I could tell what state it was by lookin' at license plates. He said sometimes the cops just shoot escaped prisoners, no questions asked, so I better be careful. The only reason he was doin' all this for me was 'cause I saved his family an' he owed it. If they ever did catch me, I had to tell 'em I stole these clothes an' food outta their house. They never saw me an' never helped me."

"So do you mean that when you got off a freight train, once you knew you were in Nebraska, you just walked along and saw this circus puttin' up?" asked Camie, with a little disbelief in her voice. She had heard a lifetime of stories, but this one was unique. Really, they were all unique, but this was one she would always remember.

"Well, we could tell there was a story behind you. Your clothes were too clean, an' your hair was too short. An' you probably weighed thirty pounds more than your average hobo. Your spirit was in one piece, too. That was obvious. An' now tell me, what would you like now, young man?"

"Ma'am, it is so nice to work for Uncle Choctaw. He really needs help. An' Aunt Jenny is good to me, an' everybody else, too. An' I get three meals a day at the cookhouse, an' people don't ask questions, an' I learn new stuff. I like this job so much. I want to work here so bad."

"You are in a trial period, now. An' everybody says you are doin' just fine. We are even going to talk about givin' you a salary. But your future is up to you. An' another time, we need to talk. You need to learn how to tell people about your past a little but not make them curious. An' we will get you a driver's license. I will tell you how. What do you think of 'Sam Goodheart' for a name, 'Samson Goodheart'? It sounds good, an' it is easy to spell, but it is not a common name, an' people won't keep asking if you are related to the other Goodhearts over in some other town. Think about that. You do have a good heart, Young Man."

The rest of the summer was idyllic for the man who grew more and more into the name Samson Goodheart, and for Choctaw and Jenny, too. Even the parrot took to Sam, sat on his shoulder, talked to him, and came out with new phrases, some of mysterious origin:

Forty miles to Fort Leavenworth!

Turn right at the first light!

Five tens is Fifty.

Before the matinee today.

Count your change!

I hate liver!

Fix your makeup

It's snowin' down South! (An expression to politely tell a woman her slip was showing)

And one phrase which made everyone laugh:

Mississippi--M i s s i s s i p p i--Mississippi

The list went on and on. And the parrot could give intonations of authority, humor, or questioning. He even seemed to imitate the voice of certain people when he came out with a line.

It would be hard to imagine a better life, and Sam was offered the chance to stay with Choctaw and Jenny at the circus winter quarters in the offseason and do repairs and paint and so on. He was becoming the son they never had. And they were becoming the family he had lost or never really had.

Shortly before the show was about to go out for the next season, Choctaw had a fatal heart attack, and he died instantly. Jenny was distraught and didn't eat for days, and maybe the person who helped her most was Sam, whom she had started calling "Son" by now, not in the generic sense, but in the "You are my son" sense. There was a funeral attended by all sorts of show people. And then the question inevitably arose, "Where could Brewer Brothers find a man to take Choctaw's place?"

The answer was easy. Sam was the logical candidate, even if he had less than a year's experience. He would drive the truck and trailer that Choctaw had driven, and he would live as Jenny's boy, as her son.

Two years later, Sam had grown very sweet on one of the Marveli girls, and the feelings were reciprocal. He converted to Catholic, and there was a nice circus-style wedding. A year later they had a son, and Jenny and the Marveli parents could not have been a prouder grandparents. Sam had also become a performer, riding jumping horses, taking a spot in one of the Marveli acts, and working one of the bulls in the Educational Elephant Act. But he couldn't spin a rope if his life depended on it.

Two years later there was another son born to the couple. The boys had been named Choctaw and Cherokee, which became shortened to Chuck and Rocky. Everybody was doing fine. That all changed early in the war when more and more men were being called up, married and with families or not. Sam was among them. It was just awful to leave his wife and sons, his mother, his in-laws, and the new life that he had grown into so skillfully, a life that he had justly earned.

He had been in the service about eighteen months and was fighting in the Italian campaign. His letters were few and far between. Then one horrible day, some colonel or general came in a fancy car from a nearby army post and gave Sam's wife the news that he had been killed in action. She was broken hearted, and so was half of the rest of the show. It was hard to tell if it was harder for her to console Jenny or for Jenny to console her. Her father pointed out that Sam had died within thirty miles of the town where the Marveli family had originated. It did not make her burden any easier. Nor did the fact that other new widows everywhere in the country were getting such visits every day. It was one price of the horrible war.

The young Goodheart brothers grew up in the business, with Jenny as a doting grandmother who saw that they got special attention in their studies and even finished high school. The little gray parrot nearly outlived Jenny. There are Goodhearts in circuses to this day. Camie told the first couple generations where the name came from and part of the story. And then after Camie died, they passed it on within the family.

The circus is one of the places in America where people can reinvent themselves. It's up to the individual. And on Brewer Brothers Circus, that was the case with two electricians. One lived his new life for decades, and the other just for several years, but they were very, very happy years.

11. TWO ELEPHANT ACTS

Dolly, Blanche and Jewel were huge animals with huge appetites and a nearly constant need for attention in one form or another from Uncle Harry, their dedicated caretaker, trainer, and presenter. Brewer Brothers' Circus was only a medium-sized show. Everybody, animals and humans, had to serve multiple functions. So these three elephants, often referred to as "bulls" in circus slang, though they were all females, had a variety of duties. They pulled the huge ropes that raised the tent. They pulled or pushed trucks that got stuck in the mud. They starred in parades. And especially Dolly, the most curious and animated of the trio, did publicity stunts out on the midway in front of the bigtop.

Dolly made more noise than the other two bulls combined. Her ear flapping expressed a multitude of thoughts, and she was terminally nosey and always on the look out for some excitement. She could effortlessly steal a pack of cigarettes out of a sponsoring committeeman's shirt pocket. It took just the right inhalation from the strategically placed tip of her truck, and out came the cigarettes. She also loved lifting men's hats off their heads, with a preference for straw hats, which she would playfully put atop her own noggin or pretend to be about to eat. Uncle Harry could always keep her under control, of course, and sometimes he even urged her on.

One of her preferred solo events was the tug-of-war contest. This was a publicity stunt performed out on the midway near a main road or street to get a maximum number of viewers and maximum attention. If a radio announcer was present or a newspaper photographer, so much the better. With a simple harness around her chest, she would pull a large, long rope behind her against ten or twenty members of the local circus sponsoring committee tugging on the other end. Dolly would be very dramatic, very measured, with much ear flapping and trumpeting, and even the occasional backward slide of a few paces as she tugged against the committeemen.

At the proper point in the drama, however, she would majestically find her pace, and with more amplification of her sound and fury, she would inch forward, and then inch forward again, all the while pretending as if this was the challenge of her life. Her steps would become larger and larger, and eventually Uncle Harry would have to stop her to keep some poor committee members from being dragged on the ground in a most undignified way. Her victory trumpet was audible a mile away, and she would turn to face her opponents as if to say, "See there, Gentlemen. I guess I showed you! Wanna try again?" Of course Uncle Harry was privy to all these shenanigans and encouraged her completely and trained her to maximize them.

The first elephant act in the performance was called the Educational Elephant Act. It was not intended to be beautiful and gracious or awe-inspiring as the Elephant Ballet at the end of the show was. And in addition to being educational, it was intended to be funny. Of course, since the audience knew little or nothing about elephants, and since for many people this was the first sighting of an elephant outside a child's picture book or a Tarzan movie, almost any-thing that was done would be educational. This act was based on a series of comic tricks developed over years and years that had gradually evolved into a complete act. No other circus, large or small, had anything that could quite compare with this "Educa-tional Elephant Act."

This act was just before the intermission, ending the first half of the performance. Uncle Harry and two other men, all dressed in black pants with white shirts, red vests and straw boater hats, raced into the three rings, each one leading an elephant. The elephants sported a headdress with a sort of fringe hanging down, and when the music switched to a Charleston song, and the men and animals imitated a Charleston step, the audience howled. For the ele-phants it was a simple one step back and one step forward, accompanied with some head swinging to make the fringe fly. To the audience this meant that they were playing "flapper girls." The men did a reasonably authentic dance step, all rotating to the right around the ring so that the audience on all sides could get a good look. Next came a surprising movement. It somewhat imitated the "black bottom," the dance in which the partners slapped each other's behinds playfully. It was easy for the men to slap the elephants' behinds. But when the men turned and bent over slightly for the slap on their behind, the elephants swatted them with their trunks and knocked them over. The crowd would roar again. And Jewel was always the "bad" elephant. She never learned to do anything gently. And her swat sent the trainer sprawling. Because she was always so rough, the men agreed to take turns working her so that no one of them had to handle her every time.

After the dancing, the announcer would begin a patter explaining that elephants could easily understand many commands, had different personalities, and were very skilled with their trunks, especially the tips of their trunks. As a demonstration, the men in the three rings threw down the canes they had come in with. The elephants effortlessly picked up the canes and returned them to the men. Next the men threw down their straw boater hats, and the elephants picked them up, but to the delight of the audience, they placed the hats high up on their own heads, and curved their trunks up in a sort of mock salute.

The announcer continued with an explanation that this must be a day when the elephants were really misbehaving, and the three men shook fingers at them, pleaded with them, and so on, all to no avail. Finally the announcer offered that maybe they were using the wrong approach. Instead, if they got down on one knee, asked nicely, and gave the elephants a kiss, the men could get their hats back. So they did so, and sure enough, the elephants retrieved the straw hats from their heads and returned them to the men.

Next the announcer suggested that maybe the elephants wanted to give a kiss to the men, and asked if the audience if they thought that was a good idea. Of course the audience screamed approval. The men stood still a little distance to the left, waiting for the elephantine kiss. When the animals extended their trunks and touched the men's cheeks, the audience applauded wildly. Some days the audience noticed that Jewel didn't give a gentle kiss with the tip of her trunk. She had such a problem doing anything gently. Her kiss was more like a sock in the jaw. This was still another reason that the men wanted to take turns working Jewel. None of them wanted to get socked twice a day.

After the kiss, the men pulled white handkerchiefs from their vest pockets and wiped their faces. Next they threw the handkerchiefs to the ground, and the big beasts promptly retrieved them, bringing on another round of applause.

The patter continued with the announcement that elephants could even pick up a cigarette, using the little tip protruding at the end of the trunk. When the men each threw down a cigarette, they were picked up without the slightest fumble.

And if elephants could pick up very small things in their trunk, the trunk was at the same time a very powerful tool. All eyes were invited to watch Jewel in the last ring as she did a demonstration of that power. Jewel loved this part of the performance. She was given a two-by-two board about five feet long, or sometimes a broomstick, and to the amazement of the audience, she proceeded to break it into four inch bits, placing it under one foot and pulling on the end with her trunk. The cracking sound could be heard throughout the tent as the people oohed and gasped.

Elephants could even hold a big hoop in their trunks. At this point, the men gave them large hoops, actually bicycle rims painted red, and the elephants held the hoops out a yard or more off the ground. A drum roll followed the announcement that Spangles, the circus Dalmatian, would do a series of leaps through the hoops held aloft by the elephants. Spangles would easily jump through Blanche's hoop in the first ring, then Dolly's hoop in the center ring, and finally Jewel's hoop in the third ring, except that Jewel's hoop could be a little more challenging, since she did not like to hold hers very still. But Spangles' tasks were not done. Poker the Clown would appear with a basket of produce.

"And now, ladies and gentlemen, boys and girls, you will see a demonstration of how elephants use their trunk to eat." And Poker gave Spangles a large carrot from the produce basket to take to each elephant. Spangles would dash to each of them, and sit up in front of each with the carrot dangling from her mouth. Each elephant, even Jewel, gently took the carrot and stripped off the un-tasty carrot top and popped the rest into her mouth with barely a perfunctory chew. The crowd awed at how fast the big animals could dispatch a vegetable. Or if carrots were not in season, then ears of corn with the husks peeled back were used, or almost any other form off produce. Carrots and corn were good, however, because Spangles could carry them easily, and they were very visible to the people.

Then Spangles would take each bull a box of popcorn. What happened next surprised people. The beasts did not put the box into their mouths. Instead, they immediately stepped on the box with one foot, with kernels of popcorn popping out left and right. Then they picked up the box and shook it a bit to get the remaining morsels out and scooped up the popcorn by curving the end their trunks slightly on the ground to grab the kernels up in little piles. The popcorn was gone within a few seconds.

The final game in this Educational Elephant Act was with water. Poker the clown came out again, wearing a raincoat and with an umbrella under his arm. He also carried buckets of water. The announcer explained that while elephants ate with their trunks, they also used them to drink, and a demonstration would now be given.

Blanche was the water-baby of the trio. She always wanted to play in water, drink water, spray herself with water, and beat the other two bulls to any water. When Uncle Harry took them to a creek or pond for a bath, Blanche could hardly contain herself. She sprayed herself, she sprayed the others, and she splashed the water with her feet. She wanted to quickly lie down in it. She wanted to go out too far in it.

All of this affinity for water made Blanche the ideal lead for this segment of the act. She hardly needed any training for it. She gladly drank up the bucket of water offered by Poker, spraying herself with the last couple gallons, or almost the last couple gallons, since she also saved a couple quarts for Poker, directing the spray a good six feet away and squarely hitting the by-now unfurled umbrella. But the fun was only beginning. Poker would approach her indignantly, shaking his finger at her and making threats. Then Blanche would make a couple of particularly plaintiff squeals. The announcer explained that this meant Blanche had something to say. Poker should go up close to her and "listen" to her secret.

Poker would approach cautiously, then put his ear near her mouth, and nod his head and nod his head some more. In just a moment, Poker would run over to the announcer and ask to share the microphone.

Blanche did have something important to say.

"What is it?"

"She says that boys and girls who come to the circus should come with their hands washed and their faces clean."

"Well, that is correct. We like clean boys and girls at the circus."

"But Blanche says that there might be a boy or girl somewhere here with dirty hands or a dirty face!"

"Oh, my, what can we do?"

"Blanche wants to go around the tent and find that boy or girl and give a shower with her trunk!"

"You means she wants to spray water on them so they have clean hands and face?"

"Exactly! She will give them a shower!"

"So, boys and girls, listen closely. When Blanche the elephant comes around, you all, every boy and girl, should stand up and smile and wave your hands back and forth at her so she can see if they are clean. Poker the clown will have an extra bucket of water if we find a boy or girl who needs a quick shower.

"Do you hear that, boys and girls? As Blanche comes by, you had better stand up and show your clean face and hands if you do not want a shower!"

Roars of laughter started as Blanche proceeded around the tent. Poker let her fill her trunk, and occasionally she would spray a few drops to the top of the tent or someplace else harmlessly. But the children loved standing up and waving their hands. They screamed with delight.

The first elephant act ended with Blanche giving Poker a final soaking with all the water she had in her trunk. The announcer said that it was Poker, he was the one with a dirty face, and he needed the shower!

Then a closing announcement was made that popcorn was available for only five cents a box, enough for an entire family, and that there would be a ten-minute intermission while the bigtop was set up for the second half of the big performance.

The second elephant act could have hardly contrasted more with the first, the Educational Elephant Act. The second act was dramatic, fast, and thrilling. There was no comedy. Uncle Harry wore a white tuxedo. His wife Aunt Hattie was radiant in a trim, feathered outfit ideal for riding an elephant. The three bulls wore head harnesses with oversize sequin-like ornaments and the large letters BBC on a headpiece – Brewer Brothers Circus.

The three elephants entered the tent at a dead run, racing around the center ring, then making a complete twirl in unison before continuing around the ring and twirling again and again. Aunt Hattie twirled with them. And then the pattern was reversed, with the bulls going counter-clockwise, with more twirls. Next they did a sort of royal march, lifting one front foot and skipping on the other and then reversing feet. Their pace was very rapid in a series of dance-like steps, but they never lost their grace.

After these beginning minutes of rapid action, they slowed and suddenly stopped and almost dropped in their tracks, lying down flat in a just a second or two. The contrast was astounding. The three animals that had been so fast and imposing on their feet were now imposing as they lay still on their side. Aunt Hattie and Uncle Harry had them hold this position and "styled" with a gracious pose and brought on a round of applause. Next, Aunt Hattie mounted Dolly's neck so that she would be well positioned for what happened next. The three animals rose together to sit up and raise their front feet and trunk up in an elephant salute, with Hattie holding to Dolly's neck harness.

Then the three rose up, and Blanche and Jewel moved to the back of the ring while Dolly stood up on her hind feet and walked across the front of the ring, with Aunt Hattie smiling and waving from the huge animal's neck. Spontaneous applause erupted. Then Dolly bowed down with one large foot in front of her so that Hattie could descend to the ground and take a bow.

Next three large "bull tubs" or pedestals were rolled out and set up so that the elephants could step on them with one foot and rotate around, then mount with all four feet and rotate.

The two tricks that followed were particularly thrilling. Blanche stayed on one of the large tubs while the other two elephants stepped to the back. Aunt Hattie jumped up on the tub beside Blanche and grabbed a part of her head harness. Hattie lifted one knee into Blanche's mouth. Blanche grasped it with just the right pressure so that Hattie was hanging by her knee from the huge animal's mouth while she rotated slowly on the pedestal. Hattie smiled and "styled" upside down during the complete turn. The audience stared on in disbelief, and then clapped thunderously.

Blanche had to turn on the tub in the next trick, too, but this time several turns, very rapidly, rapidly enough for Hattie to swing out completely parallel to the ground as she held two hand loops in the elephant's head harness. This was one of the most appreciated tricks of the entire circus performance. Uncle Harry was there to cradle Hattie as the twirling slowed and she came down and sought footing on the side of the tub.

The act ended with the Harry leading the animals out of the ring and having them line up on the narrow track in front of the third ring. Hattie was now again riding Dolly, the lead, and Blanche placed her front feet on Dolly's back, with Jewel placing her feet on Blanche's back, and all three elephants saluting with their trunks and Hattie styling broadly as they marched in this position down the track in front of all three rings. The audience applauded continuously. Those in the front row were within six feet of the animals and completely thrilled.

This second elephant act ended the Brewer Brothers' Circus performance on a very high note with very high audience satisfaction. Slowly, almost sadly, the crowd filed down the bleachers and headed to the front door where they had come in. Vendors were there with remaining popcorn and cotton candy, easily selling out the remaining stock.

If it was a matinee show, the men on the prop crew were soon at work setting up for the night show. If it was a night show, they were tearing down and taking out props before the crowd completely left. Harry and Hattie were back at the bull truck with the three elephants, feeding them with hay or grain and praising them for their performance. If the weather was hot, it was more important to get off their head harnesses and give them a chance to drink and, if they wished, spray themselves. They clearly deserved some reward for putting on two very good elephant acts.

12. WHITES ONLY

I t was not a long jump for the circus from Liverpool to the next town of Sweet Lake that day, and it was a Sunday. Gilly was riding in one of the trucks with Old Charlie, and they found the circus lot easily, but nobody was on it yet, so they pulled over to wait till Gilly's father Woody and Jake the canvas boss got there to lay things out and decide where the tent would go and where the midway and the front door would be where the people came onto the lot and so on.

The day was warming up already, and it was nice waiting on the shady street. Gilly heard some singing, and he went to investigate. It was coming from a big stone church with columns on three sides. The singing sounded good, and he went closer to hear. There was still shade on the west side of the church. He sat down on the steps and leaned against one of the stone pillars. The coolness felt refreshing against his back where he had sweat through his shirt.

The hymn was something about "The Old Rugged Cross." The voices were very well practiced. When the hymn was over, he heard the booming voice of the preacher.

Gilly did not have much idea of what *Gaudjas* did in church, and he was curious.

"Our thanks to Deacon Caldwell and Mrs. Laiterly and all the choir for their fine rendering of a beautiful old hymn. We look forward to hearing more later in the service this morning.

"And now, ladies and gentlemen, I would like to call your attention to the passage from St. Matthew, 25:45. 'And what you do unto these the least of my brethren, so you do also unto me.' Now, I am sure we have all seen that passage and verse many times, but today I ask you to take a closer look at it and what it can mean to us as Christians in our daily lives.

"It is not always easy to understand what 'the least of my brethren' means, but I can tell you this: it is not always easy to do unto them either, to treat them well, to treat them as you would treat Jesus...to do unto them as you would do unto Jesus.

"Specifically, I would like you to think about the colored people who live around us, to think about them as some of the least of God's brethren, and how we should do unto them. Oh, I am not saying that we are mean and hurtful. The people of Sweet Lake are not like that, at least not the true Christians of Sweet Lake.

"What can and should a Christian do concerning colored people? My answer to you, fellow believers, fellow Christians, is that we can be doing more than we are doing. And it is our Christian obligation to do so.

"I want to tell you a story, and I will keep it a short story, since I know Reverend MacCready has a reputation of telling long stories from the pulpit, longer than the Book of Job."

This comment brought some agreeable laughter from the congregation.

"Well, I had a Great Uncle Willard MacCready, brother of my granddad Weston. Willard is buried in Shady Rest Cemetery along with my grandparents and lots of other MacCreadys, and half the other Christians in Sweet Lake, or at least the white Christians.

"Now it is no secret that the MacCreadys go way back in Sweet Lake. Why I am sure we were here when the last of the Indians was chased off and later when the name of our town was changed from Wide Swamp to Sweet Lake. I am sure we can all agree that changing the name of the town was a wise decision." (More polite laughter followed that comment.)

"So back to Uncle Willard. Well, in the time after the War Between the States, Sweet Lake and all the people in it were having a hard time, both black and white. But in some ways maybe the colored were hurting even more. They didn't have a place to work any more, nobody to feed them, and there was not as much farm work for them to do.

"It is no secret that there have been colored Mac-Creadys around here for a long time, too. Nobody seems to know for sure how the colored people started using that name, but by now there are a lot of them. Well, Willard took it upon himself to work with three of the MacCready colored boys and to teach them some carpentry. These were strong boys, and he found they could learn some figures, too. And pretty soon they learned the differences between two-by-fours and four-by-fours, between eight-penny nails and ten-penny nails. They learned how to 'measure twice and cut once.' They even learned to use a pencil and figure how much lumber they needed for this or that and what it should cost. For example, it was very good for these boys to learn that if an eight-foot two-by-four costs seven cents, then ten of them should cost seventy cents.

"We all know that there are people who will try to Gyp a colored man out of his money as soon as look at him. And yes, it is just as much of a sin for a Christian to
Gyp a colored man as it is to Gyp a white man. I want to be very clear about that."

Gilly flinched when he heard the expression "Gyp," especially the way it was used so easily, so ignorantly, with the clear implication that everybody knew that Gypsies were always trying to "Gyp" people. Gilly had never tried to cheat anybody in his life, and he didn't know of anybody in the family who had cheated others. It was just unfair. It was not right.

The preacher continued, "And some people will try to Jew a colored man down on their wages, too. If it's just a colored man, it doesn't matter. They will try to get some old uncle, some old darky who can't read and doesn't know any better, and then give him half what was promised for the job. Well, Jewing anybody out of their money is a sin, too. We know what Jesus did with the moneychangers in the Temple!"

Gilly thought that there was another expression that was not fair, but it surely was a common one. No, don't cheat anybody, but why be mean about it and use an expression that means one group of people cheat a lot? That was not fair either.

"So Uncle Willard worked with some of the least of God's brethren, the colored MacCready boys, so that they could make a better living. And do you know what? Some of his good works are still with us today. Why those colored MacCreadys have passed on carpentry work to their kids, grandkids or whatever. And now there is hardly a chicken coup in town that was not built by them or a back porch that was not fixed by them. And I do believe that they built half the shacks in colored town. And I hope it is the half of the shacks that are not falling down!"

And there was more agreeable laughter at this point.

"Now, I know, I was raised around colored people just the way you all were. And there are things about them that nobody can quite figure out. Did you ever notice how they can sing so good, but they talk so bad? (The congregation laughed again.) And why is it that they can wash dirty clothes so well, but they go around wearing dirty clothes all the time? (Louder laughter). And I must admit, I love their cookin' Mmmh, good! But why do they just eat greens and corn bread and watermelon?" (Very loud laughter).

"No, my friends, I don't understand them, but I have to treat them like a Christian would treat them, the least of God's Brethren. Now I am of course speaking of our honest, hard working colored folks here in Sweet Lake, the respectful ones who know how to stay in their place.

"I would like to give you an example of one. A couple months ago I had gone out in the country to visit some of the members of this fine congregation, and I was headed back on a dirt road and got to the edge of town, and it was an awful, muddy road, and at a bad spot in the road, I got stuck, really stuck. I tried digging out, and I tried pushing and steering at the same time, which you know is really hard to do. It was getting on toward dark, and I didn't know what was going to happen.

"Then coming down the road I saw this man walking, and at first I didn't know it was a colored man. When I saw he was colored, I thought I would just go ahead and ask. I said, 'Hey, Good Afternoon, boy, give me a little push so I can get on into town. I have good clothes on and don't want to get dirty. And he said, 'Sure thing, Reverend MacCready.'

"It was astonishing that this colored man knew who I was. He pushed the car out of the mud, and the least I could do was give him a ride back into town. I had to ask how he knew my name, and he said most everybody knew who I was, even the colored people, but this boy knew because he was a preacher, too.

"I said, 'Are you the preacher at the little colored

church down by the creek behind the feed store?' And he said, 'Yes, Reverend. That is me, Reverend Walker, of the African Methodist Episcopal Church of Sweet Lake.'

"Well, here it was, two preachers in Sweet Lake, and we had never met. So when I dropped him off by the railroad tracks, I invited him to come by the house for some iced tea the next day. He asked if that was really OK, and I assured him that we would just sit on the back porch, and it would be fine, and nobody would say anything. He said he really appreciated the ride, since he had to go home, eat with his family, and then start some kind of night shift work at the paper mill. I said I really appreciated being pushed out of the mud. Then just before I pulled away, he said he also appreciated what some people in our church had done when they boxed up the old school books from the white school and dropped them off at the colored school. He said that was such a help, because the colored kids didn't have hardly any books at all.

"My fellow Christians, I did not know anything about those books at all, but I am so proud to be a member of this congregation, where Christians see a good thing to do and they just do it, and their pastor never even hears about it. Bless you, whoever you were, in the Name of the Lord. You helped the least of God's brethren.

"Next day Reverend Walker came by, all dressed up, and I hardly recognized him. And he had a Bible in his hand. But you should have seen the Bible! It was so old and worn and falling apart that you could hardly hold it together with both hands, and I had to joke that it must have been taken from some dead Yankee." There was loud laughter from the congregation at this point.

"Reverend Walker comes from a long line of preachers, and of course the colored preachers really don't get to go to a seminary or Bible school or anything. They just do the best they can. They have meetings and things, and the ones that went up North to some school tell the other ones what they learned.

"It was a most interesting conversation over the glasses of iced tea. He really knows his Bible, Old Testament and New Testament. We both like Saint Mathew a lot. And we both have always been curious about some passages in The Book of Kings. Reverend Walker could read pretty fair, but he said he had some problems with big words like Ephesians, and Colossians, and Deuteronomy. So we practiced them a little.

"Then I asked him what his little congregation was like. He looked at me and said, 'We are just a group of poor sinners trying to do better.' And it struck me clear as the call of the Angel Gabriel. That is exactly like our congregation here, 'a group of poor sinners trying to do better.'

"So what I offer you today, my fellow sinners and my fellow Christians, is a chance to try to do better. What can you do, in your life as a Christian, for the least of God's Brethren? What can you do that you aren't doing now? Uncle Willard was an amazing man for his time. What can you do in your time? What can you do unto the least of God's Brethren, for that is what you do unto Jesus. Who are the good colored people you should be thinking of?"

That ended the sermon, and the preacher called on a deacon to make some announcements. The deacon mentioned the church supper for that Friday and a Mexican Chili benefit over at the firehouse on Saturday. Then he mentioned that the American Legion Post of Sweet Lake was putting on Brewer Brothers Circus today, right over by the park west of the church. And that it was a fundraiser for all the good works that the American Legion does for all Americans.

Gilly really loved to hear the plug for the circus, and he wondered if anybody could have guessed that one of the Brewer Brothers' sons was listening to it. Then there was another hymn.

Gilly looked up and saw that his father was now on the circus lot, and it was time to get on with setting up the show.

But he left the side steps of the church where he had been sitting very confused. Is this what these *Gaudjas* did in their churches? It was such a contradiction. It sounded like the preacher was saying that you should be nice to the poor colored people, because that is what you are supposed to do as a good person or a Christian. But at the same time, he said some really mean things. He made fun of them. He got everybody in the church to laugh out loud at them. What did he mean? What was he trying to say?

And on this day Gilly was about to hear more confusing things, confusing about how people treat one another and also about how people can do more good than what is expected.

A good crowd was showing up for the matinee performance that afternoon. There was a long line of people who had bought their tickets and were filing into the tent. Then suddenly, a loud noise broke out.

It was the chief of police yelling at the top of his lungs. He was yelling, "This is illegal. We are closin' this thing down right now. Who the hell is the boss around here? What do you think you are doin'?"

Woody quickly stepped out of the office, and with his best manners asked the police chief what the problem was. By this time, the police chief was acting in a rage. And Woody had to repeat himself.

The reply was, "You are about to be arrested for breakin' city an' county ordinances an' lots of state laws. Do I have to handcuff you?"

Woody explained that he and the Sweet Lake American Legion Post were doing everything they knew to be completely legal, and if there was any problem it could be corrected quickly.

"You can't let colored people in here, an' you know that. It is illegal. Are you just plain stupid or what?"

Woody quickly explained that the colored people would all be seated in the back of the tent in their own place by the side of the third ring. He added that this was like the system used in the Sweet Lake Picture Show, where there is a balcony for the colored, and the main floor is for whites only. Everybody is separated.

But the chief would have none of that. "Boy, you are lettin' the colored come in through the white entrance, an' you need to be arrested for that."

Woody apologized profusely and called over one of the American Legion Committee members to help smooth things over. Woody explained that one of the working boys had forgot to hang up the Whites Only sign. The colored had to go around to a side entrance. Woody yelled at Old Charlie to get that sign out immediately and hang it up. And he told the two ticket sellers that they could not sell tickets to colored people. The colored could not get in line with whites. The colored would have to be sent around the side to buy tickets there and go in their own entrance. The law required it!

Jenny understood the situation immediately and grabbed a roll of tickets and a change apron and went out and called all the colored people in the line and around the midway to come around the side of the tent right away and buy their tickets from her. In a few minutes, the crowd was suitably separated, with the whites having their place in the lines on the midway. The colored people quickly filed around to the side. Even the popcorn and snow cone vendors picked up on the situation. The vendors sent the colored to the side windows of their booths to buy what they wanted there, once the whites had been served.

By now, more committee members from the American Legion had joined in to calm down the police chief, the Whites Only sign was up, and the colored were going where they belonged. The yelling had stopped, and the afternoon circus performance could proceed.

All went well for about ten minutes, and then an unusual situation arose. A colored girl in a nanny uniform came up with three white kids she was obviously looking after. It was also clear that she was going to have a kid of her own, and probably soon. Ethyl saw her and explained that the oldest kid could take the money and get in line to buy tickets for all four of them, and then they would figure out how the seating would be.

The white kids could not be left alone in the white seats during the show, and the nanny could not sit in the white seats. The compromise that was worked out was for the kids to sit at the end of the white bleachers and for the nanny to stand at the end there near them. She was neat as a pin and in a clean uniform so it was obvious that she was just doing her job as a nanny. She would just have to stand throughout the show.

But then Grandma Camie saw what was going on and took pity on the girl. She asked one of the clowns to take a horse bucket over and turn it upside down and tell the colored girl that she could sit on it with no problem. The youngest kid was a little afraid of the clown with the bucket, but the two older ones thought it was a good idea for their nanny to have something to sit on while they watched the circus.

Later, Grandma Camie took one of the folding chairs

from near the back entrance and asked the clown to take it to the poor girl, who obviously had the worst seat in the house and needed a little more comfort in the final days of her pregnancy. The clown figured out that it was smarter to bring the chair around back and take it under the sidewall of the tent so the audience wouldn't notice what was going on.

But the story did not end at this point. During the second half of the show, the clown came running to Madam Camie and said, "You will never guess what happened. Ms. Camie! That colored girl peed all over that chair I took her. Her dress is soaking wet. I guess she felt she couldn't leave the kids an' go pee in the woods or somethin'."

"Oh, no," said Madam Camie, "She didn't pee. Her bag of waters broke, an' that means she is gonna have her baby right here an' right now. We have to get her out of the tent. We will lift up the sidewall canvas of the tent an' take her out like that. People can't see this. We have to carry her over to my fortunetelling tent. Get some help. An' I need three or four bales of straw an' the cleanest horse blanket you can find. Do it now. I will find somebody to look after the three kids. Now first help get her over to my fortunetelling tent. Get any able-bodied man you can find to help. Hurry!"

While two men and one of the Suarez girls were getting the girl over to Madam Camie's *dukkerin'* tent, Camie went quietly over to the colored seats and asked if anybody knew the nanny and if somebody could watch over the kids. She found two nice women who volunteered to stand by the children. They said they were from the church. They talked briefly. Camie heard something she did not want to hear. They told her that there was not a doctor in the town who birthed colored babies. The nearest one was over in Wallaceburg, an hour or so away, but nobody knew if he would be home on a Sunday or not.

Camie had delivered a dozen babies herself over the years, including some of her own grandchildren, and it was becoming clear that she would have to deliver another one, very soon. Camie collected her oldest granddaughter Mattie, and then she found a colored lady who had seen babies born, and she dragged the two to her tent.

The girl was waiting there, very confused and afraid, and in some pain. At least the bales of straw had arrived and the horse blanket. Camie spoke calmly and sweetly to the girl and worked quickly with Grandpa GR and the other two to make the bales of straw and the horse blanket into something that resembled an emergency birthing bed. The mother-to-be could sit at an angle so that gravity could help a little as the baby came out. Camie told the colored lady and Mattie to cover the straw bales with the horse blanket and then cover the horse blanket with a clean sheet, and she asked Grandpa GR to get some water boiling on the stove in the nearby house trailer, a lot more water, and not just in the tea kettle, and to bring some clean towels and one of his razor blades, a new one, and not to take the wrapper off.

Then she said, "No, GR, just put a pot of water on an' get the towels out an' the razor blade, an' let our granddaughter take care of the rest. You gotta leave. A baby is going to be born, an' this is not a place for men.

Keep everybody out unless a doctor or a veterinary shows up, or any of the girl's family. Oh, an' take down my *dukkerin* signs. I won't be tellin' any fortunes this afternoon."

Then Camie pulled her wicker chair over to the make-shift birthing bed and held the hands of the mother-to-be. She said, "Honey, your baby is comin' soon, real soon, an' we are gonna help you. I have birthed babies before, an' we are gonna work together. Honey, how many babies have you had?"

"Why, ma'am, I aint had none. This be my firs'. I'm scared, real scared. They say it hurts bad. It hurts awful. An' who's gonna tell Benny an' Mama an' Daddy that the baby is comin'?"

"That's OK, sweetie. We will find a way to tell your family. An' everybody has a first time, a first baby. You are a young girl, an' you are healthy. An' I know how to keep it from hurting so bad. These two ladies are here to help, too. This is my granddaughter Mattie. She is really smart an' real helpful. You know this lady. What is your name, darling? Ramona? That your name? You know this girl?"

Ramona replied that no, it was just the girl's parents that she knew, but she would do all she could to help. And Mattie's eyes were wide with concern. Camie whispered in an aside to her, "*Raklie*, this aint the first time *tutti's sikkered lellin' ticknas. Tutti gins* it with *grais* an' *juckles*. Now it's with a *jouval*. " ("You've seen having babies. You know it with horses and dogs. Now it's with a woman.")

Then Camie spoke to the girl. "Now, honey, it is goin' to be OK. I am gonna tell you what to do, an' you will have a brand new baby. What is your name, honey?"

"I'm Jelly, ma'am, Jelly Mae. My daddy call me that 'cause he said I was a sweet baby, jus' as sweet like jelly."

"Jelly, now maybe you have seen a baby birthin', an' maybe not."

"No, ma'am, I aint never seen, but they say it hurts so bad you wanna die. An' who is lookin' after my three kids, the MacCready babies?" Ramona explained that two other ladies were now standing with the three kids, looking after them real good.

"And right now, we gotta get you outta that wet uniform an' get off your wet panties an' clean you up. An' Mattie, run to the trailer an' get my blue cotton dressing gown outta the bottom drawer under the back bed. We're gonna put it on her.

"Jelly, I want you to watch what I do. It looks funny, but you gotta do it. You know what breathin' is. Well, I want you to breathe like me. I want you to breathe kinda fast, like this, like a dog on a hot day, an' it has gotta be taking a lot of air in at the same time. Now watch."

Camie demonstrated the breathing she wanted, while she looked right into Jelly's eyes to see if she understood. And she seemed to understand. "Now you try. It's like pantin', you know, like a dog pants."

Jelly did a decent job of panting. She took in air and

let it out in rapid succession. Camie told Mattie to see if the water was boiling yet in the pot on the stove in the nearby trailer, and she told Ramona to bring over the clean towels, and she asked Jelly to practice breathing once again. And they all had to scrub their hands with lye soap and hot water up past the elbows, thoroughly. And they washed Jelly's hands. And Mattie brought three clean aprons for them to put on.

She held Jelly's hand and explained that there would be pains that would come and let up. And she shouldn't panic, cause each time the pains started, they would let up a bit, and the baby would get a little farther along. Each time the pains came, she would be able to tell when she had to push. And then she would have to push out as hard as she could. And the breathing and panting would help it all and make the pain be better. Then she said, "Jelly, Honey, do you have any questions?"

And Jelly said, "No, ma'am. No questions, but yes, ma'am, how long do it take?"

"Well, Jelly, some babies come in a hurry, an' some are afraid an' take their time. We will see what your baby decides to do. An' they say that colored girls do it faster. They can push harder or somethin'.

"Now, Jelly, we have to let you spread your legs so we can come an' see where the baby is coming out. You usually see a bit of the top of the head first. Can we come around now? You seem to be goin' along pretty fast."

Jelly nodded her head, and then some pains came.

"Good, Jelly, you gotta do that. We are here with you. Breathe like we said, an' push. Breathe right an' push hard." Jelly did her best, and everybody encouraged her. Ramona and Mattie were on each side holding a hand. She did scream a little, and Camie said she could scream as much as she wanted to. Everybody was watching the circus and could not hear a thing over the band that was playing and the crowd.

"I can see some of your baby's head, Jelly! That is the way it is supposed to be. You are doin' a good job. You are doin' a good job. It is already started."

Then she turned to Mattie and said, "Sweetheart, I have to have you here. I know you are supposed to be helping your daddy with the dog act pretty soon. But somebody else can help put on the act this time. I will explain to your mama an' daddy that you were here helping me birth a baby."

The labor continued for another twenty minutes. Mattie had seen animal births several times, but this was a human, a human baby. It was the same but different. She could not take her eyes away. It was something she would never forget. She watched everything her grandmother did. She did exactly what her grandmother said to do.

Once the head of the baby was coming out, the rest was easier. Jelly was exhausted but smiled when she heard her little child cry. Camie used the new razor blade to cut the cord. Then she tied the cord off.

"It's a little girl. You got yourself a little baby girl." The little girl started to cry as soon as Camie held her up side down. There was no need to pat her behind. Mattie helped Ramona clean the baby off very carefully and wrap her in a clean towel to give to her mother. What astounded Mattie, however, was that the baby wasn't so dark. It looked kind of white. She looked at her grandmother, but she could tell this was not the time to ask questions.

The placenta came quickly. Ramona gave Jelly water to drink. Mattie fixed tea with cream and sugar and brought it out on her grandmother's fine china from the trailer. But Jelly just wanted to hold her new baby. She wasn't interested in tea or anything to eat.

After a bit, Camie continued, "Now Jelly, I know you are tired, but you are gonna have to get some liquid in you, an' you gotta eat, Girl. You probably haven't had a bite since breakfast.

"No, ma'am, I aint," said Jelly. But I aint hungry. I just wanna hold my baby."

"But, child, you are still eatin' for two. You gotta make milk to feed this baby," said Camie. "You gotta drink water an' milk yourself an' eat enough food so you have good milk, you understand?

"Now I am gonna tell you some stuff you might not know about mama's milk an' nursing a baby, or maybe you do know some of it. You know you gotta keep your titties clean where the baby sucks. Ramona, come help me clean Jelly's breasts right now. Mattie, you hold the baby, real careful, for just a minute. She might want her first meal real soon.

"An' Jelly, you gotta feed your baby, nurse your baby,

about every two hours, real often, an' not just when she cries. That means you gotta give her your breast a lot of times every day an' every night, too. Do you know how big her little tummy is?"

"No, ma'am. I don't. I never thought about that."

"Well, child, her tummy is not much bigger than a thimble. It can't hold very much yet. So she is emptying it out all the time, an' you gotta keep filling it, even at night. Don't let her sleep too long, even if she's not fussing. Pick her up, an' put your tittie to her mouth. Encourage her.

"An' you gotta drink a whole lot of water all the time. If your pee is real yellow an' smells, you need more water. You gotta make a lot of milk, good milk. Eat whenever you're hungry, an' even when you are not hungry. There is absolutely nothin' your child can get to grow on except what comes out of your titties. That means it's got to come out of you. You gotta eat it or drink it.

"An' a couple other things. Now you know you always gotta give your baby a clean tit to nurse on, but you have to make sure she drinks from both sides, your left breast an' your right breast. Don't let one side start givin' more milk that the other. Keep that milk comin' on both sides real strong.

"The first milk that comes out doesn't look like milk. It is clear. But give it to her anyway. She needs it. She needs to drink real soon. She had a big change today. Now did your mama tell you what to do to make your nipples tougher?"

"Oh, yes, ma'am. She's been havin' me wash 'em a lot with a rag to get them tough so it don't hurt so bad when the baby pulls on 'em. An' I been doin' that."

"That was smart, Jelly. And Ramona, you probably nursed babies. Tell Jelly what it is like. Tell her things like her mama told her."

"Well, child, you do get used to it," said Ramona. "You do get used to it. I really like nursin' babies. An' I do know your mother. She will help you. You know what to do if your baby gets colicky, don't you? She don't want to eat or nothin'. She just want to be cranky an' cry all night long."

"Oh, yea," said Jelly. "My little brother was like that. Wasn't nothing we could do. Mama an' Daddy just used to hol' him an' sometimes take him for walks, even in the middle of the night. Then one day, it stopped. Nobody knew why. It just stopped, an' he was like his old self again. We was so happy!"

Then Camie said, "You gotta rest now, child. An' you should not work for a week. You gotta take care of your wonderful new baby day an' night. An' you gotta get strong again. So don't work till next Sunday."

"But, ma'am, my boss lady, Ms. MacCready, she aint gonna like that. She needs me. I don't come to work, she gonna get some other colored girl. I gotta work, ma'am."

"Sweetheart, maybe I can talk to her. She has to understand. An' maybe your folks can find somebody to help out at the MacCreadys' just for a few days. An' your boss lady knows that you have to be able to stop an' feed your baby while your are working."

"Oh, yes, ma'am," said Jelly. "Josie said she always let her take her babies to the back porch an' nurse 'em, as long as there weren't any menfolk around. Josie says she just don't want any colored babies cryin' right in the house."

The conversation continued among the three women, and Mattie listened to every word. It was so interesting and so thrilling. And it was scary. Would she ever want to have babies of her own? Wasn't that what girls were supposed to do? Would she be able to do it? Would she want to do it?

Meanwhile the show had ended, and the matinee crowd had mostly left. GR Brewer, who had been mostly sitting outside the *dukkerin'* tent keeping an eye on the crowd, heard a car horn blowing rudely. He looked up and saw a new car driven by a smartly dressed woman. She kept blowing the horn.

GR got up and walked over to her and in his best English accent introduced himself, "I am Gilderoy Brewer, and this is Brewer Brothers Circus. How can I help you, young lady?"

"I am here to pick up my children. I had to send them here with their nanny so I could get them out of the way while we had the barbeque at our house. Where are the children? I told them I would pick them up here. What has happened to them?"

"Well, young lady, you certainly look like a woman of good taste and someone who knows how to take care of things. If you will just follow me…"

"If you don't bring my children to me immediately, I will go get the police. I have good high heels on, an' I don't want to get out in the dirt. Have Gypsies stolen my children? Have they been stolen? I will have that nanny of theirs horsewhipped if anything has happened to them."

"Now, young lady, Gypsies don't steal children. They have their own children. An' the police are right here. Two Sweet Lake officers are down there with my son by the ticket office."

"Gypsies do too steal babies. I know they do. Everybody knows that!"

GR basically ignored what she said. "If you don't want to get out of your car, then just follow me, an' I will let you drive right into the bigtop. Your three children are with Pinky the Clown an' two colored ladies from the church. This is the circus. This is where children come to have a good time!"

"I am Mrs. MacCready, Mrs. Malcolm MacCready, and Mr. MacCready is a lawyer. Take me there immediately. An' I am going to have that nanny put in jail."

GR knew the first priority was to reunite the woman with her children. There was no use trying to explain anything. He motioned for her to follow him in the car, and he asked a ticket taker and a workingman to pull some canvas aside so she could drive right through the front gate of the bigtop. At first they were confused, but GR was adamant. His son Woody heard GR talking and figured out that GR was working with some kind of major problem. Woody watched what was going on but stayed back. He knew that his father GR could handle just about anything.

"Mama, Mama, look. They gave us balloons an' snow cones! An' Pinky the clown is doing magic for us! An' we saw a yama. It is the same as a camel, but they cut the hump off. An' we saw the circus!"

"An' where is Jelly Mae? Why isn't she doing her job? Why do you have to have two other colored women with you?" asked the mother.

"She got sick, an' they took her to make her better," said the older boy, the one who was given the money to buy the tickets.

And out of sight of the children, one of the colored ladies made a motion like a pregnant woman having a baby.

"You kids get in the car, right now. Stay there," said the mother sharply. "I have to talk to these people." The kids got into the car, bringing their balloons and snow cones along. Pinky waved to them and made them laugh one last time.

The mother walked over to the colored ladies and the clown. "I have to know what is going on here. If she was going to have that baby, she should have come home. Where is the doctor? I need to talk to him. Where is Jelly?"

One of the colored ladies spoke up, a difficult thing to do, given the difference in status in the community. "Ma'am, I am Ms. Walker. Jelly is fine. She had a baby girl. Ms. Brewer did the birthin'. They are over in a little tent. Everybody is fine. It happened right during the show. They had to take her right out of the big tent when her bag of waters busted."

"Why, I never heard of such a thing! What kind of family lets their nanny have a baby in a tent at a circus? Why you would think we were some kind of, I don't know, low-class hillbilly or something! I want to see Jelly, an' I want to see her now!"

"Ma'am, one of us can stay by the kids in your car, an' the other will walk you over to the little tent to see if Jelly is awake now or what."

By this time, GR had warned his wife that trouble was on the way, that the girl's boss lady was coming and was mad as a hornet. "The *divia hona dias of the trin kushti Gaudja chavies*," was how he but it. 'The crazy mad mother of the three nice white kids."

But what happened was surprising. As soon as the woman laid eyes on Jelly and her little baby, she just melted.

"Well, my word! Jelly Mae, you did it! You went an' had yourself a baby! How about you! Oh, an' little colored babies are always the cutest. It is a little girl. Oh, how sweet! Jelly, I am gonna give you five dollars, an' I will give you five dollars every time you have a baby. An' I wanna make a little dress for her. I'll have the other maids pick out some old material an' make something sweet for her. Why, I believe I already gave everything away from when my last boy was a baby. But we will find something.

"Jelly, when you come in tomorrow, we are gonna look for different material in the trunk in the attic. Let's make her two little dresses, so you can have her look nice even when one is bein' washed. I'll have Mr. MacCready make a picture of you an' the baby, a picture you can keep.

"An', Jelly, who is the daddy? We want him in the picture, too. Have him come tomorrow when you come to work. Who is he?" But before any answer could be given, the baby started crying, probably the first loud cries of her young life, and Jelly smiled down at her and offered her a breast. And the baby took her first sips of milk.

'Well, looky there! Isn't that somethin'?" said the woman. "It is just like the way white babies nurse. It is all the same. Why I remember when I had my first child. It was wonderful. It still is. Jelly, how are you going to get home, you poor thing?"

"Well, ma'am, Madam Camie here, she the one who did the birthin', she say I can't come to work tomorrow. She say I can't work for a week. I gotta get strong," said Jelly.

"That's correct," said Camie. "She needs to get her strength. She can't be walking miles to work yet. She has to stay home for a week."

"Well, I never heard of such a thing!" replied the Mac-Cready woman angrily. "You aren't a doctor. An' besides, she is just a colored girl. Everybody knows they just do birthin' fast, faster than an alley cat, some people say. An' besides, I need her. How can I run my house with no nanny? The other maids can't do her work!"

"Lady, you will have to do for a week without her. She is an excellent nanny. We watched her. The children love her an' obey her. An' she loves them. But if you want her to be healthy an' strong, you have to let her stay home for a week. She is my patient. I know what she needs. That is all there is to it!"

"Four days. I will let her stay home for four days. An' after that she has to work."

"You seem like a good woman, ma'am, an' a leader of the community. I believe if you make a promise, you will keep it. So if you promise four days, an' you send a driver to pick her up for the first week after that so she doesn't have to walk so far yet with the baby, an' if you give her all her pay for those four days, well, then, under the circumstances, I can agree to that," replied Camie, with her most official and English-accented voice.

"An' we'll see that Jelly gets home to her people. You just take your own babies home now. Send the car for Jelly an' her baby on Friday," Camie said.

The woman paused, then agreed. She left the *dukkerin'* tent, worrying about her high-heeled shoes on the dirt and in a hurry to get to her car back in the bigtop.

Camie worked out an arrangement with Pinky the Clown. Pinky drove Jelly and her new baby and the two colored ladies home in a circus pickup truck, with Jelly and the baby up front and the two ladies riding in the back. As they drove away, Jelly waved weakly, and called out, "Madam Camie, I am namin' her after you. You been so good to us. Her name gonna be 'Camie Mae!'"

It ended up that colored town in Sweet Lake was not really that far away from the circus, closer than the main part of town, and Jelly's family was so happy to see her. Dozens of people gathered around to welcome her. They wanted to hear the story, but quickly the two ladies said that Jelly needed to go into the house with the baby now. The ladies said they could tell a lot of the story.

At supper at the circus cookhouse that evening, it was one of those instances that all the Brewers sat together and discussed something that was not official business. Long after the meal was over they continued talking, adults and kids. They all wanted to know about the new colored baby.

But finally, the conversation got slower and more serious when Mattie asked why the baby looked so white. The image of a baby of such a light color coming from a black mother was burned in her mind.

"Honey child," said her grandmother, "there are some things you need to know, an' some things you already know or kinda know. Your own mama an' daddy an' your cousins need to be in on this conversation.

"First of all, little colored babies are not so dark when they are first born. They usually look light. I don't know why, but they really do, almost all of them.

"An' you know we don't know who the daddy is. It is

none of our business."

"You mean the daddy could be a white man? But a colored girl can't marry a white boy!" said Mattie.

Then Mattie's mother came in, "Yes, we all know that. It is against the law. But of course that doesn't mean they can't make a baby together. They can. It happens."

"Is that why some of the colored people aren't so colored?" asked a younger cousin.

"Yes, people get mixed together, just like different breeds of horses or dogs do. It is the same. They make babies together. An' everybody here knows how babies are made. Which of you kids can tell me?"

There was a long pause, and Mattie replied, "The *gara's cova* goes in the *raklie's cova*, the boy's thing goes in the girl's thing, and when it rubs, there are seeds, and the *raklie* can *lell* a *tickna*, get a baby."

"That's pretty good, honey. Do the *gara* an' the *raklie* have to be *rummered*?"

"*Keker*," said one of the cousins. "they don't have to *rummer*, to be married."

"Can they *lell* a *tickna*, get a baby, from just one time?"

"*Ava*," said Gilly, "the *racklie* can get *bora* from just one time. The girl can get pregnant."

"Do they have to like each other or love each other?"

"*Keker*," said another cousin. 'They just have to do it."

Then Jesse said, "Dad, I heard from some town boys

that there are girls who will do it for money. You just pay them, an' they will do it with you. Is that true?"

"Oh, boy, our children are growing up fast!" said Lucky. "But yes, that is true. We call those girls *livinias* in *Rumnis*. You have heard us use that word, an' it doesn't mean just a bad girl; it really means a girl who takes money from a man for doing it."

GR added, "You need to know that it is illegal, that a man can get arrested, and sometimes the girls have to give some money to crooked cops to get away with it, or to some man who pays off the *mushkras,* the police. Crooks are always involved in one way or another. And sometimes the *livinias lell bora*, get pregnant, and then there is no *dadus* around for the baby. There is no father."

"It is so sad. The poor *livinias* are usually just from poor families an' need money, or they already have some *chavies* an' want to feed them," said Amy. "An' they get diseases. You know you can get diseases from *sevin',* from doing it. And the diseases are painful, an' if a girl gets one of the diseases, she may never be able to have a baby the rest of her life."

"But do the men give the girls the diseases, or do the girls give the men the disease?" asked one of the male cousins.

Tillie answered, "Who knows how it started? It doesn't matter now. You just need to know that the diseases are awful an' that people who do it with people they are not married to can get the diseases. The diseases are hard to cure. The medicine does not always work."

"So, Dad, the colored women have a hard life. They have to work hard for not much money. People cheat them. Men might do bad things to them. They don't get to have a free life like other people. That is not right!" Gilly said.

"You are right, Son. It is not right. It is *vaseta*! It' horrible! But we do not have to be bad to colored people. Your grandmother was very good to a colored girl today. We are a different kind of people ourselves, so maybe we understand better what it is like to be different. And we have to be very careful of how the *Gaudjas* see us and treat us. We don't even want them to know that we are *Romanichals*. We don't tell them. If we have to, we just tell them we are English," Woody explained.

One of the cousins spoke up, "*Dortie*, well, do the colored boys have a hard life, too?"

"Yes, Nephew, colored men have a hard life, too, a lot of them. They get sent to prison a lot, a lot more than white men. You have seen the chain gangs of colored men cutting the grass along the side of the road. There is always a white *mush* on a *grai* with a *yargamingra* watchin' them and makin' them work in the hot sun. He sits on a horse and has a gun. They can't stop to drink water or to eat, or even to *mutter*, to take a leak, until the *Gaudja mush* lets them."

"Do colored men get sent to prison even if they are innocent?" Little Fred asked, very wide-eyed.

"Yes, it can happen. Or some judge can give them a lot

of years in prison even if they did something small. An' that is just because they are colored," Lucky said.

"But that is wrong! What can we do about it?" Gilly said.

"Son, I don't know of anything we can do about it. All we can do is treat the colored people who work for us right, or any colored people who we see. We have to be fair an' kind an' polite. We can do that.

"This is a good time to mention something else, too. Sometimes colored men don't even make it to prison. They don't get a trial. Innocent or guilty, they just get hung. They get lynched over some little thing or something they never did.

"Every year, there are colored men lynched in a lot of states. A couple years ago, the whole show had to completely drive out around a town. They were lynching some poor colored boy down by the courthouse. A cop stopped us on the edge of town an' said we needed to stay out of trouble an' just take a side road out around this town. So we did. It took an extra hour, but we did it."

"But Dad, when will the lynching of the colored men stop?"

"I don't know, Son. I just don't know."

This selection of old family and circus pictures is intended to help the reader visualize and understand the background and setting of the stories. The stories are historical fiction, but these pictures are real. In this first photo, the author's grandparents, great grandparents, and extended family are at a camp in Oklahoma or Texas circa 1905. The author's mother is hidden in the baby buggy in front of her parents.

The author's mother and her first husband with their circus in the background, circa 1928.

The author's mother in wardrobe for an aerial number, sometime in the 20s.

The author's parents with trained pony Teddy in the 20s.

Performers in front of a somewhat ragged circus tent, indicating that the picture probably dates from the Great Depression.

The author's mother with the original Dolly, Blanche, and Jewel on Russell Brothers Circus in the 30s.

The author's father with Domino, one of his performing horses.

The author as an infant with his mother on Hunt Brother Circus in the season of 1943 someplace on the Eastern Seaboard.

The author at about eight years old with a newborn pony. Note the beaded dress of the Native Americans barely showing on the edges of the picture.

The author's mother with one her performing dogs, probably in the late 40s.

MADAM CARNEAL KNOWS ALL.
LIFE READER

ADVISOR, SPIRITUAL AND ASTROLOGY

By visiting MADAM CARNEAL you will recognize the facts as she convinces the most skeptical. MADAM CARNEAL tells not flatter you, she tells you your life as it is, and as it should be. For most every trouble there is a remedy, and in most cases the remedy is within your reach. If you only knew it, MADAM CARNEAL advises you, she suggests wisely. She combines fully.

Not to know is to suffer. Knowledge is power. Ignorance is the root of all evil. Seek before too late.

MADAM CARNEAL does what others claim to do. No one in trouble turned away. She has helped thousands and she can help you. Suggests on Business, Changes, Journeys, Sickness, Mortgages, Wills, Love, Courtship, Marriage and Divorce, If you wish to marry the one you love, she can help you.

All interviews private and confidential.
READ OTHER SIDE OF CARD

Ask MADAM CARNEAL she will tell you

Life is not half as bad as some people would make you believe. There is no life so sad or dreary that I cannot bring happiness and sunshine into it. If you are in doubt about anything, worried or unhappy, making changes in business or doubtful as to friends or family matters, do not hesitate to call upon me. If you are in trouble I can assist you. My aim in life is to aid and assist humanity to a better and happier understanding in life. I turn no one away who is sincere and deserving. Today is the day. Tomorrow may be too late. All interviews strictly private and confidential.

LOCATED AT ALBANY, LA.

On Highway 190, one mile West in my own home. Reading daily and Sunday.

READ OTHER SIDE OF CARD

The fortunetelling card of the author's grandmother from around the 50s.

The author's eldest brother with his trained zebra, Miss Zulu, circa 1950. Trained zebras were very rare.

The author with father and brother in western wardrobe posing by side of mobile home, circa 1952.

The author's eldest brother with Big Jim, probably from the 60s.

The author's older brother and sister-in-law with young performing elephants in 1990s

13. HOUDINI'S GREAT ESCAPE

Houdini was from Mobile, or at least that is where the Brewers had found him. It was late in a season before the Depression started. The show was playing a string of towns from Pascagoula to Apalachicola along the Gulf of Mexico where it was still warm that time of year. Many people said that this was the prettiest stretch of highway in the country. There were palm trees and big old live oaks dripping with Spanish moss that hung out over the highway. There were places travelers could pull over and wade right out in the Gulf if they wanted. The beach was very wide, and children loved playing in the sand. There was a lot of good seafood, too.

Houdini was well mannered enough. He seemed to enjoy seeing people come into the menagerie exhibit. He was happy to stay on his leash and a couple yards back from the rope that kept visitors at a distance. It was when visitors would push against the rope or step over it that there could be problems. His legs were so powerful that he could break bones with one forward kick, though we hadn't done such a thing in years, and then it was to a strange dog that threatened him.

It was not surprising that people did not know what to make of Houdini. Houdini was an ostrich, a large male ostrich with beautiful black and white feathers, the kind that were seen on the hats worn by ladies on the cover of fashion magazines. Of all the feathers used in millinery, ostrich feathers and ibis feathers were the most coveted.

Sometimes it was just meant as a joke, but on rare occasion some brazen person would try to grab one of Houdini's feathers. "I just wanted one, you know, as a little souvenir to put on a hat." That was the kind of comment the workingmen heard. The same thing that made Houdini such an attraction was what put him at risk. Houdini would usually defend himself and his plumage with a rapid peck at the offending hand, and then there might be some "fixing" to do, minor fixing if there was no blood, or every few years, major fixing with a bandage if there was blood. Children were usually too intimidated by Houdini's height to get close enough to grab a feather. The offenders were more often young males trying to impress a girlfriend.

When the Brewers first found him, Houdini was on display at a gas station near Mobile and living in deplorable conditions. When some show trucks pulled in for gas, the owner noticed that they were circus trucks. He came up and asked the drivers to please take his ostrich.

"What are you doing with an ostrich at a gas station?" they asked the owner.

"Well, a zoo up North had ordered four ostriches, an' when they came into the Port of Mobile from Mexico or someplace, there were five of them, including two males. That zoo just wanted one male an' three females. It told all about it in the paper. The zoo would not pay for five of them. They would only pay for four to be hauled on the Illinois Central. So there was an extra ostrich at the port that they were keeping in an old milk wagon. Nobody knew what to do with it. The dockworkers were just feeding him doughnuts an' stuff. One guy wanted to take him to butcher an' see if it tasted like chicken or turkey.

"I called up an' said I would buy the extra male ostrich for five dollars to use as a roadside attraction to make more people stop at my gas station. But I told them I had to have the milk wagon to keep him in. Three days later, a pickup truck came here pulling him in the milk wagon."

"So was he good for business?" asked Uncle Harry, as he stood by the elephant truck.

"For a little while, he was. All kinds of people stopped, even if they didn't buy gas. I put up a little pen for him to come out of the milk wagon, but not so that you could see him from the road. I wanted to make 'em come buy gas. My daughter sold little bags of corn an' peanuts to feed him. It took a while, but then everybody had seen him. Only kids on bicycles come by now.

"He got sick or something. Nearly all his feathers came out. I talked to a chicken farmer an' even called a vet. They said he might have mold. It is not like the green mold you can see. It just makes them lose their feathers every once in a while. If you feed them right, they grow back. Well, it has been a month now, an' he still looks naked. He is ugly! Please take him!" the man said with exasperation.

Uncle Harry went to look at the poor bird. The pen had not been cleaned for quite some time. It was very muddy. So was the ostrich. There was no water for the animal to drink. It was not clear what he was being fed. Harry waited, and when Woody started to drive by the station, he motioned for Woody to stop. By the time Harry had explained the plight of the animal to Woody, the owner came over. He repeated his offer. "Just take him off my hands. I am in the gas station business, not the animal business. You can have the milk wagon an' everything. Just take him off my hands."

Woody was pretty sure he wanted the ostrich, if only to give it a better life for a while. The larger problem was if the milk wagon was roadworthy and if one of the prop trucks could pull it. When Uncle Choctaw stopped, they took a look at the tires and pumped them up and tried to put some grease in the wheels. Woody got a Tennessee license plate out from under the seat of his truck and put it on the back of the milk wagon. One of the working boys got a shovel and started cleaning it out, with another man standing guard with a broom in case the ostrich attacked. None of them knew anything about ostriches. The faded lettering, "GREATER GULF COAST DAIRY," was visible on the side of the milk wagon.

They decided to leave the generator trailer at the gas station temporarily and pull the milk wagon to the next town with the prop truck. A driver would double back later and get the generator. This would work till a longer-term solution could be found.

"If you want to get him in the milk wagon, give him this candy bar. Just throw it down where you want him to go. He loves candy bars. He will always go in the wagon for a candy bar," the station owner said.

The first five miles on the road was just a test to see if the milk wagon was roadworthy. Uncle Choctaw drove about fifteen or twenty miles an hour. Then he drove faster. He was concerned about the coupling on the milk wagon and how it was hooked on to the prop truck he was driving. It seems that at one time a horse pulled the milk wagon. Somebody had made a new coupling so that a truck could pull it. The coupling was just a pipe coming out with a loop welded on the end. The loop was too big and had to be chained onto the coupling on the truck. There were no lights and no brakes on the milk wagon either. It would need a lot of work, if it were kept at all.

"Woodvine Brewer, what on earth have you dragged in this time? I do declare, Man, if it is not one thing, it's another. What are we going to do with that old rattle-trap excuse for a trailer?" Amy was not at all happy with what she saw when Woody and Choctaw pulled on the lot at the next town.

"Just come over, an' take a look, darling. I got a little surprise for you. You've never had anything like this!" Woody replied to his wife.

"Well, what is it? Did you find it hit on the road? What are we going to do with it?" Amy asked when she peeked inside.

"You mean it is a real ostrich? We never have had one of them. Who knows how to take care of them? Oh, Lord. That baby is going to need a lot of takin' care of!" Amy exclaimed.

Almost immediately, there were a dozen people around the milk wagon, looking in. Then there were twenty and then half the show. They all wanted to see. They all wanted to hear how it was going to fit into the show.

The ostrich was not going to fit into the show for quite some time. He would have to be kept out of sight till he put on weight and grew back his feathers. Maybe then if he didn't fit into the show, he could at least find a home in some zoo.

Harold got the job of taking care of the bird and training it. After all, he had experience with ducks, geese, and peacocks before he joined the show, and that was about as close to ostrich training as anybody had ever been. The first step was to see if the bird could be broken to lead on a rope. If he could, there was a better chance that he would fit in the show somehow.

Given the lack of ostrich experience on the show, horse experience was substituted. If a horse is mean, one of the best ways to break him to lead is to get two long lead ropes on his head. Two men can lead the mean horse by keeping him between them but too far to bite or kick either man. After a while, the mean horse usually settles down. If the horse is really mean, it may take four men, two on each rope. But the first challenge was to get two ropes around Houdini's neck. Nobody wanted to go up close to him. It was clear that neck of his had a long reach. There were no volunteers to be the first person ever bit by an ostrich on Brewer Brothers Circus.

Chief Red Hawk got a rope over Houdini's head and down around his neck. Gilly got a second rope on him. Harold and Red Hawk tugged on the ropes to get the ostrich to come out of the milk wagon. They took their time. They were gentle.

Gilly pushed from behind with a broom that he stuck through the front of the wagon. It took about ten minutes till Houdini finally stepped out onto the ground. He looked around right and left inquisitively, and then he lowered his head and got a mouthful of grass. It had been months since he had been able to graze on fresh green grass. He started gobbling greedily.

Harold and Gilly just let him take his time. They wanted him to have a good experience coming out of the wagon with ropes around his neck. They tugged him forward a few feet, and all went well as long as there was grass to be had. This first foray lasted a half hour, and the men got him quite a distance from the wagon. The green grass was the big attraction. He returned to the milk wagon willingly.

It was clear that the bird needed to put on weight. He was expected to look very thin because he was almost featherless, but clearly, Houdini's body needed meat on it. A daily half-bucket of sweet feed was added to all the hay he could eat and all the green grass he could graze on his walks.

It was also clear that he was weak. He seemed out of breath, and he panted after only fifty feet of walking. He just had not been getting enough exercise in his pen at the gas station. One mystery that could not be solved was why he drank so little water. Harold assumed an ostrich would drink as much water as a pony, at least, but Houdini would go for a day or more with barely a sip.

After a week of daily excursions, the two men decided to try leading Houdini with only one lead rope and to let the other rope drag on the ground, ready to be picked up quickly if there was any problem. This was real progress, and it continued nicely for nearly a week, and then Harold got hit. It was a serious blow to Harold's stomach. Thank goodness he had on a belt with a big buckle, because the buckle probably saved him from serious harm. Harold had no idea why the ostrich would suddenly turn and strike out like that, but he did not want to take any more chances. It was back to using two lead ropes with two men for the walks.

A couple days later some clues about the attack were offered. A man came on the lot who identified himself as a veterinarian. He welcomed a break from seeing the usual farm animals and was happy to have a tour of the more exotic species on the show. The ostrich fascinated him. He listened closely to the story of how the animal came to be on the show. That afternoon, he brought his twelve-year old daughter to the lot with the O-P-Q volume of the *Encyclopedia Americana* so that she could read the entry on ostriches. The girl was a good reader, and the article was only two pages long. Harold, Woody, Gilly, and others sat around and learned important facts. Ostriches live in dry or desert-like areas and are not big water drinkers. A male ostrich can grow to over six feet tall so Houdini still had some growing to do. Ostriches can live for forty years or more in captivity. They are raised in captivity for their feathers and meat. They eat mainly grass and grains and an occasional insect or lizard or other small animal. Ostriches are birds, so they do not have any teeth. This means that the do not chew food. Instead, they like to pick up pebbles and shiny things to swallow to help grind up their food in the stomach, similar to the way that chickens like to eat an occasional pebble.

This last point caught Harold's attention. He took off his belt and put in on the ground, and sure enough, Houdini pecked at the shiny buckle and tried to grab it and swallow it. Harold grabbed it back and hid it behind his back. Then Harold took of his shirt and put in on the ground. Houdini inspected it briefly; then in the flash of an eye he picked it up and began chewing on part of it. Harold grabbed the shirt, but he was too late to save what had attracted the animal. Houdini had swallowed a shiny button. Then the veterinary pulled a nickel from his pocket and shined it on his pant leg before throwing in front of the bird. When it hit the ground, Houdini gave it the briefest of inspections before ingesting it.

"Don't worry," the vet said. "That won't harm him. For a bird this big, well, larger things are fine. You know how you see rocks and gravel in a chicken's craw when you cut it open? Well, a chicken swallows these to help grind up the feed they have eaten. Ostriches need things for grinding in their craw, too."

This was a major lesson in ostrich care. Ostriches in general, and Houdini in particular, had a great affinity for shiny objects. It was only natural for the animal to peck at them and try to swallow them. Buckles, buttons, and jewelry would always be at risk. The vet said that it would do him good occasionally to pick rocks up from the ground.

The ostrich became well broke to lead around, and he slowly put on more feathers. It took time for the people on the show to learn not to come near him if they had anything shiny on their person. The red coveralls worn by the men who put up the props in the tent were just fine because the buttons did not show. Sometimes, if Harold forgot, he would rapidly remove his shirt and put it on backwards to keep shiny buttons out of sight, and he would pull his shirttail out to avoid a blow to the gut when Houdini was attracted to the fancy belt buckle. It was all just part of the routine of handling an ostrich.

Houdini had another quirk that it took a bit of time to figure out. He flapped his wings and danced around vigorously whenever he saw the plumes on the Suarez bareback horses or even the plumes that the Suarez women wore in their hair. It was hard to keep him under control. The feathers in Chief Red Hawk's war bonnet brought no notice. Aunt Jenny was one of the first to comment that the Suarez plumes were ostrich feathers, but Red Hawk's bonnet was not. The plumes might seem a threat to Houdini, or maybe they might look like an ostrich hen he would like to meet. She pointed out that this was like when a new rooster is introduced into a flock of chickens, he has to do some display and show his feathers to all the hens and maybe pick a little fight with the other roosters.

The show folks made arrangements to keep a distance between the bareback horses and the ostrich. He would never follow them in the spec parade at the beginning of the show, and he would always be tied in a place where he could not see them. The Suarez women stayed away from him when they were in their wardrobe with the plumes.

How Houdini earned his name is another story. There were times when he would suddenly show up with no rope on, standing calmly or wandering slowly where he wanted to go. This was often in the morning, but it could be anytime of day. Nobody could figure out how he could get the lead rope off. At first it seemed like some sort of strange accident, but then it happened repeatedly. It was like an escape trick of the famous magician, the Great Houdini.

One day Gilly Brewer happened to catch Houdini in the act. It was hard to explain how he did it. The motion was so quick and effortless. Houdini could stand on just one leg and draw his other leg up under him, if he wanted to, the way a chicken does. He also just sat flat on the ground, especially at night. But if the ground was cold or uncomfortable, he stood on one foot, leisurely alternately from left to right. What Gilly caught him doing was standing on one foot and making a scratching motion with the other foot, the way a dog or even a chicken does, if there is something irritating. He scratched at his lead rope with the other foot, right where it came down to the loop at the base of his neck, as if it were irritating him. When he got the loop loose enough, he would simply lower his head and let the loop drop to the ground, as if ridding himself of some uncomfortable insect. He did it innocently and with no mind to run off immediately. He just stood in place. That was fortunate, but if he ever wandered away, he would be in danger of being lost or struck by a vehicle like any other circus animal.

Harold had to hear Gilly's story twice before he really understood. Obviously, a simple rope around the neck, even if it were pulled snug, would not work. Horses had halters on their heads to keep the lead ropes from coming off. Houdini's head was too small for a halter. What would work?

The solution was a strap that looped around the base of each wing and crossed in a figure eight on Houdini's back. A ring was attached at the crossing on his back. It snapped to the collar on the bird's neck. He could no longer scratch to loosen a loop and free himself. For the moment at least, Houdini's escape trips were stopped. He was safe.

The old milk wagon was spruced up nicely. It took a couple coats of fresh red paint and a new tarp on the roof. Windows were added on each side for better light and ventilation. Taillights were added, and the open part in the front where the milkman had once sat was enclosed except for another window. The structure of the wagon was quite sound, apparently to accommodate the considerable weight of full milk bottles and crates. After a couple seasons on the circus, the wagon had lost its look of a dairy wagon and become another show vehicle. There was a bit of jerkiness in pulling the wagon because of the slack in the coupling. The metal loop that served as a hitch was sturdy, but a bit too large, and it clanked and jerked when the truck started or stopped.

Brewer Brothers was coming into a town where the people took their horse racing seriously. The show was allowed to use the large infield of the racetrack, but there was to be no traffic whatsoever crossing the track where the racehorses, mostly sulky horses, trained and later raced. All the traffic had to go through the underpass that was built to prevent even pedestrians from being on the track at any time. The underpass was only one lane wide and flooded frequently in heavy rains, but it was effective in keeping everything off the racetrack except racehorses. This was a totally acceptable arrangement, one that had been used in other places with racetracks. The people in the town would know that they, too, had to come to the circus through the underpass going under the track.

The unexpected happened when a show vehicle was going through the underpass. As the truck towing the former milk wagon went down the incline to the underpass, there was a stronger than usual jerk as the hitch slid up a bit toward to the truck. Houdini was slammed against the front end of the wagon. When the truck came up the ramp on the other side, there was another jerk, a rougher one, and Houdini was thrown against the back of the wagon. For whatever reason, the hasp keeping the backdoor closed was not strong enough, and the backdoor flew open, freeing Houdini.

The ostrich landed on his side on the ground but recovered quickly and stood up, taking a look around. The truck had continued right along with the driver unaware of the passenger lost out of the back of the wagon. He parked the truck in the place he was assigned near the backdoor of where the tent was going up. He proceeded with various chores of setting up. It was some of the show kids who asked him why the back of the wagon was open and where Houdini was. The broken hasp dangled from the frame of the back door. The driver was alarmed. He did not know when the back door had come open or if the bird had survived. It could have been anywhere along the road from the last town. He went running over to Lucky with the bad news. Lucky and Harold came to inspect the wagon. What to do next was the question. A combination of vehicles and riders seemed the best approach. Red Hawk got on Comanche, and Woody got on Yellowstone. Both men carried ropes. Lucky unhitched his Packard from the house trailer. Harold got in the car with Lucky. Woody's young son Bart got in the back seat with Spangles, the Dalmatian. Her tracking skills might be needed.

By now Houdini had had several minutes of getaway time, but he was in no hurry. He had sauntered along the roadside on the way into the town grazing on nice grass. He had unknowingly already terrified a herd of dairy cattle in the adjoining pasture, and there would be complaints that the cows held up their milk that evening because of the fright they had had. The bird proceeded at a good pace to the town with no fear of vehicles or animals. He had become accustomed to just about anything on the circus lot. He saw no reason to hurry as he entered the town.

There was a pack of dogs that had gathered, but none of them was brave enough to approach him. All they did was bark. A horse pulling a cart stopped and reared up in alarm, but Houdini ignored that. As he came into the town, people came from shops and stores and screamed at him, but he was of course used to people and how strange they could act. A grocery store had an enticing open display of boxed fruit and vegetables out front, and Houdini enjoyed some strawberries and tomatoes. The people there, however, were rude and started pelting him with potatoes. He had never known humans to be so mean. They chased him down a small street, and Houdini stepped over a fence and into a yard where there were lines of clothes drying in the sun. When more potatoes landed on him, he unavoidably knocked the clotheslines down and went into another back yard. The noise all around him was increasing, the surroundings were strange, and he thought it wise to move on.

It did not take the Brewer search party long to learn

that Houdini had headed into town. One of the show trucks had spotted him near the cow pasture, and then a man driving a cart pointed back up the road and yelled at them, "There is a giant wild ostrich running all around town."

When they got to the courthouse square in the middle of the town, Lucky stopped the car and let Spangles out. Harold let her smell one of the ropes the ostrich was usually tied with. By this time, Red Hawk and Woody were there on their horses and could easily follow Spangles, if she could pick up the trail.

It is extraordinarily difficult to track a scent in the center of a town. There is so much traffic -- pedestrian, vehicular, and animal. Spangles was a good tracker, but this was a challenge. She stood and sniffed in various directions, in the air and on the ground. She turned to the left and then to the right. A few children approached as if to pet her, and she backed away. She whimpered in frustration. She stood still as if to think. Lucky and Harold were patient. They knew that this might be too much from her.

Her sniffing and thinking were interrupted by noises from around the corner of the courthouse. They all looked in that direction. There was Houdini, trotting at a nice clip, followed by a motley entourage of men, women, children, and more dogs. Two of the men had uniforms on and appeared to be law enforcement officials. One man was shaking a broom angrily in the air, though it was unclear exactly what he was going to do with it. The dogs barked incessantly. Observers were coming out from every office and shop around the courthouse. There might not have been this much excitement in the downtown square since the high school homecoming parade last fall or the Fourth of July celebration a few weeks before. But those events were annual. This was a once-in-a-lifetime happening. An ostrich had never walked around the courthouse before.

Houdini was at an advantage. He had seen thousands of humans in his lifetime and was accustomed to their noise and commotion. The townspeople had never seen an ostrich, with many not even knowing what one was. They were awestruck or afraid, with a few being angry. Houdini was alert, but mostly he was enjoying the experience, with the exception of those rude potato throwers.

Woody and Red Hawk rode over to Lucky and Harold in the car. They realized that Harold could probably get out and simply walk over to Houdini and put a rope around his neck. But GR and Camie Brewer had always taught their sons the value of publicity, especially free publicity. For the moment, there was no danger to any of the townspeople or to the ostrich, so the excitement could be prolonged for a while. They decided that Woody and Red Hawk would get on either side of Houdini and ride behind him just a little so the townspeople had a good view of him. Harold would go on foot behind them, ready with a leash as needed. They would guide Houdini around the courthouse square one more time and then head out of town on the street that led to the racetrack where the show was setting up.

Their plan worked fine for the trip around the courthouse. The entourage grew. Men came out of barber-shops for a better look. Women left stores in mid-purchase to be sure they saw what all the excitement was about. But just as Woody and Red Hawk were about to herd Houdini out of town, a strange noise sounded. It was the local police car with its squeaky little siren whining. This was a sound that Houdini did not like. It seemed to irritate him. He headed to the right side of the street and went up on a wooden sidewalk that several stores fronted on. Then Houdini was startled by something he had not seen in a number of years. Right there in the front window of Feldman's Dry Goods Emporium there was another ostrich. Nothing he had seen so far surprised Houdini more than this sight. The other ostrich seemed friendly enough, but what was it doing there? Houdini walked up to the window. When he moved his head to the left and to the right in greeting, the ostrich in the window did the same thing. Then Houdini puffed out his wing feathers to show that he was a male and a powerful one. The other ostrich did the same. It was time to approach and get a smell. The other bird stepped up, too. Soon their beaks were meeting, or seemed to be. He pecked, so did the other bird.

Harold yelled at the others, "He could break the window if he gets excited."

"See if you can get him away," said Woody.

Harold came so close that he could have put a leash on Houdini's neck, but Harold did not want to interfere with the publicity strategy. He gently herded Houdini back in the middle of the street. Red Hawk and Woody on horseback could guide him out of town, and the publicity opportunity could continue.

But the police car came right up behind them, with its siren slowing down in mournful rhythm. The police chief got out of the car. "Make that damn thing hold still so I can blow its brains out," he screamed to the circus men. The police chief had a pistol in his hand.

"Oh, no, sir, he is harmless. We are just taking him back to the circus now," Woody replied, and both he and Red Hawk circled their horses around to block the police chief from seeing Houdini.

"He is a wild an' dangerous animal. I have to protect the people of this town!" the police chief replied. Now get out of my way, an' I am going to blast that pile of feathers into kingdom come!"

"Officer, please, he has done no harm. An' we are taking him away immediately," Woody pleaded.

"He ate strawberries! Five people saw him right in front of Len Barker's grocery store."

"We will pay for the strawberries immediately, Sir. We will gladly pay for them!"

"Get out of my line of fire. I could arrest you for trying to protect a menace to society!"

"Sir, he is no menace. Believe me. He is gentle. We have had him for years. Let me show you," Woody replied. He called his son Bart out of Lucky's car. Bart had come along for the ride on this exciting trip, and now he was going to be useful.

"Officer, my little son has ridden this ostrich many

times, an' he is going to ride that ostrich right now all the way back to the racetrack where we are putting on the circus. Believe me, sir; I would never put my own dear son on this animal if I did not have complete confidence. Now if you will please put down your gun, put it in your holster, you will see. An' we will just continue out of town."

All the while, Red Hawk and Woody kept their horses between Houdini and the police car as much as they could. Houdini was still a good distance from the police chief, and that distance was to be maintained. The police chief's uniform featured an array of shiny buttons, and his hat had a bright copper medallion on the front. Any of these was enough to entice Houdini into what might be interpreted as an attack.

"You can't fool me, boy. I won't believe a word you are saying till I see it. You better not be lying, or you an' your horse are going to jail!" The chief of police was red faced at this point.

"Thank you, sir. You will not be disappointed. Harold, please snap that lead rope around Houdini's neck. Bart is going to ride him just like in the opening spec number of the show. Harold, you have to stay on the left side of Houdini. I will be walking on the right side with my arm around my son."

Red Hawk knew to continue keeping Comanche between the Police Chief and the ostrich. Woody dismounted and handed Yellowstone's reins to Red Hawk. He picked up his son in his arms and whispered in his ear, "*Mandi's gara*, is *tutti trashed* to do this *cova? Mandi coms tutti dosta.* My boy, are you afraid to do this thing? I love you so much. Don't if you don't want to."

"*Keker, Dadus. It's kushti.* No, Daddy, it's fine. Let me do it. I am big enough." Bart had a big smile. He could not wait.

In less than a minute, the boy was on Houdini with a man walking on either side. Red Hawk followed, riding one horse and leading Woody's. The police car followed, this time without the screechy siren going. Lucky followed in his car with Spangles, who had never needed to do any tracking after all.

It took thirty minutes to walk all the way back to the racetrack. People lined the streets to the edge of town and beyond. Some of them clapped their hands at the sight of the young boy riding the ostrich. Even on the outskirts all passersby stopped, including those in cars.

Back at the lot the tent was going up. Woody went over to the former milk wagon and took his son off the ostrich and gave him a big hug for the role he played. Houdini was just happy to get back in his wagon. The back door hasp had been repaired. All the Brewers were gathered around. The police chief and his police car were there.

"This officer here, he did a great job," Woody said in a voice loud enough for people to hear fifty feet away. "He brought order, and he kept the crowds back. It is obvious that he has a lot of respect in this town.

"Chief, it would be an honor if we could have you an' your family as guests at the shows today. We would like to introduce you an' thank you publicly for your heroic work," Woody continued.

GR and Camie knew they could do their part. They approached the police chief solemnly and extended their hands for a handshake.

Even in those days, police could go for a long time without getting much thanks or appreciation for their work. The police chief soon had a complete change of heart when he heard the flattering things Woody was saying.

"We really like to have a police presence whenever we can at our show. Police visibility is a good thing. It shows support for the community. I am sure our show sponsors, the Fraternal Order of Elks, would appreciate it, too," Woody continued.

"Gee, mister, if you really want me to, I can bring out the misses and the kids. They would like this. An' you seem to get that ostrich tamed real fast. It is amazing. Should I bring the two other officers on the force, too?" he asked.

"If you can, Chief, that would be a wonderful thing. Also, can I give you five dollars now to give to Mr. Barker whose strawberries our ostrich ate. An' here are ten free tickets for him an' his family," Woody continued. He knew that a time like this was a time to be generous and conciliatory. There was not only this year's show to think of, but if it was a good town, the show would want to be back next year.

The show had two "straw houses" that day, meaning crowds that were so large that bales of straw were broken and spread on the track around the three rings so that the clowns would invite kids down to sit on the straw and leave room for more adults in the bleachers. For the two final acts, the jumping horses and the elephant ballet, the kids would be called back to squeeze in with their parents so that the animals could run on the track safely.

Of course everybody wanted to see the runaway ostrich and the boy who had ridden it home to the circus. They had all had heard about this or witnessed it first hand. What started as an accident had become a very successful publicity event. The size of the crowds proved it.

At the end of the grand spec parade that started the show, Harold led Houdini into the center ring, with little Bart Brewer riding on Houdini's back. At this point, Lucky the ringmaster introduced Bart and Houdini, but then brought in and introduced Mac Barton, the town's chief of police. Lucky praised him for his important role in rounding up Houdini and keeping everybody safe. He invited a round of applause for him, and the crowd responded loudly. The show was off to a good start.

Houdini's "great escape" ended calmly, and he never had another one anything like it. Somebody on the show asked if in some other place it might not be a good idea just to turn the ostrich loose as a publicity stunt. He had not heard of the fact that the police chief had got out his pistol and was trying to shoot poor Houdini. Houdini lived many more years on the show, proving that sometimes animals in captivity live longer than in the wild.

He had a close scrape once back where the show spent the winter. It was one of those freak accidents that would have been hard to predict. The workingmen had been making new halter ropes for all the horses and ponies. They spliced new snaps into the end of each rope. Houdini was left to run loose at times, as long as somebody had an eye on him. In an instant, Houdini saw an opportunity. He saw one the shiny new snaps and swallowed it handily. But of course, it was attached to a five-foot length of rope, and the rope followed the snap down his throat. There was no way that Houdini could avoid choking. The rope just continued going slowly down his throat.

It took four men to grab him, tie his feet together to keep from being kicked, hold him to the ground and then slowly, very slowly, pull the rope out of his mouth. Harold massaged Houdini's long throat to help the process along, trying to squeeze gently below the bulge that was probably where the snap was. It was only as the last six inches or so of the rope came out that any blood showed. It seemed there was a chance of killing the animal in an effort to save his life. Finally, when the snap at the end of the rope came out, Houdini was still breathing. He was untied and allowed to stand up. He ruffled his feathers and looked around in a confused way. His appetite was meager for about a week, and Harold moistened all his feed and almost spoon-fed him at first. Houdini made a complete recovery, and shiny new snaps or other such paraphernalia were never allowed in his sight again.

14. THE WORST THING THAT COULD HAPPEN

The worst thing that could happen took place in Choresville, but it wasn't even while the show was playing that town. It happened ten days later, and the Brewers didn't know about it till a couple weeks after that. It was almost a life or death event for the circus people. It was a life or death event for Brewer Brothers Circus.

The show had been on the road for half the season of 1933, and the cash on hand was building up. The owners had become concerned that if anything happened to the cash, the results could be disastrous, and they might not be able to make it through the rest of the season, not to mention the months back in winter quarters till the season of 1934 began.

They asked some members of the Choresville Elks Club, the organization sponsoring the show, if there were any good banks left in town. And the owners were happy to find out that one of the Elks was on the board of the best bank in town, the Choresville First National Bank. He was Bill Creighton, also a lawyer. Bill explained there had been four banks in the town, but like in many places, the weaker banks had a hard time in the early years of the Great Depression, and they could not survive. They folded, and the depositors lost their money. But the First National had always been the biggest and the strongest. Everybody trusted it, and that is why he was on the board of directors of the bank. He would personally go with them if they wanted to make a deposit, and the transaction could be made in total security and confidentiality.

This sounded promising, because the show would be coming back through Choresville in about three or four weeks, after playing a circuit of towns in some adjoining states. At that point they could withdraw the deposit, add it to the profits for the three weeks, and maybe see if it could be sent safely by Western Union to the bank back home or at least to family there, or if somebody could even drive straight through for three days and deposit it for them. Western Union did not really like such large transfers. It meant that there would be a surplus of cash in one place, where the money was sent from, and a shortage of cash to pay out where the money was received. The transaction would all have to go through Kansas City or Dallas or some larger city, and it could take a small town Western Union office a couple days or more to set it up. They were always happy to send sums of up to one hundred dollars, but when it came to the thousands, they had a hard time working it all out.

The cash buildup during the show season had always been a problem, even before the Depression. Money was secretly kept under the floorboards of trucks, in feather pillows, and in hidden compartments in saddle trunks, but never ever in the office wagon where the tickets were sold. For smaller amounts of cash, a quart mayonnaise jar might be used, a jar from which the original contents had been used up and the inside of the glass painted white to look like a new jar. Culturally, *Romanichals* could not stand the idea of having their money stolen, so they would never keep it in an obvious place.

So when the show played Choresville, Amy and Woody quietly took thirty-two hundred dollars from the cash that was building up, almost the entire amount, gathering it from three of their secret caches. These caches were unknown even to some family members. The couple drove downtown and discretely met Mr. Creighton in the back office of the First National Bank, opened an account, got a bank book, carefully counted out the thirty-two hundred dollars with him, deposited it, and hurried back to the circus. The whole trip took less than thirty minutes, and nobody really noticed that they had been gone. They had a sense of satisfaction that they were doing the right thing.

This satisfaction was instantly crushed when they drove back through the town three weeks later on the way to play a nearby date. They had intended to make a quick stop and withdraw the money and continue on. Amy's jaw dropped when she pulled onto the side street where she hoped to park with the car and house trailer she was driving. She planned to go into the bank with Woody who was right behind her with a horse truck. She jumped out of the car and pointed to the bank. It was clear that there had been a fire, and there were large boards nailed across the door and the two windows. Her heart sank. She was trembling. Woody was soon beside her, and all they could do was put an arm around each other.

"What the hell?" he said. "How could a bank have a fire? What happened?" A thousand thoughts were racing through their heads.

They decided to go over to the saloon across the street from the bank. Of course, it was not an actual saloon any more, not since Prohibition. It was just a place that sold coffee and soda pop, a place where people could go to catch up on news. They entered and asked the man behind the bar when the fire was at the bank.

"Oh, didn't you hear? That was no fire. It was an explosion, a big explosion. A gang of robbers used dynamite to blow up the safe, an' it blew out the doors an' windows, too. It made a noise you could hear from one end of town to th'other. They killed poor ol' Mr. Donaldson, such a shame. He was the nice old guy, bald with glasses. You probably met him. He had just two more years to go before retirement. An' now he is dead."

"Oh, they shot him in cold blood?"

"Might as well have! A counter or desk blew over on him in the explosion. It crushed him bad. He was unconscious. Doc tried to save him, an' he kept him alive two days, but he was just beat up too bad from the explosion. Half the town came to his funeral. But the robbers did shoot Billy Watson, Bill Watson's oldest boy. Shot him dead. He was a cop, but he wasn't even in uniform. He was just walkin' by an' tried to stop the robbers. He left five kids an' a widow behind. Such a shame! It was another big funeral. An' people are talkin' about if Susanna, that's his wife, if she will get a widow's pension, since he wasn't really in uniform at the time. But I think she could get it, because he was in the line of duty, as they say. It would just be fair. An' the funny thing is, a woman shot Billy, at least we think it was. Or it was probably a man in a wig an' a dress. An' she had a big pistol an' shot real good, probably a man. It all happened so fast you couldn't hardly tell.

"An' then you know what happened?"

Woody and Amy realized that it could be a while before they would find out if there was any money left in the bank, but the prospects were not looking good. The man was a storyteller. If you bought a cold drink from him, you got your money's worth, with lots of news and gossip. It would not be easy to get him to their important point any time soon. And they did not really want him to know that they were big depositors. They didn't want the attention.

The man continued his detailed and animated narrative. "Well, the getaway car took off down South Main Street, an' then old man Carter at the hardware store grabbed his shotgun from under the counter an' ran out an' fired after it. He got the right rear tire, but they just kept on drivin' on the rim a' the wheel. It was something to see. But he also hit one of the robbers, because he fell out on the ground with a couple bullets in his back. An' then, an' you gotta hear this, the woman, if she was a woman, took a bag of the money an' started throwin' it out in the street, handfuls at a time. Why, there was money flyin' around everywhere! People were runnin' around like idiots tryin' to grab some one-dollar bills, or two-dollar bills, or even fifty-cent pieces, or whatever. I got a few myself.

"Now if you ever heard a' the Bonnie and Clyde gang, well, you know, they were worse than the Daltons. They are the ones who did all those bank jobs over in Arkansas an' then in Missouri. Well, this could 'a' been them, except this woman wasn't a blond like Bonnie. Now, they say they have some kinda dye that can turn a blond dark, but I never heard any proof a' that.

"But anyway, then Reverend Smiles at the First Baptist Church, well, you might never think a preacher could be such a good shot, but he was in the war or somethin'. He ran out of the church office with a couple pistols an' shot through the money flyin' around, an' he got four bullets right through their radiator somehow. Seems he just wanted to stop 'em an' not kill 'em. Well, you can imagine, in just another couple blocks, the radiator on that getaway car was boilin' over with steam going everywhere.

"So the robbers ducked into a side street, jumped out of that car, an' stole an empty lumber truck, quick as a flash. By this time, the whole town was out in the streets. It was like we were havin' a parade or somethin'. They were thinkin' the crooks would throw out more money. You know, a lumber truck can't really go that fast, so the sheriff thought they would be easy to close in on, but the gang went through another side street, an' then Dorothy Singletary was comin' the other way in her Studebaker Convertible Touring Car, an' they cut her off an' stole her car. She had no idea what was goin' on, but when they waved those guns at her, she just started screamin' an' they slugged here a couple times an' dragged her out an' took off with the Studebaker Touring Car at sixty miles an hour. Those Studebakers have big engines.

"Now what they did next wasn't really right. It was a shame, an' I feel so sorry for Dorothy. She loved that car. He husband bought it for her before the Depression started, an' she babied it.

"Well, they tore off on Barberville Pike, an' you know that part of the road after the curve where it gets real narrow? Well, they parked the Studebaker crosswise in the road so you couldn't get by, an' then they poured gas over it an' burned it, just like that. They had their real getaway car waitin' there just around that bend all the time, an' there was no way that anybody could follow them. You couldn't get around that burnin' Studebaker. Such a shame!

"Now the sheriff said it was about as professional a bank heist as he had ever saw! What with all the dynamite, an' switching cars, an' that throwin' money out in the street, that is a real first-rate professional team! People went for that little bit of money an' let the robbers go. An' they actually killed as few people as they could, you know, an' do the robbery. They didn't set out to try to kill a bunch a' folks on purpose. They just wanted the money.

"Oh, an' the preachers at both churches thanked the people for all the stolen money that they had grabbed an' asked them to return it an' put it in a special collection basket, no questions asked. Just 'cause it was stolen money dudn't mean it was yours for the takin'. The two churches got almost two hundred dollars. An' they are going to set up a widow's fund for Billy's wife. Everybody thought that it would be a nice thing to do.

"An' these reporters came down from the city, an' they were interviewin' everybody, an' they said it was the most professional job they had ever saw, too, an' they took pictures all over the place. I have some of the papers if you want to see them. Gonna put 'em up on the wall here. 'Brave Citizens Fight Crime in their Own Streets.' 'Town Mourns Officer who Single-handedly Almost Stopped a Gang of Five.' 'Depression Drives Woman into Crime.' 'Man of the Cloth is Good with a Gun.' They wrote real good stories. It was amazin'. We don't think there will be any bank robbers around here for a long time, now. Of course, there is only the one little bank left."

Amy's patience was running thin. "Well, sir, this is so interestin'. Can you tell me what people should do who have business with the bank?"

"Oh, jeepers! You mean you lost money in the robbery?"

"We want to find out about our business with them. Who do we see or what do we do?" Woody said.

"Well, I would see Bill Creighton. He is that lawyer fellow, owned part of the bank, too. He started some kind of list of bank customers. If you owe the bank, you still have to pay. If you had money in the bank, you have to say how much, an' then they will do what they can when they catch the robbers. Or somethin' like that. Bill's office is up North Main Street on the left, second story, where the window is painted 'Attorney at Law.' Say, you folks aren't from aroun' here, are you? I know everybody aroun' here. You just passin' through or what?"

"Oh, thank you, sir, you have been very helpful," Amy replied

The couple walked the few blocks to the lawyer's office and went upstairs and knocked on the door. A kind young woman let them in. Her name was Dora, but she explained that she was just filling in because Mr. Creighton and Ms. Dawson, the real secretary, had to go up to Capital City for the whole week for some kind of trial or something. So it might be a good idea for them to come back next week.

Woody explained that their visit was because of bank business, not a legal matter. They had business with the bank and needed to know what to do after the robbery.

"Oh, my," said Dora. "That is too bad. But listen, I have a book here some place that you should sign in to show you want to make a claim, or did you want to put money in? Now, if you have payments, I can take the money, too, or if you want to deposit.

"Oh, here is the book. Now, you have to have a bankbook or some other proof." Amy showed her the bankbook, and Dora exclaimed audibly when she saw how much was in the account.

And then she said, "But you aren't from around here. Why do you have an account here? You are the only customers I know who aren't from around here. How did you get an account here? I don't know what I will tell Mr. Creighton. Did you really have this much money in the bank? Oh, goodness!"

Then she rambled on with other comments. "You know, you really shouldn't take any money out. The bank is the right place to put your money. It is perfectly safe. You even get interest on your money. That means they put in free money with your money an' it just grows an' grows. Best thing in the world! Why, if I had as much money as you, I would just live off the interest."

Amy studied the book and filled out the required lines. Both she and Woody signed. They ignored what the well-intentioned young woman was saying.

"Miss, do you have a card, please?"

"You mean a condolence card for Mr. Donaldson? We have lots of them. He was a very nice man."

"No, I mean a business card, so that we can call Mr. Creighton, one of the little cards with name, address, numbers, an' so on. Oh, I see them there. I just want to take one."

"Oh, sure, they are free."

"Thank you so much. An' our visit is completely confidential. You should not tell anybody, except Mr. Creighton. You understand?"

"Oh, I never tell anythin', even if it is very interestin'."

"Thank you. We have to go now."

The couple walked back by the bank to their vehicles. They could not even bring themselves to look through the nailed up boards into the bank. It was just all too sad, too tragic. It was hard to think about what to do next. Could the circus survive with half a season's cash buildup lost?

"Honey, you know that the family will come to us smilin' as soon as we pull on the lot in the next town. They will want to know if we got the *vonger,* the money, or not."

"Yes, I know, Woody Darling. An' we have to tell them. It will be a shock. We should ask them all into our trailer an' have a meetin' an' tell them what happened. It will be awful, but we have to do it. An' then we have to plan what to do next. Why, we can't even make payday on Friday. We stocked up completely on feed, hay, gas, cookhouse supplies, an' so on. That will help some for the next few towns, but we have almost no cash. We thought we would have plenty of cash for salaries, too. Do we close or what?"

"An' one thing is clear from what that girl said. We are the only out-of-towners with money in that bank, an' they are gonna put us at the end of the list of anybody who gets money back, if anybody does. Why should they give us any money when we aren't related to them an' we won't do any more business with them? That's the way I see it. We are lookin' at ruin, like so many other people have during this Depression!" Woody said.

"But I don't think we can close the show," Amy said. "During the performance, we have to continue talkin' with Tillie an' Lucky between the acts an' agree on how to keep on operatin'. Nearly seventy people depend on us, performers, workers, musicians, everybody! An' we need the work ourselves. We have no other way now to make a livin'."

"Let's ask the family if we should tell all the performers, all the people on the show, to have a meetin' in the bigtop as soon as the crowd clears out after the matinee show. An' that will give us a little time to explain what happened an' say what we propose, when we figure out what that will be. But when we tell them to meet after the show, we have to tell them at the same time that the show is not closin'. If we don't, they will just assume that it is bad news, an' they will have a hard time puttin' on a good performance. We need to say, no, the show is not closin' but there is an important meetin'," Woody added.

Most of the show people were there in the bleachers almost as soon as the matinee ended. The Brewer brothers and their wives sat on chairs facing the bleachers for the meeting. All four of them would speak at some time during the meeting. It was odd to see the performers in the bleachers instead of in front of the bleachers. And Grandpa and Grandma Brewer were in the first row along with the Brewer kids. All the rest of the show people were clustered around. It was about the hardest meeting the Brewers had ever had.

Everybody finally got tired of waiting for some stragglers from the matinee crowd to get on out of the tent, and one of the workingmen politely told them that they would have to leave now because the bigtop was closed.

Woody looked out across the group, nearly seventy of them. They were all there: Pierre de la Croix and his two sons, who were the band; Cookie and Slim, and the cookhouse crew who fed them all; the Sugarstones; the Marvelis; the Suarez family; Jake, the canvas boss, and the dozen regular workingmen who did so many things; Poker and Pinky, the two lead clowns; Uncle Harry and Aunt Hattie with the elephants; the electrician Choctaw and his hard working wife, and of course, his own family. It was a visual reminder of how many people, how many lives, were dependent on what he would say. His father and mother in the front row sat with each arm around one of their smaller grandchildren. They looked at him serenely, and with no words they said, "You can do this, Son. And you can do it very well." Woody's brother was behind him all the way, and of course his wife and sister-in-law.

For just a moment, he reflected that if this is what it meant to have a fine family in a bad hour, this was it. If this was what it was to work and live with a fine bunch of people, he was so grateful. He would have to take on a heavy responsibility now. And as with so many responsibilities, the only way to address it was to begin.

His throat was very dry, but it did not crack. He spoke with no microphone and got right to the point.

"Folks, I have very bad news for you. As of today, the show is basically broke. We have enough money to get through the next week or two, but that is just about it. We cannot pay you on Friday," There was a gasp from the crowd.

"We can feed you in the cookhouse, but we can't pay you. An' we won't close the show. That is a promise." He paused, waiting for what he said to sink in.

"Let me explain what happened an' what we offer you. We lost money, a lot of money, from the first half of the season when we put it in the bank back in the last town, Choresville. That's where we showed about three weeks ago before we made that loop farther north an' west. It was supposed to be the best bank around, an' it seemed like the safest way to keep the cash.

"But we were wrong. The bank did not close, like so many banks have. It got robbed. A gang of bank robbers used dynamite to blow up the safe. Two or three people were killed." There was another gasp.

"This is the worst loss we have had on this show, or I believe on my uncles' shows, or any show I know of. The show won't be able to survive without you.

"Here is a some of what we found out. The town people in Choresville heard from the police that this seemed to be a very experienced gang of robbers.

They called them professionals. An' who knows if any of the money will ever be found? If it is found, frankly, I don't know if we will get any. The bank, the First National Bank of Choresville, would want to pay back the people from around their town first. These are the people who are their friends an' neighbors an' family. Honestly, we would come at the end of the list. We are just some circus people who passed through, an' we are nothin' like their regular lifetime customers.

"Yes, Amy an' I went an' signed in to make a claim for the money, an' we still have the bankbook an' papers, an' we will keep contactin' them, but what we have to do in the meantime is work even harder than we have worked before to keep feedin' ourselves an' our animals. We don't see any other way.

"Of course, you have a perfect right to quit if you want to, an' we could not hold that against you. We will talk more about that in a second.

"Now Amy will tell you of some of the things we have to do in this terrible time to keep our head above water." Woody stepped aside so that the attention of the group would be on his wife Amy.

Like Woody, Amy spoke slowly and clearly, and she looked everybody right in the eyes.

"Friends, this is hard to tell you, but we are always honest with you, good times an' bad. An' these are very bad times. I have a list of some expenses we have to cut out or cut way back on.

"First, in the cookhouse, there will always be enough to eat, but Cookie an' Slim will not be able to give you what they would like to. You will get all the rice an' beans an' greens an' potatoes an' grits an' bread you can eat. But you will probably get only one egg in the morning an' little or no bacon, an' a lot less meat of any kind. We may have to buy a pig to butcher ourselves from time to time, an' a lot of you know how to do that. This is not Cookie an' Slim's fault. It is because of the bank robbery. Now, when a town has corn in season or melon or berries at a good price, you can bet that they will be buyin' whatever is good or cheap. An' if the kids can pick enough berries of some kind, an' if there is enough flour an' lard an' sugar, Cookie says sometimes they can bake up some pies, an' we do love pies.

"Second, if we have a truck motor blow up on us, we will just have to junk the truck, or sell it for next to nothin', or try to store it with a farmer or somebody till we can pick it up another year. We don't have the money to fix anythin'. An' you know that it would mean we would have to take turns doublin' back every day two trips with a good truck to pull in the trailer that had the truck with the blown motor. We have to try very hard to take care of our equipment so that it lasts out the season. An' most any other repairs around here will just have to be patched together.

"Third, we have to keep our horses fat an' our elephants sleek, because people don't come here to see skinny animals. They have skinny animals at home. Besides, our animals deserve the best. They earn us a livin'. But we can't feed them like we have been feedin' them, with lots of hay an' grain to just put in front of them. We have to do more work. We have to stake them out to get all the grass they can. Whenever there is good grass on a lot, our animals will get little or no hay or grain. We will just keep movin' them to good grass. We can even move the horse trucks thirty feet every fifteen minutes so our horses have new grass, an' they can eat right from the side of the truck where they are tied on long halter ropes. An' you know how hard it is to keep an elephant full. We are going to have to just keep walkin' them an' walkin' them to wherever the grass is good, even in some pasture where there is good grass, if the owner will let us in. Wherever there is good free grass, it's for our horses an' ponies, or our elephants. This will be a lot more work, an' you are already workin' very hard.

"Also, we just won't be hirin' any extra town men to help at night to give us a hand with the teardown an' loadin' up. We all have to pitch in an' get it done. If there is some kind of an emergency, that is somethin' else, but there won't be much money goin' out for local town boys to help us teardown an' load up. Would you rather have extra help at night or more money for your salary? Same with help in the cookhouse for washin' dishes or peelin' potatoes or whatever. Please help Cookie an' Slim whenever you can," Amy continued. With every announcement, she could see that people were weighing the impact on their workdays and on their lives.

"Last, there isn't enough money for us to buy full tanks of gas anymore. We will just have to buy a half a tank at a time, with a gas tanker comin' on the lot every three or four days. We just don't have the luxury now to pay for complete fill-ups every week or ten days. We will just be limpin' along.

"An', Folks, we need to hear from you with other ideas. We will be sufferin', but the whole country is sufferin'. You see how poor the people in the towns are now, especially in some towns, kids wearin' rags. An' there are lots of skinny people, men with home-done haircuts like somebody put a bowl over their head. An' we have all seen guys who pick up cigarette butts to see if there are still a couple puffs left. But now I want to ask my sister-in-law Tillie to tell you how we want to bring in more money," Amy concluded, glad to be done but very concerned about what was coming up next.

And Tillie started. "So the other thing we need to do besides cuttin' costs as Amy explained, is to bring in more money. We want to fill those seats every time, an' even have 'straw houses' with kids sittin' on straw that we spread on the ground when the seats are full. We are already workin' very hard, an' we will need to work harder. Here are some of the things we have to add to our workload.

"The circus opens at noon everyday. Think of it that way. The midway is open at 12:00. There are attractions. The pony ride is open. The public can buy popcorn an' cotton candy. An' either the armadillo show or the headless show is open on the midway. Of course the bigtop is not open yet, but those people out there watchin' us, well, we need to have reasons for them to take money out of their pockets before the show, an' we need to get more of them into the tent. We need to have more attractions out there, more ways for them to spend money.

"The exact things may change from town to town or according to the weather, but we want those two beautiful Indian teepees put up every day at the head of the midway, an' Chief Red Hawk, we want you there in your war bonnet smokin' your peace pipe or signin' autographs or whatever. You can sell an' sign the little circus programs listin' all the acts. People just love Indians, an' we want people drivin' by for their kids to yell, 'Stop, they have real Indians!'

"An' we want a cowboy ridin' around on a horse out there, too. Just ridin' around, near the parkin' lot, wherever it is visible. Spinnin' a rope from time to time would be good, too. An' Poker, this is more work for you. We want you out there walkin' around on your stilts. Don't wear yourself out before the show, but you do it so good. People will want to come an' see what else is in the show.

"Also, Uncle Harry, Dolly needs to get out there an' in plain sight. Take her out to meet the committee, steal cigarettes out of their pockets, grab their hats with that long trunk of hers an' put them on her own head...anything to generate excitement. Oh, an' the old tug-a-war trick with her. She loves that, an' she can always drag twenty men all over the place an' completely enjoy doin' it. An' it has to be as visible as possible, where as many town people can see it, along the highway or wherever. We need to do things that people can't stop talkin' about.

"An' let's get the sound truck into the town every day for about a couple hours from say 11:00 or 1:00 over lunch time an' again in the afternoon to broadcast the news that we are here, that the circus is in town with two giant shows. An' we want a trapeze lady an' a cowboy or juggler or clown in the back of the sound truck to wave at the people. If you can bring in ten or twenty more people every hour with the sound truck, it is worth it. Get them into the seats. We have a good show. They need to see it.

"An' Pinky, you go with the sound truck downtown, an' you take 15-20 balloons on sticks along, an' you hop out an' do your walk around. You don't sell the balloons. You know, you give one away whenever you find a boy or girl who has a birthday that month. An' you give them a free ticket to the circus. We all know how that works. You give one kid a free ticket, just one kid in a family, an' they bring in the parents an' sisters an' brothers, an' so on. An' when the kids walk around in the town with the balloons, everybody wants to know where they got them. They are more free advertising for us. Pinky, you are so good at this. You can bring in Lord knows how many more families.

"Also, we want to get the sponsorin' committees to set up our free educational exhibits that we do in schools. Remember how sometimes we have been invited to bring a few animals an' do a little lecture for the kids? Well, we can throw the llama an' the ostrich in a pickup along with a trained dog or two, an' we can put on thirty minutes of show with lots of educational patter an' a few dog tricks an' remind the kids how educational the circus is an' to bring their parents along to see it, an' so on. An' if you can work out a way to give out a few free tickets, too, that always brings more in – of course no more than one free ticket per family.

"All of this is more work. There is no two ways about it. We just have to find a way to make it more routine, to make it faster. An' tell us other ways you think of to get more people here an' to get them to spend more money. An' now Lucky has the news you have all been waiting for," Tillie concluded.

Lucky stood up and said, "Now that you see what we want to do, let me tell you about salaries. As Woody said, we can't pay salaries this Friday. We just don't have the money. An' next Friday, we estimate that we can pay only half salary, an' that is just an estimate. The Friday after that, if we pull it all together, we can pay full salary, though it would not be honest to make you a 100% promise about that.

"But we would still owe you for a week an' half wages. So the Friday after that, we want to start paying back an extra half week at a time. That means you would get your regular salary plus 50% more, to start the payback we owe you. An' we would do that over three weeks. That means that in about six weeks it would all be 'even Stephen,' if we make it all work. If all goes well, we can even pay you a bonus at the end of the season, though not two weeks as usual, unless we do real good. Sure we would love to pay you two weeks bonus for stickin' with us. This year could be the year we can't do it.

"You could have emergencies of some kind where you need a little money. Hope it doesn't happen, but you might have to have a tooth pulled or something, or buy a tire. Come see us. We need you. We can work somethin' out. Nobody can work with a bad toothache or drive a truck without a tire.

"An' a couple other things. We will meet like this every Thursday after the matinee so we can hear your ideas an' tell you if we are movin' ahead or still behind.

"And you can talk to Woody or me or Tillie or Amy or any of us any time. An' if you want to quit the show, we understand. Somebody said that the Kelly Morris show is over in Illinois or Kentucky. You could call the *Billboard Magazine* to find out. The World's Fair is going on up in Chicago, an' maybe they need help of some kind. I don't know. We would miss you if you left, but if you want to go to another show, we would give you a recommendation over the phone. It would not be fair for a new boss to think you got fired when it is no such thing, an' every one of you does great work.

"If you do quit, we promise to pay you what we owe you. There has never been a performer who the Brewers didn't pay for honest work. We can't pay immediately, but in a couple months, we would get the money to you.

"An' one last thing, here is something an uncle told me when I was my son's age. He said that when we play a town, we have products to sell. Our products are not like nails or shoes or cans of beans, not products you can buy in a store. They are products that are hard to get any other way except from us. We have good times to sell, an' amazing things to see, an' new experiences, an' a big, happy change for town people from their hard, everyday life. That's the products we sell.

"We can take folks away from their hard work an' their routine an' all that they are familiar with. These are our products. For that day, we give them a new sort of life. An' it is true, folks. That is what we do. An' we want a fair price for the products that we sell, an' we want the town people to buy as many of our products as they can. An' we will spend some of our money in the town, too. It will be a fair exchange.

"But especially right now in our predicament, we want to spend as little as possible in the town, an' we want to give them the chance to buy as much of our products as we can. That's what it comes down to, fillin' the seats full, sellin' concessions, an' makin' it a good deal for everybody.

"We are very grateful to you for all your hard work so far in the season," Lucky paused after this comment. When he continued, he spoke slowly and in a lower voice. He didn't want to be emotional or cause panic, but the people knew him well enough to tell this was very difficult for him. For the moment, he was not the cheerful, dynamic ringmaster who could announce two shows a day, day after day, with infectious enthusiasm.

"We are all in this together. I'll be here for anybody who has questions. If you are going to leave us, please come up an' shake hands. We need to part as friends. Shake hands with everybody over at the cookhouse, too. Cookie and Slim need just a little time to get supper together an' put up the flag to announce that the meal is ready. Life is too short to go around with hard feelin's. Someday this country will get back up on its feet, an' we might work together again.

"If you are going to leave us, please do one last show tonight so we can round out the performance. That will give us time to try an' plan a lineup without you tomorrow. On the part of all the Brewers, I thank you from the bottom of my heart, an' I wish you well!" Lucky concluded. He looked at all of them slowly to be sure that they understood and to read the expressions on their faces.

After the four Brewers had talked, everybody sat there speechless. They had to take it all in. The show folks had known that something important was up, and that is why the meeting was called. But they would have never guessed about the bank robbery, never guessed that that their livelihood was in danger, never thought that they were so close to joining the great ranks of the unemployed in the country, not to mention the homeless people, men and women, and even children, whom they could pick out along the roads and even in towns. And even the town people who had jobs could never expect to get a raise, and even when the boss had to skip paydays, they usually just kept on working, hoping that it would get better.

The circus had to keep on going, keep on living. It was their only hope. Finally, after they had sat there in silence for some minutes, they started to look around, and they all realized that none of them would leave, none of them would quit the show, wouldn't even think of it, and more than ever, they were glad that they had one another other.

15. GOODBYE, JACK

The night show in that town was a very full house. Even when there were no more seats left in the tent, fifty people who had bought tickets were waiting outside to get in. Gradually, they were let in as their neighbors squeezed together to make room in the bleachers for them. The large audience was very appreciative, and the performers tried all the harder to entertain them. And many of the animals seemed to sense that this was a big show. All seemed to be going in a predictable pattern till about twenty minutes before the end of the show.

Suddenly, huge gusts of wind came up, and the audience cried out in surprise. A bigtop at times is like a living thing. It breathes and moves as the large sections of canvas inch up and down the big center poles, almost like inhaling and exhaling. Jake sent two teams of three men each in different directions around the tent to tighten the long guy ropes up to the center poles and then to all the much shorter ropes going to the stakes from the poles around the sides of tent. As a tent dries out it becomes lighter. In rain, it becomes heavier. At times the ropes around the tent need to be checked and tightened.

At the same time, just to be cautious, any hay or sacks of grain outside the bigtop were loaded in the trucks, and saddles and other tack that needed to stay dry were stowed.
Ten minutes after the gusts of wind were felt, a driving rain came, pounding loudly on the tent. The audience cried out in unison again. There were only about ten minutes left in the performance, and the people did not look forward to getting soaked going to their cars, or for some of them, walking a mile or more home.

The performance ended, but the rain continued furiously. Woody addressed the audience with the microphone, explaining that they would not be forced out into the rain, and that they could take their time. Woody found Will Wainwright, president of the local Lions Club that had sponsored the show. He proposed that Will speak to the audience on the microphone and recruit men who would go out in the rain, get their cars, come back and get the drivers of more cars, who would in turn get more drivers, and then get their waiting families. And everybody was asked to give neighbors who had come on foot a ride home. All of this required that the entrance to the tent would become a sort of taxi line. Actually, lots of the canvas sidewall would be lifted so that several cars could come into the tent at a time. Will Wainwright did a good job on the microphone, talking to the townspeople he knew well, many of them by name. Certainly all of the Lions Club members were cooperative, and others helped out, too.

One good outcome was greatly increased sales of cotton candy, popcorn and other items as the crowd waited in the tent. Also, six men were found who would help with the teardown of the seats for the evening and loading everything when the tent finally came down. They were attracted by the chance to earn a dollar that night, even though they knew they would get soaking wet, work in mud, and continue late into the night working with large rolls of wet canvas.

Then an alarming thing happened. The remaining crowd of townspeople in the tent was getting smaller. That was not the problem. It was the news from the old watchman who looked after the ballpark where the show had set up. He had been there many years, and he came and warned Woody and Lucky that the little gulley that they had crossed to get to this part of the grounds would surely become a wide, rapid stream up to twenty feet wide and four feet deep. It would come up rapidly in a big rain like this, a flash flood. He had seen it many times. And then it could be a day or more till a person could safely cross, even on foot, to get back to the main parking lot.

This meant that all the circus vehicles needed to get to the other side as soon as practical and onto the higher ground that was the parking lot where the townspeople had parked for the show. Will Wainwright confirmed what the old watchman had said,

Gary G. Steele

explaining that he had been there many years and really knew the place.

The sound system was about to be dismantled and packed up, but Woody and Lucky stopped the packing. They used the microphone to call all the show folks together. The message was hard to transmit over the noise of the rain, and it was just about unheard of for such an urgent meeting to be held after the night show, especially when everybody was working as hard as possible to tear down in what was promising to be a long night.

Woody announced the bad news about the gulley and what would become essentially a flash flood. He and Lucky devised a strategy to get as many vehicles out as rapidly as possible in some sort of orderly way. All the vehicles except the canvas truck were to load up right away, or not even load up, and just get across the gulley. One of the workingmen mentioned that he had already seen some water flowing through the gulley. As to the horse trucks and the elephant truck, well, the horses could just walk alongside the trucks to which they were tied as the trucks crossed the gulley slowly. The elephant truck could cross empty and then load the three elephants on the other side. Lucky explained that he would park his car and trailer on the other side of the gulley and turn around to help light the way with the headlights, and then Woody's wife would bring their car and trailer over and help light the way across, too.

All of this meant that for the moment, the tear down in the tent and of the tent would be put on hold. Cars, trailers, and trucks had to be moved hastily. Then

Woody called out the order in which the vehicles were to cross, two at a time as needed. The cars and house trailers were to go first, since they would have the hardest time getting through any rising water. The final word was, "As fast as we need to work, do not in any way take any chances that would cause any of us to be hurt. We sure need speed, but take the time that you need to keep yourself an' everybody else safe."

The show folks had been in jams like this before, and everybody chipped in to make it all work. At least the rain was not a cold rain, and if they could move quickly, they could get up to the high ground of the parking lot and not be stranded. They could even make it to the next town on time tomorrow. Of course everybody realized that the tent would be completely waterlogged and literally weigh tons more than usual. It would be a real struggle to load. The three elephants would certainly be pressed far beyond their routine service and might even have to pull or push trucks through the water.

All the cars and house trailers got across the gulley with no problem. The townspeople had all cleared out by now, and the parking lot was mostly empty, so the show drivers parked up at the very front to leave room for the big trucks. A couple more of the cars were unhitched so that they, too, could be driven back and parked with their headlights on to light the way across the water in the gulley better.

Then the water started to rise rapidly. The drivers started taking the semi-trucks across as fast as possible, except of course for the canvas truck that hauled the bigtop. Within thirty minutes, all the other vehicles had made it across and were parked safely on the other side. There was a collective sigh of relief.

Now the water was coming faster and higher, and a rope was tied from the front of Lucky's car to the canvas truck. Holding onto the rope was the only way a person could cross the gulley safely. All the workingmen could focus on the big job of loading the remaining bleachers and bringing the tent down and loading it up. The center poles of the bigtop were by now creaking, with pools of water caught in the sections of overhead canvas between the center poles and the quarter poles. The canvas was sagging threateningly.

Lucky proceeded with something that was rather rare. There could be years between when it needed to be done. Some of the less experienced people on the show had never seen it done at all. Lucky took his little Remington pistol and fired shots at the lowest point in each of the overhead pools of water. The water started squirting down immediately through the holes the bullets made. He reloaded and shot more holes where they were needed most. Their dad GR had been fond of saying that this was the only time when it was OK to shoot a gun in the bigtop. Within just a few minutes, there were many jets of water shooting at random spots below. The trapped pools of water up above were becoming smaller, and the weight on the poles was easing. But what had been relatively dry ground in the tent was becoming mud.

The remaining bleachers, ring curb, and props were soon out of the tent, and next up was something that usually called for routine caution but now needed extreme caution. The tent had to be dropped. Jake, the canvas master, gave careful directions. At the top of each of the four center poles was a bale ring. The sections of canvas at the top of the tent were laced with rope into the bale rings. The bale rings could be raised up or down the four big center poles, using ropes and pulleys that went down the center poles and were tied off near the base. The ropes pulling the rings made the tent go up or down, but all four bale rings needed to move in near unison, else a ring could get stuck or potentially the lace ropes would be ripped from the canvas because of the pressure.

Pulling the tent up in the mornings was relatively easy. The elephants easily pulled the long ropes through pulleys and pulled up the bale rings. They walked at a steady pace, stopping whenever told to, and even could back up a little if the four bale rings were not rising together.

Dropping the tent at night was another matter. Jake's system was to have a man stand by each center pole, untie the big ropes going up the pole to the bale rings, and then, upon his signal, all four men would let the ropes fly, and the bales rings would come down the poles, bringing the sections of canvas in the bigtop with them.

But each man needed to have a pocketknife with him and be sure footed. Once the top started coming down, there could be as little as fifteen seconds to get outside the falling tent. Tripping could be dangerous. The falling tent could be crushing and even break bones, and there was fear that a man could be smothered under it when it hit the ground. A man would have to use his pocketknife to rip through the canvas to get air immediately.

In this case, the soggy tent would fall even faster, and the muddy ground inside the tent had become quite slippery. Additionally, one of the men who usually did this was limping with a sprained ankle and not up to this duty. A less experienced replacement had to take his place.

Jake went over the steps very carefully with the four men, and he insisted that all four would run out the south side of the tent and make themselves immediately visible to him so that he could see they were all safe when the canvas came down. All four understood how serious this could be, and they went to their respective poles and waited patiently for Jake to blow his whistle. Jake had overseen this drill hundreds or thousands of times, and he could count on the fingers of one hand the times that anybody had actually had to use the knife. And he remembered every one of those times.

But tonight, with the rain-soaked canvas, all went well, and he was relieved along with everyone else. The tent was flat on the ground, and the canvas sections were ready to be unlaced, rolled up, and loaded with the poles onto the canvas truck. Of course tonight, what was usually only a good workout for a dozen men would become a grueling task taking at least twice the time. If only the rain would let up! And would the water in the gulley go down or would the elephants have to push the canvas truck through it while another truck towed it from the other side?

Woody's focus suddenly changed when his wife walked up, soaking wet of course, with a very troubled look on her face.

"Honey," he said, "what are you doing here? What is wrong? Are the kids OK? You had to take the rope through the water in the gulley. What is it?"

"The kids are fine," she said. "It is something else. That new truck driver we hired a couple months ago, Simpson, he says there has been an accident and he has talk to you. That is all he will say. He says you have to come over. He was acting half crazy. I could not get another word out of him. He just said there was an accident. He was almost shaking. Honey, I think you really have to leave this and go over. I know your hands are full here, but Simpson is acting very strange. Please come over."

"Come to think of it, where has he been? With all that is going on, I never noticed that he was missing," Woody said.

Woody took off immediately, following his wife using the rope back across the gulley, where the water had still not gone down at all.

"Mister Woody, I am so sorry. It was an accident! It didn't happen on purpose," Simpson said as Woody walked up to the truck.

"Are you hurt? Let me see. Who is hurt, Simpson?"

"Oh, nobody is hurt. It was not that kind of accident, Mr. Woody."

"What do you mean? Did you crash the truck? It doesn't look like it. Did you hit another truck or something? Where is the accident? Let's take care of it. We have a lot to do tonight."

"No, no, Mr. Woody, it is your dog."

"My dog? What dog? Do you mean Jack? Where is he? What happened to him? Where is he? He is not in his cage here under the side of the truck!"

"Mr. Woody, it was an accident. Please forgive me. I loaded the big roll of fence that we use for the dog pen, but I didn't know that Jack was not in his cage like all the other dogs," Simpson explained.

Jack was the only male dog on the show that had not been neutered. He was a wonderful performer, a little border collie cross of some kind, who did only one trick but who absolutely loved to do that trick. He could jump high in the air and do a backflip with a twist sideways. He became a whirling ball of black and white fur, high in the air. He was a real crowd pleaser and usually closed out the dog act.

But since Jack was an uncut male, he was separated from the other dogs and put on a leash outside the dog pen where the other dogs ran. His chief rival was Duke, and occasionally he and Duke would get in an argument through the fence.

This stormy night that Simpson drove the truck across the gulley, Jack was still tied to the truck and not in his cage.

"So what are you saying, Simpson? Where is Jack? His

leash here is cut off. Did you do that?"

"Yes, Mr. Woody, I cut off his leash. He was still on his leash when I drove off. He got dragged by the truck," Simpson said.

"You mean you dragged him through all that water an' then dragged him across the parking lot? Where is he? Is he alive?"

"No, Mr. Woody, he is not alive. I put him in with the pony ride stuff for now. I didn't want anybody to see him." Simpson was so fearful he could hardly talk.

"Why, you dumb son of a bitch, you killed my dog! I ought to kick your ass into the next state! We take care of our animals. Our animals are part of our life! We take care of them like we take care of each other. An' you killed him!"

Woody's right hand clenched, forming a fist that landed with a crunch on Simpson's nose, breaking it.

"Just please don't fire me, Mr. Woody! Just please don't fire me!"

Woody was standing by the cab of the truck. He opened the door of the cab and reached in for the buggy whip that he knew was stored under the seat. He proceeded to rain down severe blows on Simpson's head and arms. Simpson screamed.

"But please, Mr. Woody, don't fire me! You don't have to pay me no money. Just feed me. That is all I want. I went for three days without eatin' before you hired me. I just need the food. I will work day an' night for nothin', no money, an' I will ride in back of a truck with the horses."

Woody stopped beating him, because another scream could be heard. His wife was screaming at him.

"Woody, has *tutti jawled divia*? You're *murrain'* the *poura mush*. Have you gone crazy? You're killing the poor guy! What is happening?"

"Let him tell you, the son of a bitch!"

Simpson stood there with his head down, blood dripping from his nose. Then he mumbled, "Ms. Amy, there was an accident, an' your dog is dead!"

"Which dog? What are you talking about?"

Woody butted in and said, "He dragged Jack to death by the side of the truck coming over here. An' I feel like killing this dumb idiot!"

"Oh, no! Where is Jack? I need to see him."

"He's right here, Ms. Amy. I put him in with the pony ride stuff."

"Oh my God! The kids will be heartbroken. Nothing like this has ever happened. An' I am heartbroken!"

"An' I ought to beat that idiot within an inch of his life!"

"Wait, Woody. This is an awful night already. An' look – his face is gushing blood an' he has big welts from the whip," Amy pleaded.

"We had Jack's mother an' father, an' I believe Dad had the grandfather. Jack was a wonderful, innocent little dog. He never did anything but try to make people happy. An' now you kill him, an' you kill him in a very cruel way! I ought take this rope an' tie your hands up with it an' drag you behind the truck an' see how long you last," Woody screamed.

"Just don't fire me, Mr. Woody. I need the food. It is awful out there as a hobo. You never know if you will eat from one day to the next. I saw an old man jump off a bridge once 'cause he said he couldn't be hungry no more. I don't have no people. I don't have no town."

"Woody, leave him alone for now. You have hurt your own hand, too, when you punched him. You can deal with only one thing at a time, an' Lucky an' the men need you back at the tent. I will take care of this. Go. Get the tent packed up. We need to get to the next town for a show tomorrow," Amy said, trying to sound calm and logical.

Woody left, and Amy started yelling at Simpson, her own anger bursting forth when she pulled out the body of the mangled dog. Despite her strength in bad situations, her tears started flowing. She could only imagine what Jack's last minutes had been like.

"Just, Ms. Amy, just please don't fire me. There aint nothin' that hurts like being hungry. I gotta eat. I will do anythin'. I will work night an' day. Don't need no money; just feed me. I will wash clothes an' shovel manure for the whole show. But please don't let me go!" Simpson was sounding more and more desperate.

There was a long pause. Amy needed several tries to compose herself. "Simpson, I don't know what we are going to do with you. What you did was awful. I just can't believe it. How stupid can you be? You always walk around a truck before you drive off in it. We taught you that. We preached it to you! You check to see if the dollies are up. Is the gangplank closed? Are there any light cords connected to it? Is there anything under it? Yes, Jack was probably under it, out of the rain."

Ever the pragmatist, Amy paused and thought for a moment before speaking again.

"But, Simpson, here is what you are goin' to do now, an' what you are goin' to do tomorrow. Listen carefully if you know what is good for you. You are goin' to wash Jack's poor little face so there is no blood or mud on it an' so that my kids can look at him. The rest of his body is too messed up for them to see, so find one of those cloth feed sacks, the kind with the nice patterns that we save for making shirts an' stuff. Get a blue one, an' put him in it up to his neck. Then the kids can see him."

"Well, ma'am, we could just tell them that he got loose an' ran away or that somebody stole him," Simpson offered.

"Simpson, I don't lie to my own children, an' they are not stupid. They would want to go back an' look for him around the whole town. An' this is the Great Depression. People don't steal dogs now. They throw them out by the side of the road when they can't feed them anymore, or they put them in a sack an' drown them. You ought to know that.

"An' tomorrow at the new town on the new lot, I will

tell you where we will bury this little dog. The kids will be there. You will have to tell them exactly how it happened an' watch them cry. You can tell them that maybe when the truck took off it just broke his neck right away an' he never suffered bein' dragged. Maybe that happened.

"Now push his little legs back toward his body so he will be easier to bury. He will get stiff in a couple hours. You might have to tie the legs back to him till then. An' tomorrow you will dig the grave about a yard deep so that no animals like possums or 'coons will dig him up. Keep the grass together from the top of the grave so you can put it back like a piece of sod, an' it will grow back again fast. When you dig, put the dirt on a piece of canvas so that it will look neater when you finish buryin'. An' Jack will be buried in the blue sack. An' you will find a few short boards or parts of an old orange crate to put under him an' over him before you start puttin' the dirt over him. But the hardest part will be explainin' to my kids what you did.

"So that is what you will do, Simpson, exactly like that. I don't know what we will do with you after that. If we keep you, it will take a long time to get over this, if we ever do. Now do what I said an' go clean up your nose an' wash the blood out of your clothes. You are goin' to look like hell tomorrow anyway. Just don't look dirty."

"Yes, ma'am, I understand. Oh, Ms. Amy, I really am sorry, so sorry! It was dumb. I wish...." Simpson's voice trailed off.

But Amy walked away into the rainy night, wondering how she could compose herself in front of her kids and everybody else after they had slept the night and were in a new town. Then she would have to tell them that one of the workingmen was going to bring them some sad news and that they should try to be strong, but it wouldn't be easy. Cedartown would be a place they would never forget, and Cranby, the next day's town that they drove to, would be, too.

Amy told Woody what her orders were for Simpson, and it was barely light out when she and Woody found a place for Simpson to dig the small grave. It was by an elm tree on the fence line behind where the tent would go up. Woody marched out six paces from where the biggest branch of the elm tree pointed and put a stick in the ground. Amy said she would tell Simpson to dig the grave there. Woody said it would be best if he still didn't see Simpson, and Simpson should stay away from the cookhouse, too.

"I am not ready to lay eyes on him yet. I have so much on my mind. An' I can't give that son of a bitch one bit of my energy. An' when the other people on the show find out, they may want to give him a horse whippin', too," Woody said, the anger in him having subsided very little.

They both knew that if they really fired Simpson that it would be almost like killing him. He would join the legions of aimless hobos who lined up at soup kitchens or begged farmers for a plate of anything or stole eggs from hen houses and ate them raw just to stay alive. Nobody knew when this Depression would end. There was no end in sight.

Simpson quickly found the stick that Woody had put in the ground and dug the grave to all the required specifications. He dug as if his future depended on it, and it did. Then the hard part came. He had to go over to the trailer and tell Amy and Woody's kids what had happened. He had to tell them that there would be a little funeral for Jack.

He walked over very slowly, praying that Woody would not be around and wondering what he would say if the kids or anybody else noticed his broken nose, black eye, and the welts from the whip. But most of all, what were the words to explain it? The kids were seated on the trailer step, quietly waiting. They knew that something bad had happened. Simpson approached with his head lowered, partly from shame and partly in a useless attempt to hide his wounds.

"Kids, I am so sorry to tell you that Jack got killed last night. He is dead. We are goin' to bury him in a few minutes. When we were movin' all the trucks last night, he got drug an' run over. There was nothin' we could do to save him," Simpson blurted out quickly, trying to get the explanation over.

The children looked at him in wide-eyed disbelieve, and then they realized that Simpson would not make this up. It had to be true. And they noticed his nose and eye, and they quickly figured out what had happened to him. And they guessed why their father was standing in the trailer, out of sight but within earshot.

The little brother was the first to choke up, but his older sister soon did, too. They could not speak at first. They stared at the ground and then at Simpson. Then the questions came in rapid succession, all the childish questions that would be natural.

"How did it happen? Did it happen fast? Could there be some kind of mistake? Can we come when you bury Jack? When will that be?" To that last question, Simpson answered that the grave was already dug where their daddy and mama told him to dig it.

Amy stepped into make it as easy on the children as it could be. Simpson had done as he was told so far, and a parent needs to help her children get through situations in life that are new and so horribly painful to them.

The children had seen animals die before, but it was animals that were killed to be eaten, such as chickens and pigs, or a few cases of animals that were terribly sick or injured. The children had even learned how to kill and clean chickens. But Jack, Jack was something else. Amy bent over the kids to hug them, and soon her dress grew moist from their tears, and Woody could hear their sobs and decided to come out and hold them, too.

Simpson jumped back when Woody stepped out of the trailer, but Woody's attention was on his children, not on Simpson.

After what seemed like an eternity, Woody said that it was time to go look at Jack and take him to the little grave. Yes, they could pet his head, and yes, their cousins could come, too. Actually, though it was early, the scene had attracted some attention around the circus lot already. Word had leaked out. People had noticed that Woody's hand was bandaged, and he would not tell people what happened. But mostly, no explanation was necessary.

So they walked over to the hay bale that Simpson had covered respectfully with a horse blanket. Simpson went and got Jack, and the little dog's head was all clean now and the rest of his body hidden in the blue feed sack. A small crowd gathered, including the stunned cousins, and the crying continued.

"But this isn't right, Dad. Our animals don't die from accidents. They die from old age, like people do. We take great care of our animals, an' they live longer than other people's animals. An' we set an example for the town people. This shouldn't be," Mattie sobbed.

"Well, it was an accident, Daughter, a very bad accident. An' accidents can happen, on a farm, on a street in town, anyplace. But, honey, it just hurts bad, doesn't it?"

At this point, all the children and some of the adults were in tears. It was just unbelievable. A small procession started from the hay bale where the dog lay over to the grave that had been dug. Gilly carried Jack in his arms. Amy and Woody knew that this needed to be over before there were many town people around.

"But what will happen to the dog act, Mama? Nobody else can do that trick!" little Bart asked.

"That is true, my love, an' we will have to figure out

what to do this afternoon. But there will never be another dog like Jack," Amy answered.

The kids all patted Jack's head one last time, and so did Amy and Woody, and all the others too. Then Woody motioned to Simpson to put Jack in the ground. Woody couldn't look at him. He just motioned with his hand. Simpson gently lowered the little dog into the grave on the short boards he had already placed there, and then put two more boards over him.

Someone had found some wildflowers to throw in with him, too. And then the dirt started to go down over him. The kids strained to see him till the last minute, till all the black and white fur was covered, till no more of him was visible. They tried to be strong. They were strong in so many ways, but they had no experience like this before. And they would never forget it.

Simpson smoothed the grave over and placed the sod back on top to help hide the location. Woody explained that it was six paces out from the elm tree, following the direction the biggest limb pointed. His daughter and sons asked if they could come and visit the place when the show came back next year, and Woody said of course.

Amy carried Bart back to the trailer, the first time he had been carried in a long time. Woody's arm was on each of his other kids' shoulders. The cousins and Aunt Tillie and Uncle Lucky walked together, too. The whole procession back was slow and sad. They all knew that they had to act out the rest of this day as if nothing had happened. People didn't buy tickets to see a show put on by sad people. Smiling would be harder work than the performing.

Simpson came at the end of the procession, lagging behind, and then just disappearing behind one of the trucks. He could see that the family had more to deal with than what to do with him right now.

He stayed out of sight for three days, and at first none of the other workingmen even wanted to bring him a plate from the cookhouse, and he was hungry. Then Slim took pity on him and brought him some left overs, and Simpson ate them ravenously.

On the morning of the third day, Amy and Woody had a talk in bed. "Yes," Woody said, "I know he is still around. There is nothing much that happens around here that I don't know about. Let's talk to my brother an' see if it is all right with him if that jerk stays on to do some kind of work or another. But I don't want to deal with him. Let my brother be the one who is his boss. The way I see it, that *vaseta mush murraed* our *juckel,* the awful guy killed our poor little dog and hurt our *chavies,* our kids, in a way they were never hurt before, but two wrongs don't make a right. What do you think, Sweetheart?"

"Woody, I have been thinking along the same lines. There is no use making the *pourra mush* suffer. What good would that do? Let Lucky work with him for a month, an' we will see what happens. But just tell Lucky not to let any of the other workingmen beat him up."

"OK, darling, this won't be easy. But let's try it."

16. ROMAN RIDING

A man and two boys approached the chair where Grandpa GR sat by his horse truck. They looked dejected, and they led a pretty buckskin gelding with a white mane and tail. At first GR thought that somehow they had taken one of the family's horses, one that his grandson particularly liked. But even from fifty feet, his eye for equine detail soon helped him see the minor differences between this horse and the family's horse.

The man spoke first, asking if GR was the man they heard bought horses. They had one to sell. GR was slow to reply. He usually was in such instances. He explained that he had about enough horses now, and he asked why the man wanted to sell.

"Well," the man explained, "my boys love this little horse, an' I do, too. But the truth is that we just don't have the means to take care of 'im like he deserves. You can see that he lost a little weight already. Our pasture is bad, an' we have to save it for the cows that give us milk an' meat. It's a shame. This morning we watched an' saw that you treat your horses real good, an' they are all well fed an' slick. My boys would die rather than send Buckeroo to a slaughterhouse to make glue or dog feed. So this seemed like the best thing we could do with him, sell him to you."

GR noticed how the boys looked sadder and sadder, and the younger one, maybe fourteen, looked on the verge of tears. He also noticed that the man was about the same age as one of GR's sons and that the boys were about the age of some of his grandsons. Granted, they had light brown hair and a sandy complexion, and they surely weren't from his family, but still, GR was glad to think that none of his family was on such hard times, trying to sell a nice horse they loved to save it from the slaughterhouse.

"My goodness, sir, I am so sorry to hear about your bad luck, an' it looks like you have a pretty decent horse here. But I can't go around buyin' just any horse. Honestly, folks come to me about every week wantin' to know if I can give them cash for their horse, or even two or three horses. These are bad times for horses in the country, what with the Depression an' farms being sold an' all. Has your horse just been a pet, or is he broke pretty well?"

"Oh, Buckeroo is broke real good. Let me show you, sir," said the older of the two boys.

"No, Son, let Little Bub show the man how good Buckeroo is. That will be a better demonstration. You are almost as big as a man, an' you could ride any horse. Let your little brother do it," the father said.

GR was pleased and amazed by what he saw next.

It was the kind of thing you did not see often except maybe among professional horse trainers, but very rarely among ordinary horse owners. The older brother took the lead rope and put it over the horse's neck and tied it to the other side of the halter, making a substitute reins and bridle with no bit. A horse would have to be well trained to work with such a makeshift affair. Next, the younger boy climbed up on the horse in an instant, without a boost from his father or brother, and the horse never flinched. GR could tell that the horse was well treated and used to having kids climb around on him.

The boy clucked to the horse, and he took off at a walk. Then, very gently, the boy had the horse do a large figure eight, hardly using the halter rope at all, just using voice commands and a bit of a heel touch. They came back, and then the boy gave another command, and the horse moved sideways ten feet to the right, and then back, and ten feet to the left and back where they started. And the next move was very impressive. He touched the rope gently, and the horse backed up in a straight line. The boy reached down and patted the horse on the neck, speaking kindly to him. Then the boy clucked again, and the horse came right back to the starting point.

"Well, that is pretty good, pretty darn good," said GR. He handles real nice, an' he must have a very tender mouth. Don't you have a bridle with a bit for him? Don't you have a saddle? Does he have any gaits?"

"Yes," the father said, "We have a bridle, an' there is a Western saddle an' an English saddle, an' saddle blankets. But as you can see, you don't need any bridle or saddle like you would with most horses, an' my boys are good at handlin' horses anyways. Now about the gaits, he doesn't pace or canter. He trots, runs, an' gallops just fine, hardly needed any trainin' to shift from one to the other. He could probably learn to canter real fast, but we never saw much need for it."

GR asked and got permission to look at the horse's mouth, and a glance at the teeth showed that the horse was indeed a young three-year old, as he had estimated. But what he was as interested in seeing was if the horse let a stranger touch him easily, let him look in the mouth. The animal was easy to handle.

"Well, sir," GR answered, "he seems like a nice piece of horseflesh, an' I can see why you are reluctant to part with him. Are you really ready to talk business about him?"

The man paused, and the boys looked at him, knowing that this was the moment and that there might not be any turning back. If they wanted to save Buckeroo from the slaughterhouse, this was their chance.

"Yes, indeed. We are ready to talk business. That is what we came for. But first we want to know how you will treat him an' what you will do with him. You are a horse trader, after all. Would you sell him to just anybody?" the man asked.

"We would treat your horse the same way we treat our other stock. We would put some weight on him an' worm him. He would always be well curried an' cleaned. We treat all our stock very well. We would yours, too.

"It is true that I trade horses, but for an animal like you got, well, he would have to go to just the right buyer, to somebody or some family who could appreciate him an' treat him the way he should be treated," GR said.

In his head, GR had a different idea, but it was something that would not help the dealing right now. This horse was so special and such a good match for Chico, the other buckskin that his grandson loved so much, that what he would probably do is give this horse to his grandson so he could have a good Roman riding team.

"Will you ever sell him to a slaughterhouse?" the older son broke in, with a sharp tone of emotion. "Can you promise?"

"Son, where are your manners! You can't interrupt men talkin' business! You know better!" the father said.

GR replied slowly and clearly, "No, young man, I have an idea what this little horse means to you an' your brother, an' your dad, an' you can take my word for it, he would not go for dog feed. This is no old plug. This is a fine young gelding with much better uses."

"So, OK," the man said. I guess we are ready to talk money. I will come right out an' say it. How much are you willing to give us?"

GR was a wily horse trader with decades of experience. He had learned at his father's knee. He knew how to work sellers and buyers, and he did very well at the art of horse trading, even in these tough times when there were lots of sellers but not too many buyers. He decided to start with his standard patter, but he could not really work this family too hard, get too much of a deal from them.

"Well, what kind of money are you asking for him?" GR started. It was important to get the sellers to name a specific figure first. Always switch it around; get them to put the first card on the table.

"Well, we don't sell horses very often," the man said. "So we don't rightly know. We would just want somethin' that is fair, somethin' that would be reasonable."

"That would not be very much nowadays, you know. There is not a great market for horses an' mules, or even livestock of any kind. It's just the bad times we are in. It's so sad," GR continued.

"I believe a good price would be twenty dollars," the man said, his voice a little dry. He was on unfamiliar territory, and as much as he wanted to get a good deal for the horse, he also had the wariness that townspeople often have about traveling people.

"And we need that payment in cash," he added.

"Sure, mister, we would pay you in cash, let you count it right here in your hand. That is not a problem. The price you are asking is more of a problem. Would you take fifteen dollars?" GR asked.

"I was hopin' to get more than that," the man said. "Like you said, he is a mighty fine horse." The man had not sold horses much, but he had sold other animals, like hogs and cattle, and he had tried to bargain for the crops that he grew.

"He is a fine horse, indeed, an' I want to give you a good price. I will go up as high as seventeen, an' I can give you the cash in five minutes if you wait." GR offered.

"Well, mister, you seem like an honest man, an' I will be honest with you. I don't want to go below twenty. I have to tell you the truth," the townsman added.

"I am an honest man, an' we like to play your town, every year or at least every couple years. It is import- ant for us to keep a good reputation. But maybe we can make a deal this way. Could one of your boys ride the horse home an' bring back the bridle an' two sad- dles an' other tack, an' if they are in good shape, I will give the twenty dollars," GR said.

"Oh, the saddles an' tack are almost like new. We got them back in '28, but we have not used them much at all. Like you see, we didn't need to use them very much, just in a parade or something like that, or in the barrel races at the rodeo," he replied. "I will send the older son home now. I believe we have a deal."

"I believe we have a deal, too, sir. Let's shake hands then. If the saddles an' tack are in good shape, I will give you twenty dollars in cash when your boy gets back with them," GR said.

The two men smiled and shook hands. They had a deal. They were happy, or at least as happy as they could be under the circumstances. The boys were re- lieved to think the horse had a good home but sad to part from him. The older boy knew that this was the last time he would ever ride the horse.

"Tell you what," GR said confidentially to the man. "If your boys want to come back very early in the morning, just after sun up, before we leave for the next town, they will have a chance to say goodbye to their horse, if you think that would be a good idea an' not make things worse."

"That's very nice of you, sir. I will talk it over with the missus tonight, but I believe she will say it is OK. Of course the boys would sure want to see him go off," the man replied.

Within a half hour, the boy was back with the horse and the two saddles, and he had the bridle on the horse this time. GR counted out the twenty dollars to the man, and the deal was closed. The man gave a dollar to the older boy, telling him to buy circus tickets and a box of popcorn to share. When he came back, the three walked off slowly down the midway toward the entrance of the bigtop.

GR thought that he had made a good deal all around, for himself and for the man and his sons. And he liked to make good deals. He asked one of the workingmen to tell his grandson Gilly to come by when he had a chance. There was something to talk about.

Some time later Gilly showed up. "What is it, Grandpa? Is it something I can help you or Grandma with? Oh, Grandpa, what is *dova grai* doin' *doy*? *Lestie's tutti's*? What is that horse doing here? Is that horse yours? I can't believe how much he looks like Chico!"

"*Keker, gara, dova grai's tutti's*, if you like. No, boy, the horse is yours," GR answered.

"*Dortie, dortie*, Grandpa. Well, well, I don't know what to say. Why, that's terrific! I have just the right thing to do with him, too. You know what I mean?" Gilly said.

"I thought you would. An', Grandson, this little *grai* is really well broke. It has been a good while since I've *vattered* a *grai* from the *kera fokie*, saw a horse from the townspeople, so well broke. You can work him without a bit if you want to. He has a lot of brains, an' I think he could learn anything. Just talk to him, use the reins just a little, an' maybe your heel from time to time. An', Grandson, I was surprised when this town *chavie* jumped up on him with no saddle or bridle an' made the horse go straight backwards for ten feet an' then come right back. You know lots of horses can learn to go sideways, figure eight, do stuff like that, but many can never understand how to do a smooth backup for any distance. The nature of a horse is to go, not to go back. Well, this *bita grai gins* it *kushti*. This little horse knows it good."

"Grandpa, *nais tuk,* thanks so much. You know what I want to do, of course. I want to learn more about Roman riding an' do somethin' that could get more people into the tent," the boy said.

The boy knew that Roman riding would be a big attraction. He wanted to do it well so that he could do exhibitions along roads or on the midway or in parades so that people would notice and come to the show. Roman riding was the acrobatic act of riding two horses at one time, standing up, with one foot on each horse, and the reins of both horses in the rider's hands, ready to give commands to go ahead, slow down, stop, go right or left. It was spectacular. The popular belief was that it had been invented in Roman times. Many people had never seen it. Even the biggest rodeos rarely had it. And without the skills and well-broken horses a rider needed, it was easy to fall off and hurt one's pride if not one's arms and legs. The rider's feet were on pads that were cinched to the back of each horse, and the rider needed to develop a feel for the movement and control of two horses simultaneously.

Part of Roman riding was counterintuitive. The rider never stood up straight. He kept the knees bent a bit to adjust constantly to the movement of the horses. When turning to the left, the rider needed to lean into the turn and bend his left leg a little more, make it a little shorter, and to turn right, do the opposite. In slowing down, it was important to squat more and never to lean back. Leaning back could lead to a nasty fall.

The reins of the two horses were crossed, with the two left reins going to the rider's left hand and the two right reins going to his right hand. One of the key things a Roman rider needed to know was how to fall, and he had to be ready before he was going to fall. In other words, it would be too late if it became obvious that a fall was coming. The right thing to do instead of falling would be to jump down astride just one of the horses, or if it is too late for that, to grab the neck of one horse on the way down so that he still had a hold on the horses and his feet could land on the ground with little or no harm.

It is difficult to Roman ride on horses that are just walking. The walk makes the ride bumpy for the rider. A slow trot works fine, as does a gallop or a run, providing the rider has both horses moving at the same pace.

Gilly took all this very seriously. He wanted very much to contribute to the success of the circus in this really tough season. He took his father's word to heart at that meeting when his father told all the performers and crew that the bank with a big part of the season's money had been robbed and the money stolen. He listened to every word as his father laid out the survival plan for the show. The part the boy was relating to now was how to do more things, more flashy displays that would draw town people to buy tickets and fill the tent. He understood the idea that "the show had to start before the show started." There had to be various visual enticements to get ticket buyers into the tent.

"Grandpa, you have explained how Roman riding works, how you have to train the horses an' ride, but that is not enough. I have to try it. I have to train the horses to work together so I can control 'em. An' of course I have to learn my part. I really want to do this. Will you teach me an' train me, Grandpa?" Gilly asked.

"Grandson, you know I will. That is exactly what I had in mind when I *vatered dova bitta grai*, when I saw this little horse! Sure, if you practice every day for a couple weeks, I will watch you an' tell you. After that, you can mostly learn on your own. It just takes time an' brains. An' Grandson, you got lots of brains, an' you are already a pretty fine young horseman," GR replied.

"But Grandpa, there is something else. Can we be a little sneaky about this? I mean it would be great if I could make this a surprise for Dad an' Mama. It would make them really happy, an' I would be doin' my part to help out the show. Can we try to keep this a secret? You usually park up in front of the bigtop on the left side of the midway, an' they won't see if I practice mostly here. Can you tell the other folks not to say anything?" the boy pleaded.

"Sure, Grandson, we will make it our secret. You grandma will be in on it, too. An' other folks on the show, if they see you practicing Roman riding, we will tell them to *maw pen a lav,* not say a word!" GR answered.

The next two weeks went by quickly. Gilly came by with Chico and trained the new horse to work side by side with him. They needed a name for the new horse, and when GR explained that the old name was Buckeroo, Gilly said that a name like that would never work on a show. Instead, they chose the name Two Bits, which kind of meant that the new horse would be the number two horse with Chico.

Gilly was a good trainer and a quick learner. When the two horses trotted and ran together side by side in a coordinated way, he soon learned to stand up on them for short distances. Actually, he squatted at first, always ready to drop down astride Chico, who was always on the left, whenever he thought he might fall. The two horses teamed very well. Gilly was getting better and better and could stand up for longer and longer stretches. He got better at getting started, that awkward moment when he had to jump up from sitting on Chico to putting one foot on the pad on the back of each horse.

Then one day Gilly found the perfect place to practice. The show was set up in a large grassy pasture, but what Gilly discovered was that over a little knoll was an abandoned racetrack. It was not visible from the circus grounds. The racetrack grandstand was forlorn looking, with part of the roof missing and weeds growing up through some of the lower bleacher seats. The infield of the racetrack was overgrown, too, but the track itself was pretty good. It was not uncommon for various amusement facilities, including racetracks, to be closed during the Great Depression, or at least to be in bad repair and rarely used. Such seemed to be the case here.

Gilly had made a full round of the half-mile track standing up the whole time with Chico and Two Bits at a good trot. He hopped down on Chico to give the horses and himself a little rest before another practice round. He didn't want to wear them out, but he did want to get all the practice he could in this ideal place.

The second round was not to be, however. What happened next was a surprise to Gilly and his horses. Coming out of a nearby patch of woods near the creek were three loose horses. They were thin and had no halters. The leader of the three was a stallion, with his ears back and nostrils flaring. A mare and a gelding followed him. They were coming at a dead run with the obvious intent of chasing off the strange horses that had invaded their territory. Sometimes in those years, owners of horses, if they had no feed or decent pasture for their stock, just turned them loose to survive on their own if they could. Such horses could be seen at times along roads or on wasteland. Some survived, and some didn't. All suffered.

Gilly could hardly believe what he was seeing. This was not to be a friendly meeting of strange horses getting to know one another. In an instant the three loose horses were attacking his pair. He was in the middle of a five-horse fight, and his two horses were at an unfair advantage since they were tied together.

Immediately, the five were violently kicking, rearing, and biting, with frequent loud shrieks and grunts. His horses landed several solid kicks on the other three, as well as a good bite or two, but they seemed to be losing. The stallion ripped a bit of hide out of Two Bit's neck. Chico kicked high in the air with both rear feet and made a loud crunching noise when he hit the side of the mare. Gilly yelled and landed some strong blows across the nose of the stud and the gelding with his quirt, which helped temporarily. The five horses seemed to be spinning in a cluster, with flaring hooves here and arched, angry necks there. Chico and Two Bits were stronger, but the other three were on their home ground. The battle was chaotic. It was primordial, not like something taking place between domestic animals. It was more like what might have taken place thousands of years ago, before the species was domesticated.

It was one thing to break up a fight between two horses, something that Gilly had done or had helped with on occasion, but five horses in a fight was beyond his experience, beyond the experience of most horse people. Gilly wanted to save his horses, but he also had a cold feeling of fear. He knew he could be injured or even killed.

He was startled to hear the sound of Spangles' loud barks. Spangles, the show's Dalmatian, came running over the knoll toward the melee. Somehow, she had picked up on the noises from the horse fight, and ever defensive of the circus people and animals, she charged into the brawl. So much was going on that Gilly could barely see her, and he wondered what a fifty-pound dog could do to help. He had never heard her snarl and growl like she was doing. She was usually all sweetness and wagging tail. Now he saw, or at least heard, the other side of her nature. He did not want her hurt or killed. Her snarls alternated with a sort of piercing alarm bark asking for help.

He could not decide what to do next, but there was little time for hesitation. In an instant, however, any choice was taken away from him. For whatever reason, he went up in the air and landed on the racetrack railing. His left leg was under him as he came down. He broke both boards of the railing, and his arm suffered a jagged rip from the boards. A nail punched into his upper arm. He had cuts on his face and side and was bleeding in various locations. It was the pain in his left leg, though, that he was most aware of. He had never felt anything like it.

Through the pain, he tried to focus on his horses. At this point, a new sound joined the cacophony. Chief Red Hawk was running down the knoll emitting a curdling war
whoop. He had his bullwhips in each hand and was cracking them loudly. Yet it was not the noise that distracted the horses. It was not until he landed a stinging lash on the belly of the stallion that the battle changed. His other bullwhip caught the mare on the side, and the first whip got the stallion again, this time on the tender skin across his muzzle. Chief was amazing with his accuracy, soon hitting all three of the local horses and never touching Chico, Two Bits, Spangles or Gilly. The three horses were so startled by the hot pain they felt from the lashes that they lost their focus and started a quick retreat. Chico and Two Bits grabbed some deep bites from the backs of their retreating adversaries. Chief Red Hawk ran after them, cracking his whips and assuring that they would not circle around and make another attack. He had vengeance on his mind.

There was blood on all five horses, but Gilly had more visible blood than any of them. His face wore an expression of pain. His two horses were out of danger, and they stood with their heads lowered and panted. Gilly somehow grabbed Chico's neck and hopped on his good leg up on the railing at a spot where it was not broken. He gave a powerful push so that he could get up onto Chico's back, riding sidesaddle with both legs to the left side. He would ride this way to get home. When he landed on the horse's back, he bumped his injured leg and nearly passed out from the pain.

At least he could take himself to get help. He was thankful that the horses were good to him and did not take off or try to dump him. And he was very thankful to Spangles and Chief Red Hawk.

In reality, he was not the only one in pain. His two horses were in pain, too, and very worn out. They were in no mood to run. They just wanted to get back safely to the horse trucks.

They were halfway up the knoll when Granddad GR and Dad Woody rode over the ridge, coming from different directions. Both had heard Spangles' yelping, and both grabbed a horse and took off bareback to find out what was going on. Woody had no idea what it would be. Granddad was pretty sure it would involve his grandson and the two horses.

Gilly dreaded what his father might say to him. He feared he would hear no end of how he had endangered two fine horses, not to mention himself. Why he could have been killed! And how could he perform in his acts if he was all banged up? An injured performer is no performer at all. He was not supposed to be a child anymore. He was supposed to be smart enough to act like a man and not take chances. The words would be painful, maybe more painful than his physical injuries.

But such harsh words never came. Gilly's horses stopped, either from fatigue or because he was not keeping them going. His father stopped the horse he was riding on, and his grandfather stopped his. They all looked at one another. It was an intense triangular scene. It was hard to tell who would speak first.

Finally, Woody spoke. His words were soft and gentle, and he was full of concern. "Let's get you some help fast, Son. You look pretty beat up. Grandma has some *drab,* medicine, that will help. Let's ride over there real slow," he said.

Then Granddad GR interrupted, "Now, *Dadus, keker chinger* with the *gara,* --don't fight with the boy. It is my fault more than it's his."

"*Mandi gins*, Dad. I know. It doesn't matter. Let's just tend to the *chavie* an' make sure he's not broke up too bad. The rest is *chichi*, nothing."

The men moved their horses to either side of the boy and his horses. Woody went on Chico's side, where both his son's legs hung over and dangled, one of them obviously injured. Gilly's blood had now dripped onto Chico's side. It was a sign of his skilled horsemanship that the boy could ride one-sided as easily and logically as if this were just an ordinary ride and he was astride. The three generations of Brewers with the four horses rode off toward the *dukkering tan*...the fortunetelling tent, where all sorts of emergencies were handled.

For some minutes there were no words exchanged among them. They were silent, with all their thoughts unspoken. Each knew what the others were thinking, what they would eventually say. There were feelings of relief, concern, regret, forgiveness, and love, love in many forms, all being exchanged without a syllable being uttered.

Finally, Woody broke the silence, "Son, don't worry now. We are going take care of you. Things happen. It will all be OK. You are a strong, healthy young man, an' you will mend fast."

"Dad, I am so sorry. Really. Maybe I can at least do the acts where all I have to do is stand, like the trick roping. My one leg is good. I know that you an' Mama won't let me ride tonight. It was all an accident, a bad accident. I didn't mean for the horses to get hurt. Dad, I am so sorry," the boy said, his voice cracking from pain and shame.

"Hey, we used to call you 'rubber bones' when you were a *bitta chavie*, a little kid," Grandpa GR said. "You could fall out of a truck door on to pavement an' just bounce. You were like a rubber ball. You are strong, *mush!*"

"Yea, *gara,* boy, you are a bit of a bonehead, too. Now did you break that railing down with your *sherra* or your *bull*...your head or your ass?" Dad Woody quipped.

Gilly was in pain, but the humor was like an analgesic. The fact that his father would make a joke meant that somehow they would all handle this situation together. It was a close scrape, but they had what it took to get through it. The feeling gave him strength.

Grandma Camie saw them coming to her tent from some distance. She sent one of the workingmen to go get the boy's mother and even his sister if they could find her. She dismissed her fortunetelling client with a smile and invitation to come back in the evening for an additional reading at no charge.

Soon there was a group of four people at the tent waiting to help the boy. A wicker chair had been covered in a sheet and a bale of hay was situated as a sort of ottoman to put the injured foot on. There was a basin of water to wash wounds and scissors to cut away clothing as needed. White gauze and Mercurochrome were on the little table.

It was painful for Gilly to get off Chico. The horse stood very still, as if he knew that the boy was in pain. Woody held his arms out to let the boy slide into them at his own pace in his own way.

"But, Dad, I will get blood on your *kushti gad*. That is a good wardrobe shirt, and I am all *ratty*, bloody." Gilly said.

"Son, you are so much more important than my *kushti gad*. You are more important than a hundred shirts, than all the shirts in the world. You are my son! That is what matters. It's all that matters. Come on. Slide off when you are ready, an' I will catch you," Woody replied.

Gilly never felt more valued. This gave him a sense of worth that helped form his whole life. He looked in his father's eyes, and he was so happy to have Woody as his father.

Gilly started a slow slide off the horse and into his father's arms. The pain gripped him, and he could hardly keep from crying out. It was with a shock that

Woody realized how much his son now weighed and how that weight was nearly equal to his own. This was no longer the *bitta chavie* he had once cradled in his arms or held on his lap as he drove over the road.

Woody carried him into Camie's fortunetelling tent and placed him on the chair that had been set up and put his arm over his son's shoulders.

"Can you lift that bad leg up on this bale of hay for me, Grandson?" Grandma Camie asked. Gilly tried twice, and then shook his head.

"OK, Grandson, I am gonna help you, but I am gonna go real slow. You just tell me to stop if it hurts too much," she said to him. "You tell me when to start."

"You can start now, Grandma. Just please go slow, " the boy replied.

It took a minute, but Camie got her grandson's leg up on the bale of hay. Everyone gave a sigh of relief. Elevating the leg would help reduce the blood loss and make it easier to look at the wounds.

Amy came into the tent, out of breath and with a look of determination on her face. This was not a time to panic or surrender to emotion. In just a second, she and Camie had slit the boy's pants down the side and examined the leg as far as they could without cutting the boot. It was hard to tell if the blood puddling in the boot was from a foot wound or if it had just flowed down his leg and pooled there. Gilly tried to answer their questions stoically when they asked if his foot felt cut or just smashed. He could not be sure, but it just seemed smashed.

He knew that the boot had to come off, as much as that would hurt. The boot could be cut off with tin snips down pretty far to make it easier, but the bottom part of the boot would just have to be slipped off or pulled off. He prepared for the worst, but the boot came off easily.

It took time to clean all the blood away. Clearly, the foot was badly bruised, but there were no cuts and no bone protruding. The boot had provided some protection. The blood had just come down his leg into the boot.

"We can't tell yet if your ankle or foot bone is OK, or if your ankle is sprained, Grandson," said Grandma Camie. "It will take a bit. Some people say that if you can wiggle your toes, it means you don't have any broken leg or foot, but that is not true. An' we need to get started on the cuts on your arm an' your face an' everywhere."

"Yes, Son, you are a mess. You look like Scaramouch, but we will take care of you," said his mother Amy. "It will take some time. Just sit back an' relax. Your sister is here to help, too."

"An' *Dias*," Woody said to Camie, "Isn't it time to *dell* this *gara* a *bita tatapani*, to give this boy a little shot of whiskey, to help him deal with the pain?"

"*Dortie, Dortie*, Son. Well, you know he is just seventeen an' not of legal age, an' besides, we are under Prohibition. Whiskey is illegal, Son." Camie replied.

"Now, *Dias, maw chinger* with *mandi*. Mama, don't

argue with me. You know I mean 'for medicinal purposes,' as the *Gaudjas* say, just to make him feel better. An' I know you an' *Dadus* keep bottles of *tatapani* around for just such occasions."

"OK, Son. Ask your father to sneak the bottle in here from the box with the light cords. You are this *chavie's dadus,* the boy's father, so you an' his mother can give it to him," Camie said.

GR soon came in with the bottle of *tatapani* hidden under his jacket. Woody poured some of the bottle into a half-cup of tea with a couple lumps of sugar in it and offered it to his son, who took a sip.

"*Dadus*, you gonna get me *cussified*? Drunk? I never been *cussified!*" Gilly said. "I saw a drunken *mush* a couple times, but that is all."

"I know, Son," his father said. "An' right now that wouldn't be such a bad thing, maybe. We just don't want you to get sick. So here, take a sip or two. See if you can take it, an' we will give you another shot later maybe. Go slow."

The boy sipped the whiskey tea while his mother and grandmother worked on his injuries and his sister and father looked on, helping occasionally. They got all his wounds washed, gently, with soap and water. Many of the cuts were minor and would heal quickly. It was the one on the arm that was bad. It was a long gash with a couple splinters of wood from the railing in it. It was deep, too, and in one place a flap of skin hung. That would have to be cleaned out and held in place by bandages for a while till it started to grow back.

The women were using a lot of Mercurochrome on the boy, and it hurt every time, but there was no alternative. All they could do was make the wounds clean and bandage them up. Antibiotics were not known yet, and while they did know how to give some stitches to animals, doing it correctly on a human would be something else. Blood transfusions were not possible.

Amy asked her daughter to go ask Uncle Choctaw if he had any of those "222" brand pills from when he went up to see family in Canada. ("222" was the over-the-counter analgesic that was legal in Canada but not legal in the US. It was a great pain reliever and helped a person sleep. It contained a small amount of codeine.) The girl came back with two of the pills wrapped in a paper napkin. "Uncle Choctaw said to take it easy with these things, but if you need more, let him know," she said.

Gilly took one of the pills and soon felt better and became drowsy.

Woody went out and asked his brother to make some announcements asking for any doctor or nurse on the circus grounds to come to the ticket office immediately for an emergency. Even a veterinary would be welcome. The announcement was made several times, and even during the evening show, but there was no response. The local police, who were the sponsors of the show, explained that there was no doctor in the town, except for old Doctor Casey, who came by to the pastor's house once a week on Wednesday afternoons. The nearest doctor was about thirty miles away in Sanger's Junction.

But Gilly was quite strong, and his family's ministrations to him, including two more shots of whisky, got him through the afternoon. At one point, from the whisky or the fatigue or the "222," he fell sound asleep. They kept his foot elevated to ease the swelling and discourage further bleeding. Wrapping it helped reduce the swelling, too. They added a compress with ice that his sister got from the snow cone machine. The foot injury was serious, but the gash on the arm was serious, too. And they did not want to discuss in front of him the fact that they had seen a puncture wound from what must have been a nail in the racetrack railing that he had fallen on.

They left Gilly with his sister and some cousins who had come over, and the adults had a meeting on the other side of the horse truck.

"Two things worry me," his grandmother Camie started, "an' we need to get him to a *kushti drabaminger*, a good doctor, in the next day or at most two days. One thing is his foot. It looks like a green-bow sprain to me, not a real break. But if it is a break, we have to be sure it grows back straight. We don't want him to have some kind of limp for the rest of his life. If it starts to grow back wrong, they might have to re-break his ankle so it will grow back straight. An' we would hate to have him go through that."

Then she paused and looked the boy's mother in the eyes, knowing that they had both seen the same thing and even stopped and looked at each other then. It was just the two men who needed to know.

"He has a nail wound, a puncture wound in his arm, from a nail in the railing," Amy said. "We cleaned it out as best we could, but it is so painful, an' it looks deep. We know how horses can get lockjaw from stepping on a nail. People can get it, too, an' not just in their feet. There is no way to know if he will have it."

Now better known as *tetanus*, lockjaw was a dreaded disease in those days, and there was no preventive vaccine. People had to be treated after the exposure, and the treatment was not always available. The disease caused muscle spasms that started with the jaw muscles and could actually lock the jaw. The spasms spread through the body and could be fatal. It was painful to watch animals with lockjaw, and they were usually shot.

The boy's mother had hated even to say the word "lockjaw," but this was her son, and she would do whatever it took to protect him. "We have to get him to a real *drabaminger*."

Woody and GR were shocked. They had not been close enough to the cleaning and bandaging to notice anything more than the long gash. They admired the skill of the two women in tending the boy. It was one thing to take care of a wounded animal, but to deal with a son, with pain written on his face, that was another.

Woody spoke first. "I don't think this leaves us any choice. The *mushkras* here, the police, say that there is a doctor in a town thirty miles away. We can try to get one of the *mushkras* to come with us. They seem like really good men. We will drive Gilly to that town and wake up the doctor or whatever, and if that doctor is away or something, we will find out where the next town with a doctor is, and just keep going and going, if we go all night, until we get him the doctoring he needs. We can't let anything happen to our boy."

Woody's brother gave him his Packard, since it was fairly new and very fast. They filled the gas tank and checked the oil and tires, including the spare. The boy was loaded into the back seat. One of the local police sponsors gladly agreed to go along and act as guide and use his authority to get help find medical help of whatever kind. The policeman kindly ignored the fact that Gilly had booze on his breathe.

Woody drove, the boy and his mother rode in the back seat, and the local policeman rode up front to direct Woody as needed. The grandparents gave a supply of sandwiches and hot tea as well as more clean bandages and iodine, with a little more ice to help keep the swelling down.

Everybody acted very calm. It was their way in an emergency. Gilly asked where they were taking him. His mother *pookered a bita hookabin*, told him a little fib, that they decided to go on to the next show lot that night and get the doctor there to look at him. Gilly said OK and asked for something to drink. They gave him some water and some tea, and he was interested in eating part of a sandwich.

The roads were bad and poorly marked. It was almost completely dark. There were no significant lights along the way. The policeman riding with them helped with directions. Despite some fast driving, it took over an hour to get to Sanger's Junction. The policeman directed them straight to the town's police station, and the local officer on duty was happy to call the physician at his home number. Doctors were usually one of the first people in a town to get a telephone.

The doctor said it was easier for him to come the police station and take them to his office that was almost across the street. His wife was a nurse and would come along, too. The parents were starting to feel a little better. Gilly was sound asleep in the back seat, and he was woken up when his father and the *mushkra* carried him to the doctor's office. The two men carried the boy in a cradle of their arms and tried to minimize touching his injured arm and ankle.

"Let's take a look here and see what has happened to this young man," the doctor began. The parents gave a quick rundown of the how their son was injured, emphasizing the left foot and the danger of the nail puncture in the back of the arm.

"Well, who has taken care of him so far? Why did you have to come all the way over here this time of night," the doctor's wife, the nurse, asked.

"We can do cleaning an' bandaging OK, but we want to be sure the ankle will set straight, an' of course, the arm with the puncture wound is the most important," Amy explained.

"So let's take a look at that arm first. You have really

bandaged it up nicely."

They cut the bandages away, all the while keeping the arm elevated to lessen the chance of any more bleeding. Gilly was very cooperative. He knew this was serious. And he had just heard for the first time that he had a puncture wound. He knew what that meant.

"I need to see better in there, so I am gonna have you get up on this table and lie on your stomach, son. Go slow, and we will help you. Try not to bang anything that will start you bleeding again," said the doctor.

With help from his father and the policeman, the boy got up and lay down on his belly on the examination table, making the back of his right arm more visible. The examination lamp could shine on it.

The nurse complimented the mother on how well the arm had been cleaned, even the nasty flap of skin and the puncture wound. But just to be safe, they would use a syringe to squirt further disinfectant in the puncture would.

The doctor looked at the parents and said, "There is a chance of tetanus, of lockjaw, though we don't know for sure. Maybe we can control it, and maybe not, but we need to act fast. They have a shots you can give for lockjaw, but I don't have that medicine here. They have it over at a hospital in the state capital. We can keep the boy here just fine. He has traveled enough for now. But you need to be there first thing when they open in the morning to get a dose of that medicine for me to give him as a shot. I am gonna write you a prescription for the medicine, and I will call them at 8:00

in the morning just to be sure they understand. You oughta be able to be back here by say 9:30, and we will give him the shots.

"Right now though," the doctor continued, "we are going to give him about five stitches in that arm and maybe a couple on his face. It will hurt a bit, I gotta tell you, but, son, you are being a really good patient so far. Have you ever had stitches before? Do you know what they are?"

"No, sir. I mean yes, sir. I never had them, but I think they are like when they sew you up, with a needle and thread," Gilly answered.

The nurse explained that it was a special kind of needle and thread and that they would explain every step of the way. The stitches would make the healing go faster and leave less of a scar.

First came the stitches, six in the arm and three in different places on his face. They explained to Amy how to tell when the stitches could come out and how to take them out, though it would probably be better for a regular nurse or doctor to take them out.

Next came an examination of the foot. This really hurt once or twice, but the doctor needed to touch it and see if it was bad break or a clean break or a sprain. The examination seemed to go on for so long. Gilly was happy when it was over.

"You have a bad sprain, young man. You are not going to like this, but even after your foot quits hurting you, you may not walk on it for another week. You are going to need crutches. And about three weeks from now, you need to see another doctor to make sure that foot is healing right and maybe to take the stiches out of your arm and face. That's doctor's orders, and I am telling you in front of your folks." The doctor spoke as if he had said things like this hundreds of times before, but this time, he was taking a little personal interest in a boy with a travelling show who had had a serious accident riding two horses at once.

The doctor and his wife invited them to stay at their home for the night, where they all enjoyed a shot of whiskey, including the policeman and Gilly, "for medicinal purposes." They rose well before dawn. The mother stayed with her boy, and Woody and the policeman set off on a high-speed drive to the hospital at the state capital with the prescription from the doctor. It took time to find where prescriptions could be picked up, but the doctor had called ahead to the head pharmacist there, and he had the medication waiting.

Gilly had his tetanus shots by 10:00. He got a round of fresh bandages, and the nurse complimented Amy again on how well she had done the original cleaning and bandaging.

Before noon, the policeman had been dropped off back in his town, and the three Brewers were driving onto the lot of the new town where the show was setting up. They were met by half of the show. The circus people all stood in a big circle around the car, silent for the moment, not knowing what they would hear.

Then they saw the parents smiling as they got out of

the car. And Camie and GR were there with big hugs. Then the questions started coming. At one point, Woody had to quiet the group and along with his wife give a run down on the adventures of the night.

Only Camie and GR knew about the tetanus danger, something that they did not want to discuss in public. But the smiles on the parents' faces assured them that it had been taken care of somehow.

When Gilly was lifted out of the car, he was calm and polite. He smiled and appreciated the sympathetic looks he got and all the questions about how much it hurt. But it was not his nature to seek attention, to grandstand a situation. He tried to minimize offhandedly the danger and pain he had been through.

What he very much wanted to know was if the horses were OK, but he could not ask that yet.

The Brewers held a quick meeting to determine who would cover for Gilly in which acts and who would stay with him during various parts of the show. They all agreed he should not even watch the show or sit around in the backyard of the tent for a good while. All he needed to do was rest with his leg elevated and get better.

He was put back in Camie's *dukkering* tent, which became his ward for the next few days, or he could sit under the awning at the cookhouse, but he could not go right away around the animals. He had lots of visitors. Spangles was a regular. She cheered him up. The next day, Uncle Choctaw brought him a set of crutches fashioned from spare side poles of the bigtop with cross pieces cushioned with old canvas. Choctaw said that he had a hurt knee in the Great War, and he had an idea of how important comfortable crutches were. With a little practice, Gilly soon got the hang of walking with crutches. He just had to be careful on rough ground so that he did not trip.

Six weeks later he was riding again and in some acts. And then he did a little Roman riding. Two months from the time of the accident, he got to do it seriously for the first time when the show set up along a big road and some attraction like Roman riding would get attention and bring more people to the show. In the following seasons, he did it routinely.

Gilly never had a serious accident again for the rest of his life, but he would always remember everything about this one. It was not just about how he handled his team of horses when they were attacked or the medical care that he got.

It was about how families work in bad situations, what it is like to be in a family when things are bad, and what it is like to be safe and tended to when a person needs it.

From time to time, the long ugly scar on his arm would remind him of all that he had learned. The scar dimmed a little with the years, but it never went away. It was still with him when he died in his nineties.

17. NO DEVIL'S WORK AROUND HERE

Mr. Shaughnessy strode onto the lot where Brewer Brothers Circus was setting up for the day. He was well dressed and looked important, and he was. He was the chairman of the fundraising committee of the local Knights of Columbus in Port Cassidy. Sponsoring the circus was one of the biggest fundraising events of the year for the K. of C. Advance ticket sales had been higher than last year. He hoped everything would go well and the K. of C. would clear a lot of money. But he had a troubled look on his face, an angry, worried one.

The priest at his local parish church had given him a stern talking-to the day before, and he had already had a bad morning so far. He was looking around for some circus owner or boss to talk to when Madam Camille spotted him. She was dressed very nicely herself. She always was. She had a look that was classy but a little exotic, refined but not ordinary. Her limited gold jewelry was expensive but in the best of taste. She wore just a little bit of perfume called *Un Goût de la Vie*, which could be bought only in Canada. The way she dressed worked best for her and her business.

"Young Man, are you looking for someone? Maybe I can help you. I am Madam Camille Brewer of Brewer Brothers Circus, but you may call me Madam Camie; everybody does."

"Why, yes, ma'am. I am looking for the circus owner. I have an important message for him. By the way, my name is Rick Shaughnessy, an' I am Committee Chair of the Knights of Columbus, the organization sponsoring the circus today."

"Why, what a pleasure, Mr. Shaughnessy! We do indeed love to work under the auspices of the Knights of Columbus, an' we do so every chance we get an' in every state we show. It's so nice to meet you! An' you must be Irish with such a name. My, my, you Irish gentlemen are such community leaders, you do such important work, an' you are such fine family men. We just love working with you!" Camie knew that compliments from a well-dressed older woman, when pitched just right, could help make almost any situation better. By this time, the man was blushing brightly.

"You see, last year my niece married a nice Irish boy. Well, I call her my niece. She is really my cousin's daughter. Goodness, did we put on a nice wedding for them! I think we really confused Father Sullivan. He had never seen such a thing. The groom rode up to the church on an elephant, an' the bride came in a circus wagon pulled by white horses. We put up a small tent in back of the church for the reception, an' the circus band played for dancing. There were pony rides for the children, an' cotton candy for everybody. We all had a wonderful time. We joked that she converted to Catholic, an' he converted to circus. So far I hear that this young couple is doing fine over on another show," Camie explained.

"Well, thank you, ma'am. It is nice to hear that about the Irish. We appreciate it. An' I have an important message for the circus people that I must deliver right away," he said.

"Oh, my!" Camie replied. "That does sound important. Well, let's get right down to business. I believe I will be able to help you. But first of all, Mr. Shaughnessy, you must come over to my place for tea. We can sit down there, an' my feet are killing me. I have been on them too long this morning, tending to different business around the circus. You are Irish, so you must drink tea," she continued. Camie had picked up on the troubled look he had, the consternation on his face and how even his shoulders seemed tight and tense. She felt that if she asked him just the right questions in the right way, he would tell her a lot, and she could get to the bottom of whatever problem the man was carrying on his shoulders. "Come right this way. I believe I already have some hot water."

Before Rick Shaughnessy knew it, he was seated in a very comfortable wicker chair in Camie's *dukkering* tent, with a nice oriental rug under his feet and a very expensive-looking bone china tea set on a silver tray in front of him. Camie was pouring tea for him. It was the tea set that Camie reserved for certain occasions.

"Now, Mr. Shaughnessy--do you mind if I call you Rick?--one thing I know about K. of C. committee members is that they have tremendous responsibility. An' goodness! You are the committee chairman. I can only imagine what you must be facing the day the circus finally shows up! You have a burden right now. I can tell. An' I want to help you with it." Camie was so intuitive. She wanted to get the matter settled, and she wanted to help him feel better.

Rick did not know that he was sitting in a fortunetelling tent. Camie's husband, GR, had not put up the canvas banners yet that announced that readings were available, etc. And that was a fortunate thing.

"So, Young Man, let's get down to business. Can you tell me your message?" she asked.

"Why, that would be a good idea. This message is very important, an' I don't exactly know how to say it. We sure want the circus to go on, but we are not sure that it can," he blurted out.

"Rick, what you are saying really is important! What could possibly stop the circus after all the planning you have done? An' everything is already set up. An' there is all the money that would come in for your important work. But I bet I can help solve the problem. I have been in the business a long time, an' a good solution can almost be worked out," Camie said.

"No offense intended, ma'am, but Father McCauley, he

is the priest at St. Michael's, he called me to the rectory yesterday afternoon, an' that is very unusual."

"Well, I see," Camie interrupted gently. "A man in your position, the day before the big event, that is something! It must have been urgent."

"It was. I have never seen Father McCauley act so angry. He did not even ask me to sit down. He said the circus was off unless I could assure him that there was none of the Devil's business going on. He was almost yelling at me. He said he had heard from the bishop's office that some circus had been showing in the diocese an' that they actually had a fortuneteller with them. He said it was a sin, a sin to tell fortunes, since the power to tell fortunes comes from the Devil. Catholics can never, ever, ever have their fortune told or support fortunetelling. It would be a serious sin, no matter what the circumstances. That is what he said, almost word for word. So I have to have the circus tell me that there is no fortunetelling, none of the Devil's business going on here, or I have to cancel our sponsorship an' the circus." Rick's voice almost quivered as he spoke. He wanted the money that circus would bring in, but he could not commit the grave sin his pastor told him about.

"Well, Rick, I can tell you are an honest man, an' I believe you. But who on earth told His Excellence the Reverend Bishop such a story? I can assure you, Rick, Brewer Brothers Circus does not do the Devil's business. We are good people. We try to do good deeds. We are family people, like you. We work with people who sponsor us so they can do good charitable work. We would never do evil like that. So let me put you at ease. This circus today does not do any of the Devil's business. You have nothing to worry about. If Father McCauley likes, I will be happy to meet with him," she concluded.

Rick Shaughnessy's expression changed. There was some relief in it. He was still agitated, but some weight had been lifted. Camie excused herself briefly and told her husband GR to be sure not to put up the canvas signs for her *dukkering tan,* the fortunetelling tent. She would not be doing that today. He understood, and from the conversation she was having with the committee member, and the fancy tea set, he could tell that something important was going on.

"Rick, I am so glad we could settle that. Gracious, what a burden for you, a burden you did not need!" she said. But as she looked at him, based on her insightful nature and her years of experience, she could see that Rick was somewhat better but he was still suffering. She could see it in his eyes, in his expression, and even in the tenor of his voice. She could see so much in a person.

"Now please listen," she said. "There is still more. I have a message for you. We have to work on it. It is an important message," she said.

"What do you mean, Madam Camie?" Rick asked. "Is it a written message from somebody or what?"

"Oh, no, Rick, it is a message about you. Yes, you were worried about what Father McCauley said, but Rick, you have had something difficult, something very hard an' unpleasant happen to you, yesterday or today. I don't think it was too long ago, but it was painful. You must tell me about it. We have to get to the bottom of this," Camie insisted. She hoped she was on the track of getting him to open up, and then he could get some relief.

"Well, now that I think about it, ma'am, why yes, it was hard an' painful, an' it happened just this morning. It was awful," Rick started to explain.

"Rick, this would not have to do with your sponsorship of the circus, so there would be a charge for a business consultation with me, but I believe it would be rather valuable to you," Camie said. "Do you agree?"

"Why, yes, ma'am. You already understand that I have a big problem," Rick answered quickly.

"Were you injured or sick, something like that?" asked Camie.

"No, I am fine. I am just fine. Nothing like that," Rick said.

"Mr. Shaughnessy, you have to tell me the truth, absolutely the truth. Mr. Shaughnessy, you have not had eyes for another lady besides Mrs. Shaughnessy, have you? Or has some trashy woman had eyes for you?" Camie said, with a very serious look on her face.

"Oh, no, nothing at all like that. Nothing at all!" Rick said, defending himself.

"Thank goodness! I didn't think so, but I had to be sure. After all, you are a Catholic, an' I know that Catholics are very strict about any such thing. An' Irishmen are such fine family men. Oh, thank goodness," Camie explained.

"Well, what happened this morning was this, an' it has happened before. You see, my family has owned the sawmill in town, Shaughnessy's Mill and Lumber Company, since my grandfather started it. An' now we are really almost closed down, you know, with the bad times the country is having an' all. I have had to let everybody go, all my working boys. Nobody can afford lumber now, even if they need it. I have no customers.

"So every couple months my five foreman -- no it is really six, I have a colored foreman, too -- they get together an' come to me, an' they ask me when the mill will open again an' when they will have work. They cry about no money an' hungry families an' all their problems. An' you know right now the whole country has no money, an' everybody has problems.

"So I just couldn't take it. This has happened six or seven times, every few months. An' I lost my temper, an' I told them to get the hell out of my damn office an' they should all go to hell!" Rick explained, and he almost had tears in his eyes.

"Mr. Shaughnessy, goodness gracious! Where are you manners? You are forcing me to remind you that you are in the presence of a lady, an' I simply will not permit such language! What would your dear mother say if she heard you talking like that?" Camie lowered her voice, but spoke with a tone of righteous indignation.

"Oh, gee, beggin' your pardon, ma'am. I just wasn't

thinkin'. It put me under a strain. I just couldn't take it," rationalized Rick.

Camie paused, looked right in his eyes, gave him time to think and herself time to think, too.

"Rick, you are a better man than that, a far better man! If you think it was something you couldn't take, just try to imagine, Rick, what it was like for them. They came to you with their hat in their hand, begging, really, because like you, they have families to look after, an' they need hope. They need to know if they have a future in your town.

"Yes, we are all sufferin' in this country. Times are terrible. An' we have to help each other; we have to reach out a hand, give some encouragement. You are a leader, you are a boss, an' that is your job. You have to be a leader in good times an' a leader in bad times. What you said to them was not the real you, Rick. You have too much goodness in you," explained Madam Camie.

"Not quite sure what you mean, ma'am. You mean I shouldn't have kicked them out? I know I shouldn't swear at them like that," Rick said.

"This isn't about the swearing. It is about your future an' their future an' the future of your town, Port Cassidy. You have to think ahead, way ahead," Camie explained. Somehow she sounded motherly and businesslike at the same time.

"My boy, you see one day, an' nobody knows when it will be, these terrible hard times will end. Our great country has had hard times before, an' there was even a terrible war on our own soil, but we are strong, an' better times did come back. It takes time, but we will have a better tomorrow, an' that is what I want you to think about.

"I wasn't born in America. My mother an' father brought me here when I was a child, an' the United States is my home now, an' I love it. An' I bet you love the USA, too. An' you have to do somethin', somethin' that will build the future of our great country, an' of your own town," said Camie. As she said this, her mind was sorting through various ideas, ideas that could help this suffering man and the suffering people who had worked for him.

"Please explain to me what you mean. I can't save this town. I can't even save the mill!" Rick said.

"Rick, you are right. You can't, at least not right now. But here are some ideas about what you could do. I will suggest them, an' you will decide if you like them an' how to make them better.

"As hard as it might be, Rick, you need to ask your foremen, including the colored one, back to your office. Send a message to them tomorrow or the next day so that they all come back at the same time.

"Then you have to be completely honest with them, completely truthful. That is the only way. You have to tell them how bad the situation is. You have to say that you do not know when it will get better. Tell them that you keep watchin' an' waitin', but you know that one day you will need them again, even if you cannot tell them when that day will be. Nobody can. But one day, you will want them to come back to work. An' you hope they will be there to take their old jobs again. You hope it is soon, but nobody knows. Nobody knows, not the government, not anybody.

"An' you would not want to start all over again, hiring new people who don't know the work. You want to have these same good boys when the time comes, wouldn't you? Would you want to get all new people an' have them learn how to do the mill jobs from start?"

"Oh, no, Madam Camie, I...well...that would be awful. I couldn't do that. I need these men 'cause they know how to do the work. I gotta have 'em!" said Rick.

"Oh, I thought they were important to you, Rick," Camie replied.

"An', Rick, you see, it is not enough for just your six foremen to hear that one day times will get better an' one day you will need them again. You have to find a way for their families to understand, for the whole town to understand. The Shaughnessys are part of this town now, an' they always will be," Camie continued her explanation.

"Yes, but, Madam Camie, how could I do that?" Rick asked. He was interested but confused.

"Well, Rick, here is one way you could. But you know the town, an' you will know if it will be a good way or not. Let's see. You could start in the meetin' with your foremen. You could tell them the truth, kind of like I suggested just now. You are a smart boy, an' you will know how to do that. Nobody knows when this

Depression will end, but someday it will, an' you will need them when it does. You will have jobs for them. Then mention that you think it is very important for all the mill hands to come together so you an' the foremen will tell them what is going on. No, there are no jobs now, but someday there will be, even if we do not know when, maybe not for years. You an' the foremen want to tell them this directly. They deserve to know.

"An' you want to tell them in a special way. It will be at the First Annual Shaughnessy Mill picnic. All the mill hands are invited along with their wives an' children, or their girlfriends if they are not yet married. Rick, you should start by givin' them a pig or two pigs for them to butcher an' barbecue. Would some of your boys know how to do that?" Camie asked.

"Oh, yes ma'am. They sure would, an' very well, too," Rick answered.

"Let the foremen organize it. Your probably have plenty of old wood around the mill for them to roast the pigs with. And then they can bring all the trimmings, like rice an' corn bread, greens, watermelon an' whatever. I saw some beautiful roasting ears in a field as we came into town. Could the foreman organize everything, even set the date, an' so on? If you can, you need to let them handle this, as much of it as possible. Let them see that they can still do work an' be worthwhile. Are your foremen good enough for that?" Camie asked.

"They sure are! I have excellent foremen. They could put together a great picnic, an' if I gave pigs, they would be glad to do it, to bring in everythin' else. Their wives are fine ladies, too. They would do great cookin'. An' the kids could swim in the coolin' tank, too. People could have fun!" Rick was getting the idea.

"How would it be with the colored foreman an' the boys who work under him? Will they have to stay separate? Will there be some kind of problem?" Camie asked.

"No, ma'am. Our people know how to get along together. Everybody knows everybody, an' the colored folks will stay in their place over by the parkin' lot. They will have a good time an' say 'hi' an' all, an' there won't be any problem," he said.

"Are some of your hands Catholic, too, Mr. Shaughnessy?" Camie asked.

'Why, yes, a lot of my boys are. Some go to mass, too," Rick added.

"Then you might want to invite Father McCauly, too. Do you think he would come? It would help the town know that you an' your family are here for good. When the Depression ends, or even sooner if you can, you will get that mill goin' again, even if it is only half open. You will give as many jobs as you can," Camie added.

"I see," said Rick.

"Are there some Protestant boys, too?" Camie asked.

"Sure, more than half of them," Rick added.

"Then maybe you can get a Baptist preacher, or Methodist, or whatever, to come with his missus, too. It is not just for Catholics. An' if there is a newspaper or a radio station, get a reporter. What do you think?" Camie asked.

"I am startin' to see, but we have never done anythin' like this, not in this town," Rick said.

"Mr. Shaughnessy, we have never had times like we have now. We have to do different things," Camie countered.

Their conversation continued. Camie mentioned the possibility of the mayor coming, the doctor and dentist and the schoolteachers. Rick explained that there was no doctor or dentist, and he asked why the schoolteachers should be invited.

"Because they teach your children, Rick," Camie replied.

"Oh, of course," Rick answered. Now Rick was getting a clear idea of what he wanted to do and how he would do it. He said he wanted a little band to come, and some of the players were among the mill hands. He became very relieved and excited. He came up with more ideas. He was ready to do it. He was talking very rapidly as he laid out more of the plan, a plan that had become his. His demeanor had changed completely. The beaten-down man who came to Madam Camille's *dukkering* tent was now smiling and animated and in high spirits. The metamorphosis in him from how he was thirty minutes before was hard to believe. Inside, Camille was very pleased, too, though this was not quite yet the time to show it.

Camille was ready for the conclusion, and the conclusion was perhaps the most important part of an encounter with a client.

"Rick, I am so glad we had this talk. You are so good for this town. You have other things to do now, an' so do I. I can tell you are a man of faith who believes in the future. So, my new friend, here is what you must do. Listen closely an' see if you agree.

"Give me ten dollars as payment for this consultation. You may come back if you need to. I would always welcome seeing you. You are such a lovely man, a truly lovely man.

"You need to tell Mrs. Shaughnessy what you plan to do. Tell her the whole story, an' get her ideas. You have to have her advice an' her help. You will be doin' a job that needs a woman's ideas an' insight, Rick.

"Then of course there is explainin' all this to your fine foremen, so that they can get goin' on it, an' they will really be doin' most of the work, them an' their wives.

"Of course, you can expect some difficulties an' some setbacks in doing all this, but you are not a quitter, Rick. That is very clear. An' finally, Rick, when you go to mass on Sunday with your family, you should put three dollars more in the collection basket than you usually do. Let it be a sign of the goodness in your heart an' in your soul.

"Rick, you are an honest an' truthful man. I am sure you can do all this, but tell me if you really will," Camie requested.

"Why of course, Madam Camie, I sure can," he said as he reached for a couple five-dollar bills in his wallet.

"That is wonderful, Rick," she said as she took the money. An' next year, please come by an' tell me how it all went. Your leadership will make the difference," she concluded.

Rick Shaughnessy left with a smile on his face and a spring in his step. He could hardly wait to tell his wife. Before he left the circus grounds, he told three of his fellow K. of C. committee members that he had had a wonderful conversation with Madam Camie and that they should talk to her, too. She was a very kind woman with a lot of wisdom. And she even understood business.

Camie was busy the rest of the day. One after another, members of the Knights of Columbus or their wives consulted with her. There were seven or eight altogether, and she hardly had a chance to eat. She tried to explain to GR what was going on, but she did not quite know herself. Apparently, her reputation for wisdom and helpfulness had grown as the day went on. There was a frequent call for more tea in her tent, and the fine tea set got a real workout. The day was really quite lucrative for her.

And the next Sunday after mass, Father McCauley was very puzzled. He recounted the money in the collection baskets three times. He could not come up with any explanation of why all of a sudden there was twenty-four dollars more than usual.

18. ICE, HAY, GRAIN, AND GAS

I f a circus ran out of ice, there would be no snow cones to sell, and some milk and meat might spoil. Yet the show would go on. Brewer Brothers had a large icebox in the cookhouse, and a few folks on the show had smaller iceboxes. These were literally "iceboxes," insulated chests with room for twenty-five or fifty pounds of ice and some shelves for a couple quart milk bottles and some beef or chicken.

If a circus ran out of hay and grain, it could go for a day or two without animal feed if there was good grass on the lots where the circus was showing. The horses could get by temporarily by grazing on the grass, but especially the elephants wanted more than what they could find just by grazing on the circus lot. They would have to have hay or grain or both within a day or two.

If a circus ran out of gasoline, it couldn't move. It couldn't even move to a place where it could get gas.

Getting a gas tanker to come on the circus lot and fill all the vehicles was the most convenient way to resupply gasoline. Usually, with a tanker there was a lower bulk gas price with only one total bill to pay. The tankers of the time were small four-wheeled affairs, somewhat like heating oil trucks of a later day.

Somebody on the show had to tell the man driving the tanker which vehicles needed gas, monitor the gauge on the tanker, and pay the driver the grand total. This was a job that Gilly often did on horseback, leading the tanker driver around and keeping a list of how many gallons went to each vehicle. So Gilly was very surprised when a tank truck pulled on the lot with the name Esso on the side, since he was expecting Sawyer Oil, and then he saw that the driver was a girl with long dark braids who looked about fifteen years old.

"Who are you, an' what are you doing here?" he asked her.

"I am Cindy Sawyer, an' I am here to deliver gasoline to the circus," she replied, looking at him intently.

"Well, we ordered gas from Sawyer Oil Company this morning, an' you don't look old enough to drive, let alone to drive a tanker!" Gilly replied.

"Oh, that!" she answered. "Our truck is in the shop so we had to borrow Mr. Burrows' Esso truck for the morning, but the price is all the same. An' I am old enough to drive. I am nearly sixteen. The police chief is a friend of my dad's, an' he says that as long as I stay in town an' drive real slow an' careful an' only in daylight, there should be no problem. You see, my mother is real sick, an' Daddy has to stay home with her a lot," Cindy explained.

Gilly couldn't help but notice her big brown eyes and her long dark braids. He also noticed a big dog, a shepherd or police dog, on the seat beside her, and the dog was keeping a close eye on him. "Are you sure about all this? Can you drive a tanker around through a bunch of trucks an' cars, and can you handle the hose to put the gas in?"

"I been doin' that since I can't remember when. I can handle a hose real good. Just don't let me see anybody smokin' while I do it. I'd have to shut it down, an' I will," she answered.

The tone of her voice conveyed that she knew what she was doing, and she would be in charge of the operation, or at least the selling part of the operation. She was a little nervous, but she definitely had a kind of spunk to her, and Gilly knew that kids in families did what they had to do for the family to make a living. He wanted to get this girl to smile and maybe tell her a joke, but this was a business deal.

"Well, Miss, you can follow me on my horse, an' I will tell you which truck or car to go to an' keep a record of how much goes in each one, an' then I will take you to the office an' we will count out the money to pay you. That is the way we do this. By the way, my name is Gilly, Gilly Brewer. Is your dog OK? I don't like how he looks at me," he told her.

"That will be just fine. Nice to meet you, Mr. Brewer.

Don't worry about my dog. If you don't come in this cab, he will be OK. Let's get started. But don't you need a saddle on that horse?" she asked.

"No, no, Chico, that's his name, he's very well broke an' rides fine without a saddle. An' on horseback it is faster to get around with you than if I am walkin'."

Gilly rode to the first truck to be filled, and she followed with the tanker. After two trucks, however, he asked her to fill two empty jerry cans of twenty gallons each. He wrote down the reading on the gauge before she began filling the cans. This was a strategy his father had taught him to use to confirm the accuracy of the dispensing gauge on the tanker. Usually the reading for the two jerry cans came out very close to forty gallons, twenty gallons each, maybe just a little below or above, not enough to make a real difference in the overall reading and cost.

Today's reading was different. He did the arithmetic quickly. When the two cans were full, the reading came out to forty-six gallons. He stood there for a minute or so, his horse standing beside him. This was a fifteen-percent difference and could not be seen as an accidental overcharge. The jerry cans could hold only forty gallons.

"Miss, I have to tell you something. Look at this. Look at what I just did. You saw me write down the gauge number when we filled the cans, didn't you? Your gauge is way off. It is fifteen percent too high. I have to see if we can continue to buy your gas. Stay here. I will talk to my uncle over there."

Cindy was blushing deeply. She stared at the numbers Gilly had written down. She could not do the arithmetic in her head as fast as he could, but it was clear that she was overcharging, or rather that the gauge was overcharging. This was something she had never come up against before. She tried to think of what she should do besides be so embarrassed. It was hard to look at Gilly. All she could do was mumble, "I'm sorry."

Gilly asked Cindy to wait in the tank truck for a moment while he rode off. His Uncle Lucky was not far away. He hopped down from the horse to talk. It took only a minute to explain the problem. It would be difficult or impossible to get to the next town without more gas.

He and his uncle wanted a third Brewer to weigh in. They went to the ticket office. Aunt Tillie listened to them, and then the three sat there silently for a moment. Lucky asked if the girl seemed basically honest and if she was surprised and ashamed at the reading. Gilly explained that she was seemed sincerely surprised and ashamed, really ashamed. Lucky asked if under the circumstances they could take the risk of just filling all the vehicles and then going with the girl to her family office to make the adjustment with her father. After all, it was not as if it was their own company tank truck. And the show really needed gas to get to the next town. The three of them then went to the tanker where the girl was waiting, her gaze down and her fingers nervously tapping the steering wheel. It seemed better for Tillie to speak first. She was very gentle with the girl but clear at the same time. She told the girl what the Brewers proposed to do.

"Oh, ma'am, we definitely need the money from sellin' this gas today. An' I am so sorry that the gauge is not right. I can't believe that Mr. Burrows' truck had a bad gauge. I just don't understand. I am so sorry." Cindy was near tears. She wanted to be businesslike but didn't quite know how.

"Well, young lady, will you sign the list there where it shows that with the two twenty-gallon jerry cans the gauge registered as forty-six gallons, an' then again when you fill each truck. Will your father accept this at your word? Will he believe what happened?" Tillie asked.

"Nothing like this has ever happened before. It is so terrible. I will have to explain to him. He trusts me. I am so sorry!" Cindy explained.

"Miss Sawyer, we just want to do what is right. We want to pay the right price. That is all. We will go with you to your father's office. We will sit together. We will count out the correct money together. How does that sound?"

"Oh, Ms. Brewer, will you come? Daddy is doing the best he can. Mama is quite sick. We can't afford anybody to take care of her. We don't know what will happen. I have to help out all I can. These are hard times for our family right now. Our office is just the front porch of our house."

"OK, so just go then with Gilly to fill up the trucks, sign each time, an' then we will go to your house. We have to get back before the matinee show this afternoon. Please hurry."

Gilly and the girl continued around the lot as fast as they could, writing down the gauge reading and signing at each vehicle. He wished that the overcharging had never happened because he really liked this girl. He stared at her surreptitiously from time to time and kept noticing things that made her more and more attractive. There was a problem involved so he didn't want to be too friendly, just businesslike. His eyes followed her. He noticed how well she handled the hose, even when it seemed pretty heavy for somebody her size. He liked it when a girl was capable and not just all "frills and bows." He wanted to say something, but no ideas came to mind. Under other circumstances it would have been easy for him to start a conversation. Finally he just blurted out that he liked her long braids. She smiled at him for just an instant and then added that her grandmother was Ojibwa.

"What is Ojibwa?" Gilly asked.

"Oh, the Ojibwas are an Indian tribe," she answered.

He felt foolish and thought it best to get back to business. He could almost calculate in his head what the total due would be. He went to the office and showed the list to his aunt so she could count out the money, subtracting fifteen percent from what the total would have been because of the bad gauge. Tillie stashed the *vonger* discreetly in her bosom, and they left to go to the tanker truck. Gilly tied up his horse back at the horse truck and stepped up on the left running board of the tanker to ride to her house, knowing it was better not to get inside with the girl's dog.

Lucky and Tillie followed in a car.

Cindy drove the truck into the back yard behind the house. They entered through the back door. The curtains were drawn, and the rooms were dark. The girl called to her father, and he came out from one of the side rooms.

"Hi, baby, how are you? How did it go? Is everything OK? Who are these people?" The questions from her father rolled out fast.

"Daddy, I have to explain. They are here to pay us. But there was a mistake. Let me explain. The circus people have been very nice. I made the sale. This boy here could not have been nicer," the girl blurted out.

They all continued out to the front porch. The father invited them to sit down. "Oh, what kind of mistake? Baby, I am sure you did the right thing," the father said.

"Mr. Sawyer, let me help explain," Tillie spoke first. "Your daughter has acted very properly, and we are here to pay you the correct amount. She said you were using a borrowed tanker that was not your own truck. The problem was, and she didn't even know this herself, that the Esso truck has a bad gauge. We tested it with two twenty-gallon jerry cans, and you can see right here where your daughter signed what the gauge said. It was overcharging by fifteen percent.

"And Mr. Sawyer, if you like, we will go out in your backyard right now an' fill a jerry can again. Do you want to do that?" Tillie asked. She was polite but businesslike and not threatening.

"Baby, is that how the gauge measured on Mr. Burrows' Esso truck? Was it fifteen percent over? Kind of like it would charge for 115 gallons for 100 gallons?"

"Yes, Daddy, it really was. It was terrible. After that I watched the gauge at every stop. The circus people are right, Daddy. I think we should take the money as they figured it an' tell Mr. Burrows to fix his gauge. Is it all right that I went ahead an' filled the other trucks? I didn't know what else to do," the girl asked.

"An' I have to tell you, this boy here, Gilly Brewer is his name, he was a perfect gentlemen about it all. He didn't yell at me or anything. He was calm and polite and found a solution. So thank you, Mr. Brewer," Cindy looked at Gilly as she said this. It was a little confusing, since there were really two Mr. Brewers present, but she was clearly meaning the younger one. Gilly felt flattered that she noticed how he acted. Maybe she took some notice of him after all. That would be nice.

"Yes, baby. I see why you look worried. It is OK that you went ahead an' filled the trucks. Honey, you did a good job, an' it wasn't easy. Come here. I need to hug you. You did a grownup's work, an' you are only fifteen. Your mama would be proud of you." The man said.

"How is Mama?" Cindy asked.

"Pretty good, just like you left her. But we have been talking about you, honey," her father answered.

But the conversation with the Brewers started again,

the money was counted out, and Woody and Tillie prepared to leave. Gilly kept staring at Cindy, trying not to be caught at it but definitely staring anyway.

When the money was all counted out and verified with a second count, her father asked her to come back in the house so they could "talk some business" a bit. He asked if Gilly could stay for just a few minutes more. Gilly did not know what was going on, but he was happy to wait.

Cindy went back into the house with her father to the kitchen in the back of the house. "Your mother an' I are a little worried about you, honey," her father said.

"What do you mean, Daddy? I am fine," she answered.

"Well, you have been working an' working all summer long. If you aren't driving the truck, you are here looking after your mama. An' she and I talked about that, an' we just don't feel right about that," he said.

"But, Daddy, I am happy to do all I can. These are hard times, with Mama bein' sick an' all. An' my little sister an' brother, they are too young to do much yet," she replied.

"I know, darlin', but it is just not right. A young girl your age, you should be havin' some fun in the summertime. You are a pretty young lady, an' I am not sayin' that just 'cause you're my daughter. It's just true. You just can't work an' work an' work. You will have plenty of time to work when you get older. An' ever since you quit seein' Hub Markham's oldest boy, why you haven't been goin' out at all, not even hardly with some of the girls you are good friends with, an' it's been months and months," he added.

"Your Aunt Lucy came over today, an' she said they are havin' a dance down at the school again tonight, but it's somethin' kinda new. She said it is gonna be a 'ladies' choice' dance. That means the girl asks the boy," he said.

"Really, Daddy? But what if the boy says no?"

"Well, honey, that is just a chance the girl has to take. Lord knows the boys get shot down sometimes. So turnabout is fair play, as they say," he answered.

"But I don't know of any boy I wanna ask to such a dance. An' if I did an' he said no, then he would tell, an' everybody in town would know about it. A lot of girls always tell the other girls if they turn a guy down for a dance or somethin'," she explained.

"Cindy, your mama an' I would really like to see you go out an' have some fun. An' did you notice that there is a very nice boy sitting on our front porch. You yourself said he was a perfect gentleman, even in a hard business situation. I looked at him, too. He is very mannerable, the kind of boy I would let my daughter go out with. An' he couldn't ever tell the other boys in town that he said no. He doesn't even know them," her father continued.

"Go ahead, honey. Take a chance on this 'ladies' choice' dance. You got nothin' to lose, an' you might have some fun. It would be fine with your mother and me," the father said.

Her father always wanted the best for her, and he had

just come as close to pushing her as he ever did. She thought about it for a moment. Her father's blessing meant a lot to her.

"OK, Daddy, I will try. I have never asked a boy to a dance before, but I think I can do it. But don't tell anybody if he says no, promise?" she asked.

"Of course, darlin', I promise. I would never tell anybody," her father said.

She slowly rose and went to the front porch. Her throat was a little dry, and she hesitated for a second and then went on.

"Uh, Mr. Brewer, Gilly, thank you for waiting," she said.

"My pleasure, ma'am. Do you have some business you would like to discuss?" he asked.

"No, not really. It is something else, not about business," she said, trying to gather courage.

"What could that be, ma'am, Cindy?" he asked.

"Well, Mr. Brewer, Gilly, I want to ask you something."

"What's that, Cindy?" he replied, warming to her now that business was over.

"Well, we have a dance down at the school every month all summer long. What I am sayin' is that tonight it is the new 'ladies' choice' dance."

"What does that mean, Cindy?" Gilly asked.

"It means that the girl asks the boy," she replied.

"What? Gee, I never heard of that. Oh, does that mean that you are askin' me right now?" he asked.

"Yes, I am askin', if you would like to," she said, a little hesitantly.

"Would it be OK with your father? He seems like a very nice man," he said.

"No, it would be fine with Daddy. He even said he likes you," Cindy replied.

"Well, gee, I would like to," Gilly said. "I can't drive a car after dark. I would have to come get you on my horse. Would that be OK?" He asked.

"Oh, that would be fine. I can ride. An' it's not very far," she said.

"Could you come after your show tonight? You don't even have to dance. I just want to show you that we are good people in this town, an' you mustn't get the wrong idea."

"Why, that is mighty nice of you, Miss Sawyer, Cindy. Would 9:30 be too late? An' you can ride on the back of my horse. Like I said, my folks don't want me to drive after dark. But I do know how to dance. I dance pretty good." Inwardly, Gilly felt a little miffed. He was a Gypsy, and of course there hardly ever was a Gypsy who was not a good dancer. But he couldn't say this to her. He just smiled.

"Oh, that would be just perfect. I am used to ridin' horses. It is just one of our dances we have every month. We have a lot of fun. I will be right here on the porch waitin' for you at 9:30," she said.

Gilly was excited. He had gone out with some *Gaudja* girls before from school, and he was pretty sure his folks would let him go to the dance with this one. When he got back to the lot, he caught his two parents together and decided he'd better ask early so that the arrangements could be made in time.

Woody had a big smile when he heard the news. "Why sure, Son. You are sure old enough to decide if you want to go with a girl to a dance, either a *Gaudja* girl or a *Romanichal.* Now, you have to get somebody to do the chores you would usually do after the night show. That is your responsibility to line up somebody. An' your mother an' I insist on two things: no drinkin' and no fightin'."

Amy broke in, "Yes, even if the *Gaudja* boys, the town boys, are *cousseyin'*, drinkin', don't touch their alcohol. You could get in all kinds of trouble, an' we could, too. An' no *chingerin'.* No fightin'. You know how there are some people who just love to cause trouble. An' you know that the *muskras* always side with the *gava fokie,* the town people. The police side with them, the people they know in the town, an' not with us.

"Your aunt an' uncle met this *raklie*, an' they *pookered* us that she seemed *kushti*, they said she was nice, an' her *dadus*, too, a nice girl with a nice father. She has *bora rinkna yocks*, big pretty eyes!" Amy added.

"Well, my darling, maybe our son hasn't just noticed that she had big beautiful eyes!" Woody quipped.

"Honey, you shouldn't talk like that. You'll embarrass

him," Amy said.

"Why not, darling? He is a healthy young man. An' we know he is not blind!" Woody said. "An' she has pretty long braids, too, like some *Romanichals*."

"*Ava, Dadus*, her *bora dias* was *Veshna*," Gilly said. Yes, Dad, her grandmother was Indian, Ojibwa Indian.

Gilly asked his sister, a cousin, and one of the working men to handle his usual work after the night show. Of course, they had to know why. He had to tell them. Soon the news was all over the lot. He didn't like being the center of attention, but he was going to go to the square dance with this girl.

There was so much advice for him about what to wear, a lot of it obvious. His mother, his sister, his aunt, his cousins were all on hand. Yes, he had every intention to wash and shave and wear a clean shirt and comb his hair. Then the discussions became serious. Should he wear a cowboy hat or not? Many men coming to the show in this town had worn cowboy hats, so locally it was the style. Should he wear a neckerchief to look a little dressier, and should it be red or blue? Should his boots have a riding heel or a walking heel? Where could he get a corsage to give her? Didn't *Gaudjas* do that? The trailer was fairly bursting with advice givers until they moved out under the awning.

Over a two- or three-hour period, certain consensuses were reached. Yes, wear a hat, and if he saw that none of the other boys had hats on, he could just leave it tied to the horn of the saddle. Take along a blue and a red neckerchief in his pocket, and then ask the girl or see what the other guys were doing. Be sure not to tie it tight and to put the knotted part to the side, since that is how boys wore them, and not in the middle, since that is how girls wore them. Use Brylcreme on his hair, but just enough to make it shiny and keep it in place, not enough for it so smell like Brylcreme. It was better to wear boots with the shorter walking heel so that he could dance well in them. He was a good rider, and there was no danger of his foot sliding through the stirrup, so no need for the higher riding heel. But they had to be nice boots and real clean. It was just a monthly square dance so he didn't have to bring flowers.

He should put a nice saddle on Chico, but not that silver one, since that would be too showy. And the saddle and saddle pad should extend far enough behind the seat for a girl to sit sideways behind him and put her arms around him to hold on. There was no question about it. She would not ride astride when she was wearing a dress. This was the part where his sister and female cousins got all excited. Yes, she would have to hold on to him or she could fall off, but she would want to hold on to him anyway since they would be holding each other if there were any slow dances between the square dances. There were lots of giggles. Inevitably, the question rose if he was going to kiss her. At his point, Gilly just put on a little smile and stared at the girls, as if to say, "Do you think I am gonna tell you?"

They all wanted to know what the girl was like and what her name was and so on. Gilly was very gentlemanly at this point. He threw them a few details but was a little evasive beyond that. Cindy was a very nice girl who was smart and could handle business. She had long dark braids down her back. Her grandmother was Indian. She had a big dog that sat in the cab of the truck to protect her. She could handle the tanker hose very well, and she could drive in the daytime. She was in high school and almost sixteen years old. Of course what they wanted to know was what her dress was like and if she was pretty. Gilly honestly didn't remember details about her dress, but yes, she was cute, and he liked her.

With his mother's help, he had his clothes all laid out so that he could clean himself up and do a quick change as soon as the show ended, or even before it ended. His parents told him to have a good time, and they tucked an extra dollar bill in his shirt pocket. He was on Chico and riding to the girl's house before the crowd was coming out of the tent.

He didn't want Chico to run on the slippery pavement, but he went at a pretty good pace. It was a bit harder to find her house because the little town looked different at night. Then there she was, sitting on the front porch, smiling. He rode up and got off Chico. Her father came out and said hello and that they should be home before midnight. She looked very different from the girl driving the tanker. She wore a pretty lacy dress, the style worn at square dances. She had ribbons in her hair. She wore just a little makeup. There was no way to tell that she was a girl who could conduct business for her family.

"If you like, I can help you up on the back of the saddle first, and then I can get on throwin' my leg over

Chico's neck. Or would you rather than I get on first and then let you grab my arm to help you jump up?"

"Well, you are very polite, but if you get on first, you can give me your arm and take your foot out of the left stirrup, I can put my foot in it and swing up pretty well," she said.

Obviously she knew her way around horses, and this was not the first time she had ridden in a dress behind somebody. Gilly went more slowly now that she was on the back of the horse. "It is a good night for a dance," she said.

"Yes, I think it is, Cindy," he replied. "Will there be a good place I can tie my horse?"

"Sure, Mr. Buckley, he's the school janitor and watchman, well, he will be by the side door, and there is a railing there you can tie to. Some of the kids are coming on a wagon like a hayride, and that is where they will tie up," she explained.

The dance was in full swing by the time they arrived. They had to wait till a group of four couples could be formed so that they could join in. Some people made much of how square dance steps changed from one region to another or even one part of a state to another, but Gilly could see what the steps were, and the caller gave out good directions that were easy enough to follow. He also noticed the band, especially the three fiddle players. They were good, and he wanted to go closer and watch them before the evening was over.

It wasn't long before he and Cindy joined three other couples to complete a group, and they could join in.

Cindy said he was a good dancer, and Gilly returned the compliment. After about a half hour, the band took a break, and he asked if they could walk over and look at the fiddles. Cindy said, "Sure we can. I know two of the fiddle players."

Cindy took him over and introduced Gilly to a couple of the musicians taking their break. They gladly offered him a violin to look at.

Gilly was examining it and held it up under his chin to get a feel for it.

"Do you know how to play?" one of the fiddlers asked.

"Yes, Sir, I play pretty good, but every fiddle feels a little different. Do you mind if I borrow your bow just a bit?"

"Not at all. I got an extra fiddle here. How would you like to join in?" he asked.

Gilly looked at Cindy, and she had a big smile on her face.

"Well, it would be just great to join in for a couple songs, but I want to dance with this young lady, too," he replied.

"Oh, I've known Cindy for a long time, an' maybe she won't mind. Why don't you warm up a bit? When the caller comes back, we will be doing 'Red River Valley.' Have you heard of that one?"

"Why, sure. That's a pretty song. I know it," he said.

It was the first time he had ever played just spontaneously like that with a band he did not know, but it felt very good. It was completely enjoyable. He did not play lead fiddle. He just followed along.

He kept looking at Cindy to see if she liked to have him playing or if she was about to start dancing with some other guy. She was smiling back at him and clapping her hands to the rhythm.

The second song, "Orange Blossom Special," was faster and harder. Then the lead decided to do another round of the last verse and do it even faster. Gilly could mostly keep up till almost the very end. At that point, he just had to nod his head and move the bow as if he were playing, but he did not want to play off key and mess up what was really a fine rendition by the band. At the end of the piece, he thanked the fiddler and returned the instrument and said how much he liked playing with them.

"Come back any time, mister. We can always use another good fiddle player," the lead told him.

But it was time to get back and dance with Cindy. "I didn't know you could play a fiddle," she exclaimed. "An' you seem to ride real good, too!"

"Gee, thanks," he replied. "An' you are good at handling a tanker. I would sure hire you if I was in that business!"

At the next break, she introduced her to some of his friends. They were very polite, and so was he. They were all curious about where he was from and how Cindy met him. He had always been taught by his family that one good way to handle such questions was to give simple answers and then to ask questions about the town people.

"Oh, we bought gas from the Sawyers, an' that is how we met. Are all of you from here or where? Do you have these dances all the time? This seems like such a nice city." And so the local boys and girls were all talking at once, and he was off the hook. He could just smile and nod. He didn't have to tell them anything about being with the circus and certainly not about his family background.

It was after 11:00, and the dance was winding down. "Cindy, tell me when you would like to leave. Your dad said we needed to be home by 12:00. We could just walk back to your house. I could just lead Chico," he said.

"We could do just one or two more dances an' then leave. That should give us enough time," she said.

At 11:30, they bowed out of their group of four couples. Groups were already reforming, rounding up four couples, as other dancers left. Gilly and Cindy left through the side door. It was a pleasant walk home. He held hands with her, keeping Chico's reins in his other hand. Chico followed behind them. The streets were very quiet. Cindy assured him it was perfectly safe. He told her that he had a very good impression of the town. They stopped a half block from her house at a dimly lit spot. He hooked the reins of the horse over a picket fence. Her father might be waiting on the front porch or have left the front porch light on. Her dog might be there, too.

She faced him and took a step toward him, putting an

arm on his shoulder. "I was afraid that after what happened this morning you would say no. You would not want to come a the dance with me, but I am sure glad you did."

"I am sure glad you asked me, Cindy," he said, smiling back at her. He put his hand on her waist, the same place it had been during many of the dances. There was a little more conversation; then, it became pretty spontaneous when they both came together to kiss. It had been quite some time since Gilly had kissed a girl, and maybe it had been some time since she had been kissed, too.

Sometimes Gilly thought about who he was and what kind of girl he would marry and what that would mean. But right now, his only thought was about kissing this *Gaudja* girl right then and there, in this dimly lit place, after playing the fiddle and dancing with her. That was all that was on his mind. The kissing didn't last very long, and then she said, "Gilly, I need to get home." And they headed on toward her house.

"Would you send me a letter some time?" she asked. "Do you know my address?"

"Of course. It's Miss Cindy Sawyer, 17 Sycamore Street, Coffeyville, Kansas, United States of America. It's easy."

"Oh, you don't have to put 'United States of America!'" she said.

"I know, but I wouldn't want it to get lost!" he smiled back.

"But my real name is different. It is not really Cindy," she said.

"Oh, that is good to know. What is it?" he asked.

"Well, I never let anybody but a teacher maybe call me by it, and maybe you are supposed to have it on a letter. I don't know. But it is really Cinderella," she said.

He was surprised, but he had enough diplomacy to say, "Oh, I always thought that was a very nice name. I like it!" he smiled at her.

"An' I have to tell you that Gilly is not my real name either," he continued.

"Oh, my goodness! Who are you then? What is it?" she asked.

"OK, but don't call me by it. Just use it on a letter. My real name is Gilderoy. I am named after my grandfather and his father," he explained.

"Well, I never heard of that name before, but I like it. It sounds good, like a gentleman's name," she said.

"Will you send me an answer when I write you a letter?" he asked.

"Sure," she said. "I'll write you, but what is the address for a circus?"

"It will be Brewer Brothers Circus, General Delivery, with the name of the town. In the letter I send I will give you the name of a town we will be playing in two weeks later."

"I hope your circus comes back to our town soon. If there is not another dance, maybe we could go to the picture show or something."

"Or maybe this time you could come to the show," he replied.

They were at her front porch now, and it was really time for him to go. He started to lean down for a good-bye kiss, but there was an interruption when Chico started eating the flowers planted by the railing.

"Chico, stop it! You can't be that hungry!" he told the horse as he pulled on the reins. Cindy just laughed.

"Oh, that is OK. The flowers will grow back," she said.

Then he got on Chico. Cindy came up to the horse, and he bent down again for the goodbye kiss.

In some ways it would really be great to live in one town and have a regular girlfriend and know when all the dances were and all that. It was plain to see that there were good things about the *Gaudja* way of life, too, even if the Depression was going on. He understood this from living in one place and going to a school six or seven months a year. He had *Gaudja* kids who were friends. Some of them he had known for years. He had learned to pass in and out of the larger world, the *Gaudja* world, pretty easily. Maybe that was because he knew he could always go back to his own world, to who he really was, a circus Gypsy.

He got back to the circus lot and unsaddled Chico and fed him. He tried to go to bed quietly though he knew his parents might be awake listening to be sure he got home safely. The next morning his mother saw lipstick on his shirt collar but said nothing. She just smiled and would wash it out. There was no denying it. Her son was growing up. She would have to start letting him go. Gypsy mothers nearly die when they have to let go of their children. It is one of the biggest struggles of their lives. Some of them never manage to do it.

What Gilly's little sister Mattie noticed was the smear of lipstick on his neck. *"Maw pukker* me no *hookabin,"* she chided him. *"Mandi gins* you *choomed dova raklie!* Hehe. Don't tell me no lie. I know you kissed that girl!"

He looked at his sister confusedly. She took her finger and rubbed his neck to get a sample of the lipstick. She showed it to him, with a wicked gleam in her eye.

"I am gonna tell everybody!" Mattie giggled.

"No, you are not! 'Cause don't forget, Sis. I got some real secrets on you, too!" he chided right back.

"Uh oh. I forgot. Oh, please, Bub, don't tell!"

"Guess we better both *kliven* our *muis*! Keep our mouth shut. Deal?"

"Deal!" she replied. They both laughed. Then she started peppering him with all kinds of questions about the dance and the girl and the other kids and the fiddle playing. Then she asked if Cindy had a nice brother, and they both laughed.

19. SOUP

"**D**addy, why are those men lining up like that to go to church? An' the *Gaudjas* go to church on Sunday, anyway. Sunday was yesterday. They aren't even wearing clean clothes." The comment came from the next youngest of Lucky and Tillie's four children.

Usually, the parents had to split up and drive two different vehicles over the road between towns, but today the family was all together, stopped at a long red light in some town on the way to the town where they would show that day. Three of the kids were in the front seat with their parents. Two of them were standing up so they could see better, and the third was seated on her mother's lap. The fourth and oldest was seated in the back seat.

"Well, *raklie*, girl, they are not really going to church. They are going behind the church. They are hungry, an' the church is going to give them soup back there," her father answered.

"But why are they hungry? Didn't they eat breakfast?

Is the church like a restaurant that sells soup? An' they should put on clean clothes to go to church," she replied.

"*Keker*, no, sweetie, the church is giving them the soup, just *dellin'* it free. The men are very poor an' hungry. Probably a lot of them did not have breakfast. The church is doin' a good thing so the men can eat," her mother explained. "Lots of churches try to do good things for people, not just singin' an' prayin' an' preachin'."

"Mama, the men are all ragged an' dirty. Why don't they wash up?" Little Fred asked.

"Son, they probably don't have any *kushti hezes,* any good clothes. They don't have a town or anything. They don't have a home or a family," her mother said.

"Well, that's *kekushti*, that's awful. They should go someplace an' get a job," his older brother, Jess, said.

"*Gara*, there just aren't many jobs, boy. These are hard times. These *mushes* lost their job or they lost their farm. Every one of these men has a story, a very sad story, to tell. There was no work an' no money where they lived, so they had to start walkin' someplace else to see what they could find," Lucky said. "They left everything they knew. They left what family they had."

The red light seemed to be lasting far too long, and the children were staring at the hobos waiting quietly in the line. The children were thinking, trying to understand what they were seeing.

"*Tatchi*, truth?" Jess asked. "You mean if the church did not give them soup they wouldn't have anything to eat?"

"*Ava, chavie, no hobin to haw*. Yes, child, no food to eat. They would go hungry. There have even been people who died. You know, it's what they call the 'Great Depression.' Depression means things are pushed down, an' nothing is moving like it should, not money, not jobs, not even food.

"There is not much *vonger* in people's pockets. It is why we have to charge low prices at the show. It is why Cookie an' Slim at the cookhouse give out plates of food if men will wash dishes or peel potatoes or clean greens an' chop them up for cooking. Slim told me that once it was so bad an' the men were so hungry that he had to give them the plate of food first, a plate of any kind of food, stuff we left on our own plates at breakfast or anything. He even saw some old hobos gobble up two plates. They were too hungry to do any work till they got something in their belly," their father explained.

"What that church is doing is really important. Nobody should be hungry," Jess said.

"Yes, Son, you are completely right. The men at the town where the Knights of Columbus sponsored us last week told me about it. They said every morning, all week long, Sundays too, the women come to the church early in the morning an' start cooking big pots of soup. They boil the water an' put in it whatever they have, rice, potatoes, grits, macaroni, things like that. Can't waste anything. An' if they can find onions or collards or carrots or celery or bones from the butcher shop, they put it in, an' as much salt as they have. They don't peel the potatoes, just wash them good and cut them up. They don't throw anything away.

"The K. of C. men said that in their town dogs don't get bones from butcher shops much anymore. People do. Those bones go in the soup. One time, all the women had was bread, an' they just had to make bread soup. It was all they could do," Lucky explained.

"But, Dad, what do they do for supper? Aren't they hungry again?" the boy asked.

"Yes, Son, I am sure they are. The church just does all they can do once a day. I think they don't have any more food after that."

"Daddy, what happens if there are too many men in line? Don't they get any soup?" his daughter Mearlie asked.

"The people at the church try to guess how many people there will be. If they have to, they just add more water to the soup. It gets thinner an' thinner, but they want to have something for everybody if they can. The Catholic men in that town told me about stale bread once. A baker, a man in the church, had three or four loaves of stale bread an' brought it to the soup kitchen at his church. He thought it would be nice if they gave each man a piece of the stale bread to go with the soup. So they sliced the loaves of stale bread up an' put it in a bushel basket. Then a man took the basket, an' a lady went along with him down the line to give each man a slice, one at a time," Lucky explained.

"The men were all very quiet in line. They always are, but every one of them said 'Thank you.' By the time they started getting toward the end of the line, the man an' woman knew they would not have enough bread. They had to start tearing slices in half. It was all they could do. But the men still said, 'Thank you.'

"When they walked back up to the front of the line, all the men had eaten their slice of stale bread. They could not wait till they got their soup. They were too hungry."

"*Dadus*, Dad, that is just awful! They couldn't even wait, so they ate the slice of stale dry bread! I don't think I could even get stale bread down," one of the kids said.

"Honey, if that's all the *hobin* you have, you'll *haw* it, you'll eat it," Tillie told her child.

She looked over at Lucky to get a sense of if he thought they were going too far with their children. Lucky looked serious, but when he glanced back at her, the expression on his face said, "No, they need to know more about it. This is the time."

"I just counted how many men are in the line real fast, an' I think there are about a hundred an' fifteen. That's more people than are on the show. So the church is cooking for free for all those people, every day. Wow!" said Jess.

So Lucky started in again: "The *Gaudja* churches do good work with those soup kitchens for hobos. The guys at that town told me that if the Catholics have anything extra they don't need for their soup, they call up the Lutherans or the Episcopalians to see if they need stuff for their soup. Or if the Catholics need stuff, they call around to the other churches. They forget about how one church prays or another church prays. There are just hungry people to feed."

"I have heard that a lot of butcher shops don't throw out the chicken feet any more. They give it to churches for soup," Tillie said.

"Do you mean like drum sticks, Mama?"

"*Keker, mandie's chavie.* No, my child. It's the chicken's real feet, the part they walk on the ground with, with the nails. They wash the feet up real clean, an' then they boil them an' boil them in the soup. And they add flavor to the pot an' maybe a little meat from the feet, too," Tillie explained.

"Why, I have never eaten chicken feet. Should we start doing that in the cook house, Mama?" asked little Fred.

"No, *mandi's gara,* my boy, we don't have to do that yet," Tillie replied.

"Daddy, there are *trin kawla mushes* at the end of the line, an' those three colored men let some white *mushes* get in front of them. Why is that?" the youngest of the kids asked.

This was a tough question. There was no easy way to

explain it. Lucky looked over at Tillie, and she looked back at him.

"*Dortie, chavies*, well, kids, it is not right, but people do that. They put the colored last, an' the colored don't want to *chinger*, so they don't fight. They just go along. It is even the law in some places, colored toilets, colored water fountains, colored schools. You've seen it. An' the things for the *kawla fokie*, the colored people, are always worse. In some towns in some states, they make us rope off a special section of the tent to put the colored people in. They have to sit there.

"We understand how bad that is more than *Gaudjas* would understand, because we are *Romanichals*, Gypsies. People don't like us either. Well, some people don't like us. We know what it is like for people to look at you in a funny way, or think you are going to steal from them, or laugh at you, or even hate you. *Chavies*, that is why we can never tell the *Gaudjas* that we are *Romanichals*. An' they would not understand anyway. We have to make a livin' an' do business with them, an' we are just as good as they are, but some of them don't know that.

"Be good to everybody, an' more than likely they will be good to you. The world is a funny place, but we have to live in it." And Lucky reached over and put his arm around the child nearest to him and kissed her.

Finally the light changed, and Lucky took his foot off the clutch, and eased the car and trailer forward. But the conversation continued. Two of the kids kept staring back at the soup line.

A thought crossed his mind. It is not what we tell our children. What really matters is what they see us doing. Am I doing that, being good to everybody, so that they see it? Are they seeing that? Is Tillie doing it, too? Our *chavies* are such copycats.

"Why don't the *kawla mushes* go to a colored church to get soup?" asked Jess.

"I don't really know," Lucky said. "Maybe they could. Just about any *gav*, any town, with *kawla fokie,* will have a colored church or a couple colored churches. Colored folks go to church a lot, more than *Gaudjas* do sometimes.

"Well, maybe the colored church can't even afford a soup kitchen, or maybe the colored men think that the white church would have more soup," Tillie said.

"*Dais, vater,* there are *dui bita chavies, a raklie* and *a gara,* with that *mush* in the line for the soup to *haw.* Mama, do you see those two little kids, a little girl and boy with that man?" Mearlie asked. By now they were looking back at the line of hobos. It extended around the front of the church and down the sidewalk.

"*Ava, Raklie,* yes, my girl, I see them. He is trying to see that they get something to eat, too. They are hungry. They are probably his son an' his daughter. It is awful," Tillie said.

"Daddy, will we ever run out of money an' food an' have to go to a soup line?" little Fred asked.

"No, honey bunch, we will never have to do that, not as long as your daddy an' your mama an' all the show keeps goin' on bringin' in enough *vonger* for us to live on during the season an' to make it through the winter. We won't let that happen. We love you too much."

The parents looked at each other again. They both hoped what Lucky had just said would always be true.

20. THE SUAREZ TROUP

The Suarez Troup Bareback Riding Act was subtitled as "The Acrobats on Horseback." It was an act of grace and beauty. The riders and horses were a visual splendor. The band played Cole Porter tunes with just the right rhythm to bring the whole experience together. There were even performers from other acts who stood around the back door of the tent and watched it on a routine basis.

The three Percheron horses in the act were like additional members of the Suarez family. They were babied and fussed over constantly. They were scratched just they way they like to be scratched. They were given treats. They were talked to. They were petted. It was enough to make the others horses jealous. Percherons are a wonderful breed, huge horses, with a great disposition and a very attractive appearance. Their dependability and gentle nature, as well as their broad back, make them ideal horses for bareback riders.

Percherons were originally bred in France as draft animals for farm work. But when the Suarez Troup dressed theirs up for show work, nobody would guess that they had ever originated in a barnyard. Their long flowing manes and tails were left to grow. Their heads were adorned with beautiful white ostrich plumes. Golden reins ran back from their bridles to cinches that ran around the middle of their waists. Of course there were no saddles. They were sleek but not fat, and in great condition. After all, the Suarez family depended on them on a daily basis.

The horses were named for archangels: Miguel, Rafael, and Gabriel. Within the family, they were referred to as "*los angeles*" rather than "*los caballos,*" "the angels" rather than "the horses." They always performed like clockwork, circling the ring counterclockwise at just the right clip as the men and women of the family leaped up and stood on their backs to perform, then going at the faster clip when cued, and finally going side by side all abreast when the family formed the "Pyramid on Horseback." Marco Suarez, patriarch of the family, served as ringmaster in the middle of the ring and cued the horses with two whips. One was simply like a long wand, which the horses had been trained to follow. The other was a whip with a long cord attached, the purpose of which was to crack and make a loud noise meaning to go faster or to stop. It was not to hit the horses.

Bareback riding horses were often referred to as "resin backs." This was because powdered pine resin was rubbed into their backs before each performance to add stickiness and give the riders' feet better traction. A well-washed horse's back is smooth and slippery, and the performers needed steady footing. The resin was washed out each day so that it never irritated the horses' skin.

One secret of bareback riding was for riders to develop a sense of timing in running to and mounting the bareback horse circling the ring. This took practice. As the rider on the ground began a run to the horse, he or she needed to aim up toward where the horse's head would be so that by the time the animal arrived, the rider would end up right on the animal's back. A rider who ran too soon would slam into the horse's head or neck. A rider who ran too late could miss the horse completely and end up on the ground.

Shorter people could benefit from a small riser placed on the ground. This was like a very short stand with a slanted top that would provide a step up for the running rider. Taller riders did not need the stand if they could train themselves to run just fast enough to go from the ground to horseback without having too much speed and going over the horse and out of the ring.

Another important secret for bareback riders was to keep the knees and waist slightly bent and to bounce gently along with the rhythm of the horse. Additional prerequisites were years of practice to develop a fine sense of balance and completely reliable horses.

It was essential to learn how to fall from a horse in a way that would prevent or minimize injury. A bareback rider needed to keep a slight tilt to the left so that he or she would always fall to the left and into the ring and not right and out of the ring and onto the hard ring curbs. It was important to jump off the horse in advance if a rider sensed there might be a fall. If it was too late to jump off, the rider really needed to grab the horse's mane or neck on the way down. Lastly, another member of the family would rush forward to catch the rider or at least to cushion the fall.

Every day and every performance, the riders had to be focused with full concentration. They wanted to get through each performance without even a minor accident. They wanted to go months and years with no incident. Yet all the while they had to be graceful and smiling as if it was a pleasure to perform. And it was a pleasure to perform, the highlight of the day, the chance for the riders to offer their artistry to audiences. It was always a challenge and always a thrill. Every time they performed, before they entered the ring, the Suarez family could be seen quickly making a little Sign of the Cross and kissing their thumb to honor the Virgin of Guadalupe, patron saint of Mexico, so that she would protect them from harm. Some other performers were Catholic, but they did not manifest their piety in that way.

Like many circus acts, there was a technique in making it not look too easy. One of the more difficult tricks was to swing the arms wildly as if about to come crashing to the ground but to regain footing and balance. It was also good to include at least one failed attempt at something, necessitating a second try. And most performances included a daring jump to the ground with the rider just grabbing the cinch around the horse to prevent a serious fall.

The act started when Miguel, the slightly larger horse, entered the ring and began circling it, and Lupe Suarez ran in, jumped on the little riser that was strategically placed, and landed astride Miguel's broad back. Next, Rafael, the second horse, entered the ring, running just a couple yards behind Miguel, and Consuelo leaped on his back. Lastly, Gabriel, the third horse, entered, and Anita, sister-in-law of the first two women, leaped on him. All three of women wore a headdress of white ostrich plumes matching the plumes on the heads of the three Percherons. Simultaneously, the three women rose on hands and knees on the back of their horse, holding on to the two leather loops on the horse's shoulders. Then they would raise their left leg and point it high in the air. Next, their left leg would come down along the side of the horse, and the women would rise on their right knee and balance with their arms above their heads. Then they jumped up completely, standing and making a ballerina pose with their arms. People wondered how anybody could ride a horse standing up with no saddle, no reins, and nothing at all to hold on to.

Two of the men in the act would enter on foot and hold a large hoop in the air, just above the heads of the horses. As each horse passed, the woman riding the horse would leap through the hoop. After that, the women were handed jump ropes, and they would execute a flawless series of jumps on horseback as they swung the ropes in their hands.

The last trick in this series was for the women to sit back down on the horses again and put their right foot through a small loop attached to the right side of the horse's cinch. Then they would swing their left leg over the horse's neck and lie crossways over the horse's back, held only by the loop on their right foot. Their head and shoulders would curl to the ground, with their fingers nearly scraping the ground as the horses loped along. Then the women would rise, sit on the horse, remove their foot from the loop, and dismount gracefully to the ground. In the middle of the ring they would make a deep curtsey to the audience.

This was a signal for three men to come from the back of the ring and each mount a horse. They were more athletic or muscular but tried to be as graceful as the women. They began by bending forward and grabbing the cinch on each side of the horse. Then they would bend down placing their head to one side of the horse's neck and raising their torsos and legs into the air to do a shoulder stand on the running horses.

The speed of the horses would increase a little as the men rose to their feet on the backs of the horses. The men would stand tall and do several leaps in the air in which they touched their toes. This was followed by a movement that was like Cossack dancing on the backs of the horses.

When the men dismounted, they would grab the cinch on the left side of the horses and do three or four forward somersaults by the sides of their horse.

At about this time, a poorly dressed "drunk" would stumble into the ring. In reality, it was Nicolo Marveli joining the act. One of the Suarez men would pull him out of the way just in time to keep a horse from running over him. Then Nicolo would turn around and face a second oncoming horse before making a frightened leap to the center of the ring and knocking over one of the Suarez men. This would begin a mock fight, before Nicolo, using some sort of sign language, would agree to leave the ring if he could just ride a horse for a bit. Then two of the Suarez riders would laugh uproariously at this and then fling him up on a horse, or rather over a horse, to be caught by a third rider strategically positioned on the other side. Finally, they would get Nicolo astride the horse.

Nicolo had two thin ropes in his pocket that he would snap into the cinch on the horse so that he could stand up and hold on, weaving about drunkenly. Then his suspenders would fall from his shoulders and his pants fall down revealing red bloomers. While the audience responded with uproarious laughter, this was actually a precarious time for Nicolo, and two of the Suarez riders followed along closely on the ground. Nicolo's legs were rather immobilized by his fallen pants, until he could bend down on his hands and knees on the horse's back and pull them up. But before the audience could stop laughing, Nicolo was on his feet again, holding onto the ropes snapped into the cinch. This time he gradually let out more slack in the ropes and bounced farther back on the horse. In no time he was dangling off the rear end of the horse, playing along with the crowd and grabbing the horse's tail with one hand while tipping his hat with the other and landing clumsily on the ground. As he stood up and attempted to take a bow, we was unceremoniously grabbed by two Suarez riders and tossed out the back of the ring.

The next segment of the act involved the two youngest Suarez riders. Tito entered, carrying his nine-year old son on one shoulder. As Miguel passed by, Tito would help his son mount the horse. The little boy could briefly stand up holding a rope tied to the cinch to help him keep his balance. His father trotted along solicitously by the horse, ready to catch the boy at a moment's notice. Ricardo came in next with his little daughter who could only sit on the horse's back and blow kisses to the crowd. Both children got a loud round of applause.

The "Pyramid on Horseback" required four horses. Big Comanche, the horse that Chief Sugarstone had done rope tricks on earlier, was brought alongside the three Percherons in to make the fourth. Instead of galloping single file around the ring, the horses were slowed and lined up side by side all abreast with Big Comanche almost at the middle of the ring and Miguel at the edge of the ring. The three men, Tito, Ricardo, and Enrique, mounted the four horses with one foot on each of two neighboring horses. Tito rode with one foot on Miguel and one on Gabriel; Ricardo with one foot on Gabriel and one on Rafael; and Enrique toward the center of the ring with a foot on Rafael and on Big Comanche. The four horses and three men were the first two layers of the pyramid. The next layer was two women. Lupe climbed up and stood with one foot on Tito's shoulder and the other on Ricardo's shoulder. Consuelo stood with a foot on Ricardo and one on Enrique. Ricardo, as the middle man of the layer, actually carried more weight, since both Lupe and Consuelo had a foot on him. The crowning point of the pyramid was Anita, who climbed higher and stood up with a foot on one shoulder of each of the other women. She managed to wave an American flag in this position.

They all held this pyramid position for a complete circle of the ring before Anita came down, followed by Lupe and Consuelo, then the men.

The finale of the act was when Miguel, the largest horse, would circle the ring and the three women would all do a running mount to get on him. Then Tito brought out his son again and placed him on Miguel in front of the three women. Then Ricardo placed his little daughter in front of the boy. At this point there were five people on Miguel, and his pace would necessarily slow a bit. Then each of the three men would do a running leap and land on Miguel's back, adding riders six, seven and eight. Just when it seemed impossible for another person to get on the horse, there would be a comedic climax. Nicolo Marveli, in his drunk's costume, would come back in the ring and leap onto what little room was left at the back of the horse behind the eight Suarez riders. Nicolo would be partly held in this precarious perch by the last of the three men, and he would gradually start sliding backwards off the end of the horse, holding onto the tail for a while, but eventually falling off.

Soon all the riders were leaping to the ground again and lining up in the center of the ring to receive the applause from the audience. Even Miguel was brought to the center of the ring to bend one front knee and stretch down in an equine bow.

The family had done this act or various versions of it for generations. But in the summer of 1933, the Suarez Troup had a new experience. They were not wearing their wardrobe, and it did not take place in the ring. A half-dozen countries were implicated directly or indirectly.

It was very worthwhile for Brewer Brothers Circus to cross into Canada each year. Sometimes the show went to Quebec, sometimes to Ontario, and sometimes to the Prairie Provinces out west. This year they went to Quebec for a couple weeks. Claude Levesque was hired to serve as announcer, since a French speaker really was needed. The dates in several towns went very well. The problem was when the Suarez Troup and for that matter, the whole show, came to reenter the United States.

Many current readers will find it hard to imagine how informal and unsystematic crossing international borders was in the 1930s, especially the U.S. border with Canada. Agents sometimes barely looked at license plates. Many visitors were simply waved on across. It was more complicated for a circus than for a private party of people, but it was usually just a formality.

Typically when crossing into Canada, a manifest listing all the people on the show and all the show vehicles and animals was drawn up and presented to the American and to the Canadian officials at the border crossing. The listing included year of birth and country of birth for the circus people. For the vehicles, the state of the license plate was included. For the animals, the species was sufficient. This year the show entered from Stanhope, Vermont, to St. Albertville, Québec. The agreement was that all people, vehicles, and animals that went into Canada with the circus would come back out with the circus. Any changes could cause serious delays, fines, or worse. As the show lined up along Rue Principale de St. Albertville and started to reenter the US, all was going smoothly. The Canadian officials were just waving everybody on through as the show left Canada. But on this day coming back into the US, two things were working against a rapid crossing for the show. One was boredom, and the other was curiosity. The US officials were having a very slow, boring day and wanted something to occupy their time; plus some of them were very curious about the circus, its people, and its animals. They proceeded through the manifest slowly, paying attention to detail.

A ridiculously funny question was asked, but nobody could afford to laugh at it. The American border guard asked Chief Red Hawk, who clearly had Indian features and was actually wearing a leather headband, if he was an American citizen. GR intervened to explain delicately that indeed, all American Indians were automatically given American citizenship. All of the Sugarstones were citizens. GR and Red Hawk would later laugh long and loud in the retelling of this incident many times.

Then another official commented, "Why, you have foreigners from all over on this circus!"

"Yes, we try to get the very best from all over the United States and the world," GR explained, using well-worn verbiage and sounding very American so that the officials might not notice that he was born in England. Then the processing all came to a sudden stop.

The US border guard asked what "Gt." meant after Anita Suarez' name. All the other Suarez family members just had "Mx." GR looked at the listing closely with him. Then GR remembered that Anita was not Mexican by birth. She had been born when some Mexican circus was showing in Guatemala and had gotten Mexican citizenship when she was just two or three years old. The US officials asked to see her identification, and Anita gladly produced it. The document was written in Spanish, but the officers could make it out, and it did indeed show her as a resident of Mexico.

"But where is the proof that she changed citizenship?" the official asked.

GR paused, giving himself a moment to think. "You see, sir, the U.S. Immigration Agency does not require that sort of documentation to bring the family to the United States. But let me get you a copy of what they do require." GR made it a point to sound as cordial and business-like as possible. He didn't want to come across as, "You are the U.S. Immigration Service, and you should know this!"

He produced a copy of the letter that had been written and sent to the family in Monterey, Mexico, certifying that Brewer Brothers Circus would contract these performers and their children for the six-month season of 1933 to show in the United States and Canada. This certified letter was what the family used to cross at Piedras Negras, Mexico, into Eagle Pass, Texas, each year.

The customs agent had never heard of such a situation, and he was not buying any of it. He had been on the job only a few months, and he wanted to take no chances. GR approached the subject a different way to see if that would work. "Sir, another way to look at it is like this. The lady is just transiting the United States, doing work along the way, till she can get back to Mexico."

"Well, if she had some documentation that she was Mrs. Enrique Suarez, legal wife of a Mexican citizen, then that would be fine. I would know she was his wife and not some Guatemalan trying to get into the country illegally."

This conversation was going poorly. The agent did not know that Latin cultures have a different naming system, with some variation by Spanish-speaking country. Latin women, Latinas, might not change their "last" name, the name they got at birth. Their identification might just stay the same. They could add their husband's name as a suffix on some documents, for example, "de Garcia." They often included their mother's names, too. A Latina's name might look like the equivalent of "Mary Ann Jones and Smith of Johnson." Any attempt to explain this to the agent was likely to be counterproductive.

GR proposed for the agent to call on the telephone to get clarification from a supervisor. The agent said his supervisor down in Montpelier was off for the day and would not be back till Tuesday, since Monday was a holiday.

The agent had said that all the rest of the Suarez family could come on through, and the rest of show, too, but not Anita, who was born in Guatemala.

GR and the Suarez family stepped a few feet back into Canadian territory, or rather the no man's land between Canada and the US, to have a conversation. It was a Friday morning, and they wanted to play a town in Vermont that evening. What could expedite this border crossing?

Tito Suarez, who spoke the best English of the family, explained that it could take days to get any documents from relatives in Mexico or from the church where Enrique and Anita had been married. Was it possible to even get a call through from Canada to Mexico?

Enrique, the youngest of the three brothers, spoke in broken English. "If they won't let Anita in, I will not go in. I will not leave my wife."

"If my bother does not go back in, I will not go back in," added Ricardo.

"*Ni yo tampoco*, me neither," added Tito.

"We cannot go without our sons and daughters-in-law," added the parents, Marco and Conchita.

GR could not be angry. He understood family strength and family cohesiveness. He knew the power of it in trying situations. He knew how it worked in his own family. He called Camie and Woody over, and they reviewed the situation. They all agreed that they would never leave a family member in a foreign country either, even for a very short time, even if it was just Canada. They understood.

They were thinking about calling ahead to cancel the show. Then GR happened to look down the road. What he saw gave him an idea. It was a Catholic church. He asked Nicolo and Rosa Marveli to come over, since they spoke passable French. It was getting complicated. He conferred with Camie first about his idea. Here they were, people born in four different countries—England, Italy, Guatemala, and Mexico—but not born in the US or Canada, standing in the narrow strip of land between Canadian customs and US customs.

GR was now speaking to ten or so people. "Sometimes good ideas come from bad ideas. Didn't that customs agent say that if he had a document that said 'Mrs. Enrique Suarez' on it, he would let Anita back into the States?" Enrique, Anita, Tito, and others nodded.

"Well, you all are Catholic, an' that is a Catholic church right there. Nicolo an' Rosa, can you get the priest an' explain in French that we need to have an emergency wedding?"

"What are you talking about? Is somebody pregnant?" one of them asked.

"No, don't say it that way. It is a different kind of emergency wedding," GR clarified.

"Are you saying that we should ask a priest to marry us right now, to marry us again? Is that what you mean, GR?" Enrique asked.

"Yes, Enrique, I guess I do. It is a crazy idea, but why not try? All we need is a document with your wife's name as 'Mrs. Enrique Suarez.' Do Catholics let you get married twice, I mean married twice to the same woman?"

Tito had been listening and turned to put the proposal to his relatives in rapid Spanish.

Then he turned back to GR and Camie, "We never heard of getting married when you are already married to that woman, but that doesn't mean you can't do it," he said to Amy and GR, and to Rosa and Nicolo, and the others who were gathering. This crowd of people was starting to look like something illegal, all these people standing in the no-man's-land between the US and Canada. Some of the kids wanted to come, too. They were tired of just waiting in cars and trucks.

"Rosa, Nicolo, what do you think? Can you find a priest an' explain all this to him in French? We will gladly pay whatever the church offering is for a wedding," GR said.

"We will do more than that," Camie added. "If you need to, promise him free tickets to the circus for all the priests an' the altar boys."

"We will give him some of those bottles of French wine we bought here an' we are sneaking back hidden in the horse feed," added Ricardo.

"We will come back an' do some benefit acts for free next week to help the church," Woody offered. "But what is something we could do to make a good impression on him to start with, since only Rosa an' Nicolo speak French? Oh, Choctaw's mother was Canadian, an' he speaks French. Let's get him, too"

Anita spoke for the first time. Her English was faulty but clear. "I am sorry to be so much trouble. I am willing to try anything. I have to be with my husband, my family. I think we should all go to the church and go in and get holy water and make the Sign of the Cross and sit down, at least the Catholics should. And then Nicolo and Rosa can talk to him. Who are the Catholics beside the Marvelis and the Suarez family? Oh, and of course the de la Croix from Louisiana!"

"Do they let black people in a white church in Canada?" somebody asked.

"I think so. It is a Catholic church, an' they usually let them in anyway. This is Canada too," came a reply from someplace.

"And I think maybe Willy Truman an' Mike Shaney. Those two are Catholic. Get them. Tell them to put on clean shirts. Tell them they are going to church on Friday!" said GR.

"But Rosa, Nicolo, what do you two think of such an idea? Will a priest do such a thing?"

"GR, it all depends on the priest and how you approach him. It just might work, Rosa replied. "So let's get the Catholics together and go over and sit in the church. Bring a few Protestants, too. Nicolo and I will do our best to explain and make the priest happy. Nicolo was once an altar boy, kind of a good one, his father says. He could be an altar boy if the priest wants one. Can we say there is a best man and a best woman? We need to work fast and get that document that says 'Mrs. Enrique Suarez,' right?"

Père Le Mieux, the parish priest, was not in the church. He was sitting on the porch of the rectory next door. He had been trying to read his daily breviary, but he was distracted. He was enjoying all the commotion of a circus stopped on his street trying to get back to the US.

It was surprising to see about twenty people, men, women, and children, going into his church. They were not his parishioners at all. If they were some kind of pilgrims, they must be truly lost. He went over and entered the church from the back door. The sight of all these people sitting politely in the pews, some of then kneeling, made him smile.

Rosa and Nicolo approached him and began to explain the special situation. It was becoming clearer to the priest with the third explanation. He said he had never heard of such a thing, but if the man and the woman had never been married to any other persons before, in the Catholic faith or any other faith, then he could schedule a ceremony. Since the man and woman were obviously not from this parish, there was no need to publish the Banns of Matrimony. The priest asked when would they like the wedding to take place.

It was not until Rosa replied, "*Dans trente minutes ou une heure,*" that the priest really understood the situation. They wanted a wedding in thirty minutes or an hour. At first, the priest's laughter sounded impolite. It was really just from the surprise and the delight of such a wonderful idea.

"*Oui, mes enfants, bien sur !*" he replied. "Yes, my children, certainly!"

The next forty-five minutes was semi-coordinated chaos. GR went back to the customs agent to be absolutely sure that if they had the signed marriage document in an hour that Anita Suarez could cross back into the US.

Anita's mother-in-law Conchita was working with her daughter-in-law to pick out a dress from what Aunt Jennie could find in the entire circus wardrobe. It looked like it might be a yellow gown Tillie wore for a dog act. Conchita just loved weddings. She was almost crying. Both Enrique's brothers wanted to be best man for him, one claiming that he was the real best man since he had that role at the first wedding and the other claiming that it was his turn to be best man.

Père Le Mieux came in with lots of roses from his garden. They could be made into a bouquet for the bride, boutonnieres, or whatever. Consuelo and Lupe worked with the flowers.

Anita soon had seven bride's maids, lining up quickly and at least trying all to dress in the same color. Should it be green? Or should it be yellow? Her sisters-in-law would be her matrons of honor. In an unprecedented situation, her husband was playing the role of her groom. Eight children were lining up to be flower girls and ring bearers, but there was a procedural question: Should the bride and groom remove their rings and then put them back on or what?

Aaron de la Croix and his sons were happily assigning themselves their roles in the wedding. Aaron was practicing on the church organ. Then his sons proved to be good vocalists, loving the chance to sing as a duet for everybody.

Chief Red Hawk and his band came in, looking all around. One of the children said in Osage, "Gee, Catholic churches are beautiful. They are so much prettier than the Protestant church at home!" Then they had to experiment with the movable kneelers that could be placed up or down in each pew. One of the Marvelis explained that in a Catholic church, sometimes people sit, and sometimes they stand, and sometimes they kneel, depending on what the priest says.

Poker and Pinky became the ushers. They were not wearing clown paint or wardrobe, but very nice clothes. They seemed to be different men. They were pleasant and straightforward, but they did not give the children special attention or play any magic tricks.

The noise in the church was rising, and the preparation was getting slower and more complicated. The group was losing sight of the document needed for the border crossing and the speed needed to get to the next town for an evening show.

Lucky took charge of the situation, relying on his long experience as a ringmaster. It was different being in a Catholic church rather than a tent, but it was important to keep things moving along and ending on time. He confirmed the order of the bridal procession, announced that they would dispense with having friends and family of the groom sit on one side and friends and family of the bride on the other side. Mike Shaney knew no French at all, but he would join Nicolo as an altar boy. They would mumble the Latin prayers together.

Next it became clear that the priest could read English but not really speak it, and he certainly did not speak Spanish. Enrique and Anita did not understand French. How could the wedding vows be handled? If a marriage is to be valid, the bride and groom must understand what they are vowing to do.

Rosa agreed to translate from French to English for Anita, and Nicolo would translate for Enrique. If they wanted to, the bride and groom could even say the translated vows in Spanish. It would work. Père Le Mieux had a broad grin on his face. He thought of a famous Latin quote, "*Amor Vincit Omnia*" or "Love Conquers All."

Camie stepped forward and interrupted Lucky. "The priest has to have that document right here, the one to sign to say they are married. It has to be ready to give to the bride and groom. We will not leave this church without it. Make sure Nicolo or Rosa gets this across!"

The signed document was certainly what it was all about, but it was getting a little cloudy. Everybody was enjoying the idea of having a wedding. The people on this circus were a community. This was a fine occasion to celebrate, to enjoy themselves. They were already having a wonderful time. There were already jokes going around that if the couple ever wanted to get divorced, they would now have to get divorced twice, since they had been married twice.

In addition, Camie and GR were seeing the publicity possibilities, not for Canada but for the towns in New England. "Pictures! Pictures!" Camie yelled. There had to be pictures of this wedding.

Aunt Hattie served as photographer with her little Brownie camera. Unlike in the Twenty-First Century, a photographer then had to be miserly in the number of shots taken. Hattie took one of the bride coming down the aisle. Since the bride's own father could not be there, her father-in-law, Marco Suarez, said he would be honored to serve in her father's place. Hattie took another picture of the waiting groom and up at the altar with Père Le Mieux, the seven bridesmaids, the groom and his two brothers, the best men. They were resplendent in matching wardrobe from the bareback riding act – white boots and slacks and a peasant-style shirt with puffy sleeves and a neck opening that went half way down the chest.

Of course there was a picture of the bride and groom kissing, and another of them existing the church. Cookie did not have any rice on hand to shower the newlyweds with, but Uncle Choctaw got some oats from the horse truck. Oats were very appropriate for a couple who rode bareback horses.

Amy had prepared a big envelope for the priest. It

had a Canadian ten-dollar bill in it, ten free passes to the circus and an autographed eight-by-ten picture of the Suarez Troop. Before the couple was out of the church, she passed it to the priest and got the signed *"Certificat de Mariage"* from the priest. Anita's name was listed as *Madame* Enrique Suarez instead of Mrs. Enrique Suarez, but that would just have to do.

The most important picture, the one that ended up in papers all over New England and even down to Washington and Richmond, was the one of the Anita and Enrique crossing into the US with the *Certificat* in hand for the border agent. The headlines on the accompanying article varied from one city newspaper to another. Most of them were in the vein of "Priest Performs Emergency Wedding So That The Show Can Go On" or "Circus Performers Remarry with Blessing of Priest and Border Guard."

Though the headlines varied, every newspaper article brought lots of free publicity for Brewer Brothers Circus, and Anita Suarez got back into the US with her husband, her family, and the extended family of the circus.

21. BANANAS IN THE CEMETERY

There was a place over in the East somewhere called Jacob's Ladder. It was probably in the Berkshires in western Massachusetts or in Vermont. Circus people enjoyed the natural beauty of the place, but they really dreaded driving through the mountains of Jacob's Ladder. Some said that the area was at its most beautiful in the fall, when the leaves turned myriad colors. Some locals claimed that it was at its best after newly fallen snow. But the truth was that is was a natural wonder all year long.

In the summer there were a thousand shades of green in the trees and bushes and the echoes of raucous birds and choruses of frogs and crickets. Clouds of butterflies might fly by. There were dense populations of squirrels, chipmunks, opossum, raccoon, deer, and even some bear. Anyone who passed through the area was certain to see at least some of the smaller animals, but the larger ones could be road hazards, too. The deer could just stand unafraid on the narrow roadway as if questioning who really had the right of way. Passengers riding in vehicles could take all this in, but the drivers would have less time to enjoy any of this beauty since many stretches of the road required white-knuckle concentration to negotiate curves, dodge on-coming vehicles, or downshift the transmission to keep from coasting downhill too fast.

The reference to Jacob's Ladder in the Bible seemed quite apt. The narrow road would go up forever and ever over each mountain; then finally there would begin a long descent with some short flat places, more sudden dips, and many curves. Then the road would start up the next mountain. Travelers really could feel like they were climbing Jacob's Ladder. It must surely still be there. Mountains don't go away. But probably modern roads circumvent them somehow.

Climbing each mountain was an exercise in patience. Truck drivers stayed in the lowest possible gear to get maximum power. They watched the temperature gauge to see if the vehicle could make it to the top without overheating and boiling over. Everybody traveled with extra water to put in the radiator as needed. For the heavy trucks, the speed could be as low as ten miles an hour, and a man would ride along on the running board with a chock block in his hand to put under the drive wheel to keep the truck from rolling backward if the engine stalled. The pace seemed so slow at times that it looked possible to run along beside a truck and count the lug nuts on the hub of the wheels as they went round and round.

Going down each mountain was a completely different experience. The engine would cool down, and almost no fuel was needed. The danger was in starting to roll too fast and then not being able to negotiate a curve. Skillful downshifting was needed to stay in a lower gear to maintain a safe speed and not overheat the brakes. It was crucial to have both good tractor brakes and good trailer brakes but not to overuse them so they would fade and eventually fail. There was often a noticeable smell of hot brakes in the air. The sound of loud engine backfires echoed down the road.

The guardrails on this road were flimsy by modern standards. Some places had no guardrails. There were breaches where a guardrail had been broken. Not all the breaches had been repaired. They served as sober reminders of what could happen if brakes failed or if a driver was not skillful enough.

There was a drivers' code in these mountains. For instance, the driver of a slow vehicle would stick out an arm and signal to faster vehicles behind when there was a safe place to pass and go on up the mountain. If someone was stopped and changing a flat tire, passing drivers always offered their help. Another part of the code was that if the driver of a descending vehicle had lost control, he would blast his horn frequently so that ascending drivers would get the message, "I have lost control, and you need to stay out of my way!" The conventional wisdom was that in such cases the driver of a runaway truck would look for a place to brush against the mountainside and slow the vehicle down or try to stop it completely. This alternative was better than risking going over the side of the mountain. Every year there was a runaway truck, and more often it was in the summer. In winter, if there was the least bit of ice or snow, the road was closed.

The weather was beautiful, and the mountain air was fresh as Brewer Brothers Circus started negotiating Jacob's Ladder in the circus season of 1933. All the drivers had met and gone over the good strategies. They tested out tractor brakes and trailer brakes. Everybody had one or more red emergency flags. They carried extra water with them, and nobody, absolutely nobody, drove alone in any vehicle.

Uncle Harry was asked to drive the long and heavy canvas truck loaded with the bigtop and to let John drive the elephant truck. The elephant truck was heavy, too, with the weight of Dolly, Blanche, and Jewell and a several-day supply of baled hay, but the elephant truck was newer and easier to drive. So in this case, for this trip, it was wiser to have John drive it. Gilly Brewer rode with him.

Halfway up the third or fourth mountain in Jacob's Ladder, both men heard a truck horn blasting. John was driving on the outside lane, meaning the lane by the guardrails, the edge of the cliff. The runaway driver would be on the inside, right up against the mountainside. It would be easier for him to take the option of slowing down by scrapping the side of the mountain. It would be a judgment call, a difficult one.

In a short time, the runaway driver came swerving around a curve just up the mountain. John had already positioned the elephant truck to give the other vehicle as much room as possible. He parked it right up against the guardrail, or rather where a guardrail should have been. But there just wasn't enough room on the narrow road for the runaway truck. It sideswiped the elephant truck starting right behind the cab where John and Gilly were. The force was strong enough to push the elephant trailer perilously close to the edge of the road. Actually, one of the back wheels was partly off the road. The truck shook dangerously.

Dolly, Blanche, and Jewel were terrified. The noise from the sideswiping had been frightening, and the side of the trailer had long rips gouged in it. The elephants cried and trumpeted. The more they rocked the trailer, the more precarious their position became.

John and Gilly jumped out of the cab of the truck, first of all, to save their own lives. But secondly, they wanted to get the elephants out before the truck could go off down the cliff to what would probably be certain death. The two men quickly decided that it would be better to open the left side door of the truck, the one that was hardly ever used, to get the elephants out. Using the right side door would mean the elephants would literally have to step off the road and down the cliff. Several layers of bales of hay were blocking the backdoor.

But using the left side door would mean that they were blocking the road for any driver going down the mountain or going up. It was the risk they needed to take.

It was hard to get the left side door open because when the truck had been sideswiped, that door handle was bent. The men tried to say soothing things to the elephants. John and then Gilly used a sledgehammer to straighten the handle enough to open the door. They wanted to sound like Uncle Harry: "Take it easy, babies. Take it easy. You are the most beautiful elephants on the whole circus. We are getting you out. You are gonna get some sweet feed!" Then John remembered that Uncle Harry had a habit of whistling to them in a low octave, and he tried to do that. It was hard to tell if it actually helped sooth the elephants or not. After several tries with the sledgehammer, the side door opened.

As soon as the door slid open, the elephants tried to get out, straining at their leg chains. They were usually calm, sensible, and obedient, but in this case they were just too scared, too panicky over what had happened, all the noise, and how the trailer they were in was strangely rocking.

It was with great difficulty that John crawled in and undid Dolly's leg chain. Dolly wasted no time in getting out of the truck. This made Blanche and Jewel all the more anxious to go with her, the lead elephant that they always followed. For the moment, Dolly was standing in the road, and John yelled to Gilly to try to lead her out of the road. As John tried to undo Blanche's leg chain, she accidentally pushed him against the inside of the trailer, putting tremendous force on his left leg. He yelled out in pain, wondering how badly his leg was injured, but he did set her free, and she bolted out of the truck to join Dolly.

Now Gilly had two elephants to keep out of the road, and he was not having complete success.

It took a long time for John to undo Jewel, who kept jerking on her leg chain. She had become thoroughly unnerved. As soon as John got her chain off, she jumped from the truck and was nearly hit by a driver coming up the road, a driver who had no idea what was going on or that running into an elephant would be very dangerous for him as well as for the elephant.

All it took was for Jewel to join Dolly and Blanche, and the three ran off into the woods and up the mountain somewhere, crashing through underbrush or anything that stood in their way. Gilly couldn't have stopped them no matter what he did. They wanted to be away from this terrible place and find somewhere safe. They were not thinking clearly. Usually, they never wanted to be far from their truck or the tent unless they went on parade with Uncle Harry and Aunt Hattie. Now they were just terrified animals.

"Did you see Blanche's head?" John asked Gilly.

"Yes, I did. It looked like a bad gash, and when she came out, Dolly started putting her trunk up to it to smell it and make chirping noises to Blanche. But somehow we have to round up those three elephants before we can doctor that cut," Gilly replied.

"Oh, my god!" John yelled. "I didn't see this! That runaway truck cut into the left saddle tank when it hit us. There is a big gash. The gas is running down the road. We gotta move this truck as fast as we can. What if somebody is smoking? Or what if it gets lit some way?

Oh, hell! Where is Woody or Lucky or somebody!"

Most tractor trucks that pulled trailers had three gas tanks. There was a small tank behind the seat, and there were two larger ones placed low over the frame of the truck on either side behind the cab, vaguely like the saddle bags on the back of a saddle. A lever under the seat allowed the driver to change the fuel source from one tank to another. It was the left saddle tank on this truck that was now leaking.

As John stood on the side of the road, he remembered that there had been a little church about a half-mile back down the mountain. There was a place to pull in and get the truck off the road. There was no question of trying to turn around on the narrow, twisting road. He would have to back down it.

If it is hard to drive a truck up a mountain, it is so much harder to back a truck down a mountain. There is only one way to do it, and that is to back down foot by foot with another person walking behind the truck, giving some hand signals in the rear view mirrors and yelling if the vehicle gets too close to the edge. This would be Gilly's job, and he also had to carry red flags to signal vehicles coming up the mountain. It was as if he needed eyes in the back of his head.

There were so many things going through their minds – loose elephants, an injured elephant, and damaged truck, a leaking fuel tank, and John's badly aching leg. He had been running on adrenalin, and now he would have to summon the concentration to back down the mountain. They never even thought about what eventually happened to the runaway truck that had caused the predicament in the first place.

Gilly got behind the truck and carried the flags. John started the engine to pull up a bit and get the back wheel of the trailer firmly onto the narrow pavement. Then he put the transmission in reverse and started the slow descent to the church. He went about fifteen yards along before Gilly signaled him with the flag to stop and pull up again, since he was so close to the edge. Then two cars passed them, and another truck came down the mountain, this one under full control and at a very moderate speed.

John took another try at backing down. He got about forty yards this time before needing to stop and pull up from the edge. This process was repeated again and again, and all the while gas was leaking out of the gash in the left saddle tank. There were interruptions three more times as vehicles passed going up or coasting down in the other lane. One courteous and concerned driver even pulled over and parked in front of the truck and got out and offered his assistance. Gilly gladly passed him a red flag to signal upcoming vehicles. Finally, after what may have been the slowest half-mile in the annals of circuses, Gilly saw the church and yelled to John that he was nearly there.

John was delighted to back across the descending lane and into the space in front of the church and get the truck off the road. He turned off the engine and climbed out of the cab. He realized he was soaked with perspiration, and it wasn't even a warm day. His leg hurt so bad he could not walk on it. With Gilly's help, he hopped over to the front of the church and sat down on the front steps.

There was nothing the two men could do now but wait for help. Gilly joined John, taking a seat on the steps of the little country church. They hoped Gilly's father or uncle or some show truck would come along soon. But what kind of help would they be given? What could be done? How can elephants be caught in the woods? Could the elephants even be hauled in this truck if they were caught? Would they even get into this truck after what they had just been through in it?

Gilly did have the idea to get as much gas out of the leaking saddle tank as possible. He got the jerry cans tied to the back of the truck and found a little siphon hose. The more gas he could get out, the more the danger would be reduced. Gilly had soon siphoned out a full jerry can of gas and was starting on the second can. John told him to take the full can and put all of it that he could into the right saddle tank, the one that was not leaking.

Uncle Harry and Aunt Hattie pulled up in the canvas truck. "What the hell has happened? Where the hell are our elephants?" Harry did not say it in a blaming way. He was just astonished.

Then Woody showed up with the horse truck. The parking space in front of the church was nearly full. John sat on the church steps while he explained to them all that had happened, with Gilly filling in details. Woody, Harry, and Hattie could hardly believe their ears. They had nothing but kind and congratulatory words to say for John and Gilly. The elephants could have been killed. The men might have even been killed. Their quick thinking and fast action saved the day.

Of course there was more to do, much more. Harry had to inspect the truck to see if it was elephant-worthy or could be made elephant-worthy, after being sideswiped. Even if the elephants were rounded up, could they be enticed to get back in it? Gilly needed to keep siphoning gas to empty the leaking saddle tank as quickly as possible, and that clearly meant putting the gas from the jerry cans into the canvas truck or the horse truck. Woody decided to get Yellowstone, the big palomino stallion, out of the horse truck and go on horseback to locate the elephants and herd them back toward the truck. The trail of three elephants crashing through the woods could not be that hard to follow. Spangles could come along. The Dalmatian might be useful in locating them faster. It would be good to get the horse out and go immediately before the frightened animals strayed any farther.

"I hope they haven't gone very far, Woody," Harry said as Woody jumped up on Yellowstone. "They are not really woods girls. They like their comforts an' the feed we give them an' the attention they get. I don't think they would go far, an' Dolly is one smart elephant. When they settle down, they will probably just stop an' rest. But on the side of this big mountain, where the hell are they?"

"I'll do my best to find out," Woody told them. "If I can get them to trumpet, I will so that you know we're are coming back, or trying to. An' they like Spangles, so she will help, too."

Hattie was asked to keep an eye on John and see that he did nothing. She gave him some aspirin and water and played the role of a stern nurse. But she had another idea, too. In the little town back at the foot of the mountain, she and Harry had pulled over at a small general store. They bought bread and other supplies, and when they spotted bananas, they practically bought the store out. Bananas were more like a rare seasonal treat in many parts of the country back then. Cookie would be delighted to have them to give as a dessert for supper in the cookhouse, and they would save a dozen or more for "the girls," Dolly, Blanche, and Jewel.

The girls really loved Hattie, and in a different way from how they loved Harry. Her role was maybe more maternal, whereas Harry provided them with more adventure. Hattie took a couple loaves of bread and a dozen bananas and went out into the little cemetery beside the church. John said that if she was hungry she could stay right there on the front steps and eat beside him. She explained that she had a different idea.

Hattie sat down quietly on a tombstone toward the back of the cemetery. She took her time, opened a loaf of bread, and ripped out a small piece. She peeled a banana and took a bite, placing the rest of the banana and the opened bread beside her on the tombstone. She wanted it to be as visible as possible, and she wanted the fragrances to waft up in the air as far as possible. This strategy required patience, and Hattie was a patient woman.

In the interim, Harry had checked out how badly the

elephant truck was damaged. The frame still looked sound, but the left side had a long gash, and some of the sidebars were bent. They could be repaired or replaced later. The truck seemed safe enough. The question was if he could he make it look fine to the elephants and somehow overcome their fears so they would actually get back in it.

If he couldn't get the elephants into it, he would be faced with the prospect of leading the elephants like Hannibal over the mountains to the town. They might be walking all night. The elephants would need water. And then what would they do? He didn't even want to think about that. He got help from Gilly to move all the bales of hay that had been placed in the back of the truck. Together they built a sort of hay wall inside the truck to hide the gashes in the left wall and to help Blanche forget where she got her head cut. Then the men opened the backdoor of the truck and went in with a bag of grain. They spilled the grain in a little trail. The trail did not start at the back door. It started several feet up inside, where it would easily be seen and smelled, but where it could not be reached without all three elephants actually entering. After that, all they could do was wait to see what Woody could round up. Gilly had siphoned out all the gas he could get from the leaky tank and put it in the horse truck and the canvas truck.

At about this point, a local man drove up in a car. There was barely room for him to pull in off the road by the trucks. "Goodness, I have heard tell that you boys have really had some adventure on our mountain here today. Is it true that you are gonna get cowboys to go lasso the wild elephants? How would that work?" he asked. The man was excited but respectful. Obviously, something like this had never happened before.

Harry asked who he was and discovered that he was mayor of the town back down the mountain. Harry took the man over and introduced him to John and Gilly. He asked John where Hattie had gone, and John pointed silently toward the cemetery.

What they saw next was hard to believe. There was Hattie sitting on a tombstone with "the girls" gathered round her eating bread and bananas. The elephants had knocked over two tombstones, but elephants are not particularly graceful when there are bananas and bread involved. With her eyes, Hattie asked them to remain quiet and stay back. But she got up and moved closer and sat on another tombstone, and the elephants followed her. She was taking the bread slices out of the wrapper one at a time, tearing them in half, and slowly giving them to the animals, making them take turns. The bananas were nearly all gone. Elephants don't need bananas peeled in order to eat them; the fruit goes down peel and all in one gulp.

It was clear that Hattie wanted to keep easing them closer and closer to the truck, and they kept going with her. She motioned for Harry to come up slowly and maybe help out with a little more bread and bananas from the truck. Harry gradually joined the group and began whistling softly, the way that the elephants were used to. He motioned with his head to Hattie that the truck was indeed ready and they should proceed to it, as if all this was just an everyday occurrence.

A car stopped on the road, and two children yelled out, "Hey, Mister, can we watch your elephants?"

But Harry and Hattie ignored them, and the local man motioned for them to be quiet. He seemed to know them. Within five minutes, the animals had transitioned from the bread and bananas to the trail of grain that Harry and Gilly had laid out in the elephant truck. After just a few more minutes, all three were inside scooping up the grain with their trunks. Gilly and Harry gradually closed the door, and Harry climbed over it to put the leg chains on them so they could be transported again.

"That is the most amazing thing I have ever seen in my life. You folks can just do magic with those animals. Wait till I tell the folks in town what I saw, what I saw with my own eyes. They will never believe it!" the local man exclaimed. "My name is Reverend Waverly, by the way, and this is my congregation's church. We just call it the 'Unitarian Church on the Mountain.'"

He was extremely agreeable. Hattie was reluctant to mention that "the girls" had knocked over a total of eight or ten tombstones. "But I thought you said you were the mayor, Reverend Waverly," Hattie said.

"I am. Nobody wants that job either, so I have to do it. But right now there is another job I have to do. Looks like you got an injured man here, an' I am the only one in these parts who has been trained in any first aid. Take him into the church, an' I will get my bag from the car. Let's see if it is serious. He looks like he is in pain."

"But we don't have the keys to the church. How can we get in?" Harry asked.

"Keys? Why, I don't believe there have ever been any keys. It is always open. Just carry him in an' put him flat on a pew with his bad leg up on one of the arms at the end. We need to get that leg elevated," the man replied.

So Gilly and Harry took John under each arm and carried him up the little steps as Hattie opened the door, which was indeed unlocked. The church was simple inside and quite well worn.

"Son, tell me what happened an' where it hurts, please," he told John. John explained how his leg had been smashed against the inside of the truck and how it had been swelling ever since and hurting more and more since the truck got sideswiped an hour or two ago.

"My, my, in all my born days, I have never looked after anybody that had a leg smashed by an elephant! Looks like you got a little fever, too, an' you need to drink some water. You gotta keep lots of water in you when something like this happens. Anybody got any water?"

"I will get some from the truck. We carried some extra in case the radiator boiled over," Gilly said.

"But I can't really examine your leg like this. I have to see if it is just bruised real bad or if there are cuts or even if it is broken. You're gonna have to take your pants down. No, you gotta take 'em off."

"In a church?" John asked in astonishment. "Why, I could never do such a thing in a church!"

"Well, young man, the Lord has seen all kinds of bodies. After all, he made our bodies. So there is no shame in it. He wants us to take care of your body. He won't be offended. An' I am a preacher, too, so I know about these things," the man explained very soothingly.

John looked around at Harry and Gilly questioningly, and Harry nodded his head in agreement. Hattie was holding back a laugh. She quietly excused herself to go out and check on the elephants. Harry and Gilly pulled off John's boots and helped slide down his pants. "Now I want you to touch where it hurts the most and tell me how bad it hurts. It is easy to see a lot of bruising already, but I want you to tell me," the preacher continued.

John looked at his painful leg, already quite swollen, and felt down along it. There was no bleeding. He couldn't tell if it was broken. It was just very painful, and he pointed to the most painful spots. "OK, thank you," the preacher said. "You did exactly what I wanted you to do. Now I am going to push against your leg in different spots with my fingers. I will push harder than you did, an' tell me to stop if it hurts too much. An' I will spend a little time on your kneecap. A kneecap is very important," he explained. He obviously knew what he was doing. There were spots, mostly in the lower leg, that were much more painful, but there was no clear indication that the leg was broken. He could not tell.

"OK, sir, here is what we are going to do, an' I don't want you to argue with me. You are not going to do any walking at all. We are going to carry you. Don't move your leg. Just leave it like it is. There is only so much I can tell about it. We are going to keep your leg elevated, keep it up, as high as possible, so the swelling gets a little relief. We gotta find a comfortable flat place for you in one of the trucks. No, that won't do, and you should stay away from elephants!" he quipped with a smile. "We will put you in the back seat of my car.

"We need to keep giving you water, an' you need some aspirin. Does anybody around here have a bottle of whiskey? This poor man could use a couple shots," he said. "No? Well, I know where we can get some in town. I'll get a bottle just for medicinal purposes, of course. An' we won't tell anybody. Now, gentleman, let's carry this poor man out to the back seat of my car."

John was placed in the back seat and made as comfortable as he could be. He held his pants modestly to minimize his exposure. Gilly ran back to the church and got John's boots. That was when Hattie grabbed Gilly's arm and pointed to the cemetery. There were a dozen tombstones knocked over. She knew she had to show this to the preacher.

"Reverend Waverly, we have to tell you something. It was an accident. Our elephants knocked down some of the tombstones. We apologize. We meant no disrespect. What can we do?" Hattie asked.

"Oh, that? Let' see. We need to hurry an' get over these mountains to the town before it gets dark. But if you boys will work with me, we can set those tombstones up proper pretty quick. We have to do that every year. You see, here in New England we have bad winters with lots of freezing an' then thawing. What it does is, it makes the ground heave. It pushes up. That always makes some of the tombstones fall over.

"So every year before Memorial Day, when there won't be too much more freezing, a bunch of us come up an' straighten up all the tombstones. It takes time. All the old families names are on them, an' we want to show some respect. We try to make sure that the right tombstone always goes back on the right grave, but there are four or five we aren't so sure about anymore. So let's get to work, an' then there is something I want to ask you for."

In fifteen minutes, the men had straightened all the tombstones, and they looked almost like they had before. "Now what was it that you wanted, Reverend? We feel indebted to you," Harry said.

"What I would really like is a couple wheelbarrows of that elephant manure an' horse manure out of your trucks. We have a hard time getting any flowers or lilies to grow here 'cause the ground is so bad. It is mostly just rock an' shale here on the mountainside. But with some of your manure, we could have the prettiest flowers in the state! Could you do that?"

"Reverend Waverly, we would be delighted. Just tell us where you would like us to put it."

In another ten minutes, five wheelbarrows of manure from the horse truck and elephant truck had been spread in the raggedy flowerbeds around the church. Just as they finished spreading the manure, Woody rode up on Yellowstone, looking dejected, with Spangles trailing behind and panting rapidly.

"I am sorry, Harry, Hattie. I followed their trail as best I could. I went up an' down the mountain three times, an' you can see this horse is getting really wore out. I am, too. Seems like they just disappeared into thin air. How can three elephants just evaporate?" Woody asked.

"They didn't, Woody. They came back on their own. Hattie lured them in, you might say. They were just dying for some of the bread an' bananas she took over to the cemetery. Maybe they didn't go so far after all. They were just hiding out in the woods behind the church, keeping their eye on the truck. You know how they get all excited if we start up the motor of the truck an' they are not in it. They don't want to be left behind. It is like a home."

"Ah, hell! Harry, you mean I was riding all over this mountain an' they were probably around here all the time. Spangles kept trying to take me back down the damn mountain, but I didn't pay her any attention," Harry said.

"Woody, this is the Reverend Waverly here, an' we are parked in front of his church. He has been awfully good to us, an' he is a preacher, so you might want to watch your language," Hattie chimed in.

"Oh, I have heard worse than that, an' I have been known to say a *hell* or *damn* or two myself, sometimes maybe something worse, depending on the circumstances. And *Damn!* This is a day with circumstances!"

"By the way, Mister Woody, you are riding a beautiful horse," the Reverend said.

"Thank you, Reverend. Yes, he is a beautiful piece of horseflesh. An' we are very lucky today. It is just a wonder that nobody was hurt in this accident," Woody said.

"Well, somebody was hurt, one of your drivers. We looked after him a bit, an' he is in the back seat of my car right now. I'll take him over the mountain to the town where you will be showing. There is better care for him there.

"But somebody else got hurt, too, the guy driving the runaway truck. He decided to scrape into the side of the mountain to stop. Guess he was just going too fast an' his brakes weren't working that good. He wasn't that far out of the town down there, but when he went into the mountainside, he got thrown right through the windshield an' out on the hood. He got cut up pretty bad from all the glass.

"One of those cars that passed here going down, well, they stopped an' picked him up an' tried to stop the bleeding. He bled all over their car. They got him to me, an' we got it stopped pretty good. It was touch and go for a while there. Now he is going to a hospital somewhere, wherever they can get him to. An' what are we going to do with that darn truck of his stuck on the side of the mountain? Something like this happens every year, sometimes a couple times."

The sun was getting lower in the sky, and they needed to move on soon. There were a half-dozen more mountains to get over before nightfall. They decided to let the Reverend Waverly go first with John in the back seat. Then Harry would follow driving the elephant truck. This would be a switch from the canvas truck he had been driving, but if "the girls" got excited when they finished their grain, he could calm them down better. They were a driver short now, so Hattie would have to take the horse truck. She had driven semi-trucks before, but not the horse truck. This was not a convenient place to learn how, but there were no real alternatives. Stops and starts with the horse truck had to be even slower and more gradual that with the elephant truck. Sudden stops or starts could throw the horses down on their side.

"Look, honey, you will be right behind me and right in front of Woody with the canvas truck. You can go our speed, brake when we brake, an' flash your lights at me if you want to stop or if you have a question. We gotta take it easy anyway, but I will be watchin' for you if you just want to stop or whatever. Will that be OK, darlin'?" Harry asked.

In some ways, circus women were feminists before lots of others. There weren't many jobs a woman couldn't do. They were also a very determined lot, very flexible, and usually ready to attack a problem in a levelheaded way. That was how Hattie was now.

"Just let me see if I know where all the gears are, the

lights, the trailer brakes an' so on," she said, as she competently located everything.

The procession of four vehicles started up the narrow road again, taking every precaution. It was not possible to enjoy the real beauty of the place. There was serious business at hand, the business of staying on the road and getting to the town safely. It was fatiguing. It took two more hours.

"They're comin'! They're comin'!" the cry went up. The rest of the show had been getting concerned when three of the most important trucks and some of the most important people were so late getting in on the circus lot. There was a flat area where the town was down in the valley, and the show was going to set up on a sort of baseball field there. The cookhouse was already in place and some of the other parts of the show. Several people had been keeping an eye on the road coming down the mountain, and Amy was certainly one of them. There had to be some serious reason why her husband Woody and her son Gilly would be so late. She was standing with Woody's parents when they all heard the news.

At first there was not time to tell the story. The latecomers were all hungry, but the hungry animals had to be taken care of first. The horses needed to be unloaded and fed and watered, and so did the elephants. Extra efforts were needed with them to make sure they stayed calm. The cut on Blanche's head needed to be doctored. The wound had to be cleansed first; then there was the standard treatment for elephant scrapes and cuts, a pomade of Vaseline and Massengill powder applied liberally. Nothing healed a hurt elephant faster than this. There was a bitterness in the Massengill that prevented the elephants from wiping it off or tasting it. Of course Blanche would have to be made over and babied, too. Fortunately, Blanche loved being tended to. Days after the cut was all healed, she would still be putting her head down to ask for it to be looked at.

Finally, all the essentials were taken care of. The cookhouse had been cleared except for one table reserved for the late travelers. Cookie and Slim knew that there must be some grave reason for them to come in late. Half the show gathered around watching them try to eat and tell the story, or rather the stories. An extra table was pulled up so that Woody's wife and kids and parents could sit down near him. His brother Lucky and his family were nearby, too. It was a slow supper with a lot of questions interrupting it.

Then Reverend Waverly showed up with the town nurse who would be looking after John, and they got plates of food, too. Another round of storytelling began.

Woody asked if they could just take a cup of tea and some cornbread and with them and leave the cookhouse so that Cookie and the crew could clean up.

"Boss, don't worry about it. Me and Slim, we're listening, too."

Eventually, though, a circle of folding chairs and bales of hay was assembled outside. The circle kept expanding as more people brought chairs and joined in.

The kids sat on canvas or horse blankets. New England evenings can be quite cool, even in the summer, so some wood was brought and a fire started. Somebody brought marshmallows, and the kids were soon roasting them on sticks.

Reverend Waverly had already administered two or three doses of "medicine" to John, who said he was feeling much better. The reverend kindly asked if anybody else needed a little dose of the Canadian medicine, "for medicinal purposes, of course," and several hands went up to signal that a little might do them good. The whiskey bottle circulated freely, and then another bottle was produced. "We don't live that far from Canada," he said, "so we can get this 'medicine' pretty easy." It was too dark for anybody to see that the reverend was winking broadly.

Woody was lavish in his praise for John, his son Gilly, Hattie, and Harry, but especially for John. Elephants were not John's usual responsibility, yet he took quick action that may have saved their lives, and he paid a price for it. The show folks gave him a round of applause. Woody did not mind being the butt of a joke, so he said that Hattie outsmarted him by sitting in a cemetery while he rode a horse all over a mountain trying to catch elephants. He asked Hattie to tell the story herself. There were a lot of oohs and ahs and laughter, and a dozen questions.

Woody also asked for everybody to acknowledge the Reverend Waverly, who had been so good to them and so helpful. He really helped John, and he helped save the life of the poor driver of the runaway truck.

Reverend Waverly said that he had had a really good day. "You know, sometimes a preacher has to try really hard to get people to church, and here I got five new people to come to church in one day, and it wasn't even Sunday!"

GR and Camie were always alert to the possibility of publicity for the circus. In this case, what could have been a fine story for the local radio and the newspapers in the coming towns was totally unnecessary. Everybody in the town had already heard about it, and the news was already reaching the next few towns. That is the way it was in smaller and more isolated communities. And while the town populations were smaller, a higher percentage of the people came to see the show. There were even times when the school principal would ask what time the afternoon performance was so that she could be sure to let school out in time for the kids to get to the show. It was not unknown for stores to close during show times in towns like these.

Amy was curious about one part of the story, and she asked Reverend Waverly why there was a church there on the side of the mountain, with no houses or people nearby.

"My dad told me that back in the old days, the two towns both wanted a preacher, and there wasn't many preachers around. So they said that whoever built a church first would get the preacher. But my town said they would never go across the mountain to the other town to go to church, and they said the same thing.

"Well, this went on and on for a number of years. Neither town built a church. Finally, a boy from our side of the mountain wanted to marry a girl from the other side of the mountain, an' let me put it this way, they kind of needed to do it in a hurry, if you know what I mean. They say it was the girl's grandmother who came up with the solution. She had always liked that little flat place not far from the top of the mountain back there. There just are not many flat places around. She said maybe both towns should come together an' clear off that flat place an' have the wedding there in the clearing, an' later they could build a real church there.

"So that was the first sensible thing that was ever said about the church competition, an' they all got together an' cleared the spot. That wedding was the first wedding there ever. It was just an open-air ceremony in the cleared space. But the funny thing is, the cemetery really started before the church got built. Ole Lady Gibbs, that is what they say her name was, she was the girl's grandmother, an' poor woman, she ended up dying before the church got built, so she is the oldest burial there. Some of the old folks still call the church Gibbs's Chapel."

It was interesting to hear this bit of local history, and it made the stories that happened at the church today even more interesting. And everybody wanted to hear the stories over and over again. They loved hearing about the bananas and the tombstones knocked over. They laughed again about poor John having to take his pants off in church. They laughed about paying back the reverend's kindness with manure on the flowers. They thought it was very smart to siphon the leaky gas out of the saddle tank and put it in other tanks. They wondered how John could back down the mountain with the elephant truck, even while his leg was banged up.

It was a very clear night, and the stars twinkled up above as the story telling went on and on. Then the fire gradually died down. The crowd dwindled. What had been a harrowing day ended up on a happy note. Everybody knew they could sleep just a little bit later in the morning, since they were already on the circus lot, and there would be no driving.

Woody and Amy gathered up their kids with Woody carrying little Bart, who had fallen asleep in his arms. Lucky and Tillie were collecting their kids, too, and Tillie was carrying Fred. They went over to Camie and GR and thanked them for their advice when they were laying out the circus route for the season. Camie and GR had reminded them of how bad Jacob's Ladder was and that they really ought not to try showing a town the same day they went over Jacob's Ladder. It was better to take a whole day just to get over it.

Woody asked, "Do we really want to do Jacob's Ladder again next year?" They stared at one another intently. Tillie replied, "Maybe that is something we don't want to decide tonight. Let's see how many tickets we sell tomorrow and how much money we take in. If we do decide to play here next year, we just have to leave an extra day to get over Jacob's Ladder!"

The Brewers all exchanged hugs and kisses and went off to bed.

22. THE SHEIKS OF THE DESERT AND THEIR ARABIAN HIGH-JUMPING HORSES

The Brewer Brothers Circus act known as "The Sheiks of the Desert and Their Arabian High-Jumping Horses" had an unexpected provenance, at least in the summer of 1933. Denny and Ernestine Dillon, the two leads of the act, were both born in the Blue Grass Country of Kentucky. Ernestine was better known as Polly. They grew up around horses and horse people. Both had been steeplechase riders. Denny had been a jockey, and though girls weren't supposed to be jockeys, Polly had on occasion cut her hair and impersonated a boy so she could ride, too. By the time they were in their twenties and had married, they still loved horses but had had some bad experiences with horse people. There were wealthy racehorse people who really loved their racing stock, cared for them, had them well cared for.

But Polly and Denny had ended up working for wealthy racehorse people who got into the business less seriously and for whom their horses were just status symbols and tax breaks. They wanted pretty barns and pretty equipment. They even bought racing stock because they thought the color was pretty or they liked the white star on the horse's forehead. They didn't really care about the wellbeing of the animals. They even ordered Denny and Polly to over-train and wouldn't give them enough time to get horses over strained leg muscles. They wanted brand-new sheepskin on the nosebands of halters so they would look nice whenever friends came around. Then there was a horrible case everybody had heard about. A wealthy woman specifically put in her will that immediately upon her death, all eleven of her thoroughbreds were to be put down. Her idea was that this would make it impossible for her horses ever to be mistreated or suffer any pain again. In only one hour, two veterinaries euthanized thousands and thousands of dollars in prize horseflesh, including some excellent breeding stock.

The Dillons hoped to have some of their own horses one day, but it was hard to get enough money ahead. When the Depression hit, paradoxically, horses were extremely cheap, but getting the money together to buy them was harder than ever.

When the opportunity came up for them to work with the circus, they were skeptical. They were looking for a new start in the horse business but weren't sure what it would be exactly. When they went to visit the Brewers, it was really a two-way interview or audition. They wanted to see how the Brewers treated horses, how well the horses were taken care of. The Brewers wanted to see what the Dillons could do with stock, how they could ride and jump, and how they treated horses. The meeting went on for two hours and then into a third and a fourth hour. It included jumping some horses over low and medium hurdles. By early afternoon it was clear that the Dillons were a good fit. Terms were agreed on. The Dillons would work with the jumping horses as their main responsibility and have more work in several other areas. For example, they would be in charge of keeping the gallon containers and the hand sprayers of DDT, the usual spray insecticide of the time. They would spray the horses, elephants, and the cookhouse whenever needed to bring some relief from flies and mosquitos. They would start their new jobs two weeks before the May 1st opening of the new season.

Performing with jumping horses in a circus was more like a steeplechase than anything else the Dillons knew, but there were lots of differences. There would be only an audience and no judges, and the horses would be on the rather narrow track around the three circus rings in a tent instead of through an outdoor obstacle course. They would have to smile to the crowd and raise their arms to acknowledge applause, something that seemed awkward to them and that would take some coaching. What they would be wearing was completely different than jockey silks or the like. Horses were still involved, but everything else was pretty much a new way of life.

A few weeks after that first meeting, they arrived where Brewer Brothers Circus was assembling. They brought only a couple of flimsy suitcases, with hardly a nickel to their name. They were optimistic and happy to have a new start.

They started training and practicing immediately with the six horses that were in the act known as the Sheiks of Desert and their Arabian High-Jumping Horses. Only two of the jumping horses were actually Arabian, the two white ones, and they were pink-skinned Arabians. There were no papers on them. But all six horses were good jumpers anyway. Nobody cared. Few people could tell a purebred Arabian from a Quarter Horse or whatever. Denny was to ride Mounty, and Polly was to ride Pablo. But their duties including assuring that four more jumping horses were always ready to go and that there were four capable riders ready to ride them for every performance for a total of six horses and riders ready and in Arabian wardrobe.

The jumping horse riders had to mount up a good ten minutes before the act to warm up their horses by running a bit behind the tent and to be sure the saddle was well cinched. There were horses that could be "puffers." Puffers just had a natural habit of inhaling and expanding their chest when a saddle is put on. Later, when the puffer lets the air out, the cinch can be loose and needs to be snugged up again.

Some people in the audience were more attracted to the "Arabian" wardrobe that the riders wore than to the performance of the horses. The wardrobe consisted of Arab headdresses, baggy white trousers with sashes, and long, flowing red satin capes that went down over the backs of the horses and made a terrific silhouette. When the horses ran, the capes flew up in the air behind the riders for a wonderfully dramatic effect. The male riders rode bare-chested, and the three women wore white blouses. None of the audience or the performers had seen Arabs before, not outside of movie representations, but this getup was close enough. Nobody seemed to wonder if women could be "sheiks." The musical selection played by the band matched the action and added to the drama. "The Flight of the Bumble Bee" was a standard for this act.

A skilled Western rider was far from automatically a good jumping horse rider. He or she had to learn to ride with an English saddle. Compared to a Western-style saddle, the English saddle was not much of a saddle at all. It had no horn, a very small pommel, and not much of a seat. The stirrups were shorter. There were no tapadores, the stylish toe covers on stirrups. It weighed a third as much as a Western saddle. It was like a saddle used by jockeys in races. Posting is never done with a Western saddle, but at the right gait, riders with English saddles may post, rising and sitting in the saddle in a rhythm to match the horse's speed.

Another difference from Western-style was how the reins were held. Instead of holding the reins in the left hand so that the right hand was free for other work, the rider typically looped the reins to hold them in both hands just over the withers of the horse. A standard practice was to rise in the stirrups shortly before the horse jumped so that the horse had less of the weight of the rider to lift, and then to sit down only after the horse was over the jump and had all four feet on the ground. The horse would be spared having the full weight of the rider come down on its back at the same time as its two front feet were hitting the ground.

The horses jumped over a hurdle that was set up between two tall gates. The gates were as tall as a man's head, set about ten feet apart. The gates funneled the jumpers toward the hurdle. As the act started, the hurdle was rather low to the ground. It was raised each time the six horses had jumped it. To add a bit of drama, a "brush jump" was added. It was a split hurdle with the ends of sawed-off brooms bolted between the two pieces of hurdle. The protruding broom bristles made the jump look a little higher, and they protected the horses' feet a bit if they ever banged the hurdle.

Since the act was on the track around the three rings, the audience got to see the jumps up close. If the ground was dusty, every effort was made to sprinkle it down with water so that the audience would not be covered in a cloud of dust. If the ground was muddy, there was another challenge. If a horse slid in the mud before rising to jump, the animal might get off the ground too late and crash right through the hurdles.

At the start of the act, each horse jumped a few low jumps, using very little effort. It was sort of a warm-up. Next came the pair jump with two horses at a time. The riders knew which of the two horses wanted to be first and race ahead of the other and which wanted to be slow and lag a bit. The object was to get both horses to jump in unison, lifting their front feet at the same time. Then there was the triple jump with three horses jumping in unison. The riders had to get the three horses to run and jump very closely side by side so that they would fit through the tall gates.

There was almost a hope that Benjy or Becky would knock the hurdle down once early in the act. They were the younger and less careful horses. If they did knock a hurdle pole down, shouts of "aw" would come from the audience, then spontaneous applause when the horse tried again successfully. Every few weeks, a rider might be dumped for any of a number of reasons. The horse might slide awkwardly before the jump. The horse might shy from some distraction beyond the jump. That is why there were strict orders for balloon sellers with their huge "bouquets" of balloons to stay out of sight and out of the tent during this act. Occasionally, just like a human athlete, a horse might just be off. Or it could be the rider who might be having a poor day and fall because of lack of concentration. Everybody agreed that it was far preferable to fall far on the other side of the hurdles, far enough for any falling hurdles not to come down on the rider. Falling before the jump might mean crashing into the hurdles. The more skilled a rider was, the more he or she could somehow grab the neck of the horse on the way down, turning a fall into more of a rapid dismount. The best riders went years without falling. Less experienced riders could fall monthly.

There was no great shame in falling off a jumping horse. Sometimes it just happened. But there was a type of shame in falling and not holding onto the reins of the horse. That was not very forgivable. The loose horse could run off to who-knows-where, and the horse might step on the reins while running, pulling harmfully down on the bit and bridle and maybe inflicting injury. There was a bit of shame in a rider showing any pain from a fall, too. The audience did not like to see pain. It was just standard practice to paste a smile on one's face, rise with a sort of dignity, even salute with one hand or take a little bow, and get back on the horse. Doing it well could elicit a round of applause.

Horse people know better than to chase a runaway horse. Horses are faster than people. Instead, the technique is to work with a few other people and try to corral the horse against a fence or building or other obstacle, speaking gently. Shaking a feedbag with a little grain in it can be very seductive, too. People who weren't horse people could be a problem. They could develop a foxhunt mentality and chase a loose horse, making the situation worse. "No, thank you, sir, but we don't need help. Our horses know us." That was the sort of comment the show folks would make in such a case. Yet some local guy might have a hard time missing a chance to be the hero who helped catch the runaway circus horse.

As the hurdles were lifted higher and higher, two horses and riders would drop out and take a place in the back of the center ring, then another and another, leaving just Sheila and Mounty in the act. They were ridden by Natalie Marveli and Denny Dillon, respectively. These two horses would do the next-to-the-highest jump as a pair jump. Then there would be a big announcement about the magnificent animal that would attempt to do the final high jump, six feet high. The animal was Royal Mounty named for his service with the Royal Canadian Mounted Police. Royal Mounty had been retired after an injury in the line of duty, but because he was so well loved, the Mounties offered him to a home that would take good care of him. Or was it that Mounty was too tall for their standards? The stories varied from time to time. In any case, Mounty began his second career as a star of the Brewer Brothers Circus Sheiks of the Desert and their Arabian High-Jumping Horses act. The audience was asked to maintain strict silence, and the band ceased playing in preparation for this spectacular jump. Mostly for dramatic effect, Mounty was ridden slowly up to the high jump and given a good chance to look at the high hurdle and even smell it. He knew the routine very well, and he would never expect to be ridden up to the high jump without this step first. Mounty just never missed the high jump. He was as dependable as clockwork. He made it look easy. He always got a great round of applause as he closed out the Sheiks of the Desert act.

Sheila was a well-behaved horse, but she was unhappy at this point in the act. She wanted to do the high jump, too. She saw no reason why Mounty always got to do it. She rankled. Natalie Marveli, who was almost always her rider, had to make a special effort to control her. Everybody knew that Sheila could do the final high jump just a well as Mounty, but the audience loved the story about Mounty and the Royal Canadian Mounted Police. No one had thought up a good story about Sheila yet.

At the end of the jumping act, there was a potential traffic jam at the backdoor of the tent. Six riders were exiting with their horses, and Uncle Harry and Aunt Hattie were lined up to enter with three elephants. The animals weren't the problem so much as any forgetful humans who got in the way at the busy backdoor. Policemen or members of the sponsoring committee had to be politely asked to step way back.

Denny and Polly Dillon were glad that they had transitioned to circus life. They could still be in the horse business but avoid some of the bad times they had had with certain racehorse people. They even started discussing buying their own first horse with Grandpa GR. Nobody could buy horses better than Grandpa GR. Denny and Polly were thrilled at the idea of finally owning their own stock. Granted, the horses would not be thoroughbred racers, but they would be great horses, horses that they could make a living with.

Their long-term goal became buying and training two high school or *haute école* trick horses. These horses did a routine based on what European show horses did in competition. Currently, there was no high school act on the Brewer show. There were horses that could do the routine, but the show had a bit too many horse acts. Maybe another season they would drop a current horse act and bring back the high school act. In any case, high school horses were a good place for the Dillons to start.

Then came the decision of which breed and color to get. This being the Great Depression, horses were pretty much a buyer's market. Polly and Denny settled on two options. One would be Palominos, which were a more popular breed than ever thanks to certain film cowboys who rode Palominos. The other option would be Appaloosas, leopard Appaloosas with the spots over the entire body instead of the Appaloosas with the spots just over the hips. GR explained that if Appaloosas did half the act that some plain sorrel horses did, the people would like the Appaloosa act much better. It was the breed of horse that sold the act. So Polly and Denny left it like that with GR. He would tell them when something came up, and they could look at the horse or horses and take it from there. They were not in a hurry.

There were so many ways they liked working on the circus, but one day all that threatened to change. Lucky Brewer told them in a very nice way that to really carry their weight on the show, they had to learn to drive truck and get a driver's license. On the face of it, this was a very reasonable request. Lucky was puzzled by how they both blanched when he brought up getting a driver's license. He just told them that they should get Jake or Choctaw or somebody to start giving them a few lessons in a pickup, and he let it go at that.

Actually, they both already knew how to drive a bit, at least small trucks, and learning to drive a semitruck would not be hard. They had been driving small trucks around barns and racetracks since late childhood. There was another problem. They were profoundly ashamed of the fact that they could not read. They could not read at all. They could not read road signs or a license test or even little signs in a store. They could hardly read prices. They could not do arithmetic above single digit numbers. When payday came and they went for their cash, as a signature they scribbled some illegible scratches in the receipt book and laughed about how they never were any good at writing.

Going to a restaurant was so hard. They usually just ordered a hamburger because they could not read the menu. Sometimes, if others had already ordered and they heard something that sounded good, they would ask for the same thing. Then there was the agony of paying the bill. They usually just put down some money, and if it was not enough, they would apologize to the waitress and add more money. They rarely went with others to a restaurant because they did not want anybody to get suspicious, though some already thought that they Polly and Denny must not be very well educated.

Neither of them had more than two or three years of schooling, and those years were interrupted by moves from one racetrack to another. There were delays in getting back in school and troubles getting to the schoolhouse. By third grade, they still couldn't read the basic primers. Other children mocked them. They gradually quit school. It was the easy way out. This of course was years before they met and married. They just had parallel experiences, each in their own family.

Neither set of parents objected to them not going to

school. The parents had not gone seriously to school either. They used to say, "What need do you have for book learnin' in the horse business? You need to know horses an' how to take care of them an' train them. That aint in no book."

In a sense the parents were right. It wasn't in a book, and Denny and Polly had a fine education about horses, a certain hands-on level of the horse business. In reality, though, they were trapped at that level of the horse business. They could never do more than train, clean, feed, and care for horses. All else was beyond them. They could never own, trade, or make a better living with them.

They could not check to see if the bill for a delivery of feed was correct or not. They might pretend to, but ultimately they had to trust the feed man. They could hardly count money, if there were more than a few coins and bills involved. They just had to smile and be agreeable and go through the motions. Life was a long exercise in hiding shame and hoping not to be taken advantage of.

This is not to say that illiteracy existed only in the milieu of horse people. It did not. It was widespread. The great American educational system was still making its mark on the population, and it was doing it far too slowly. Illiteracy was decreasing, more kids were finishing grade school, some were going on to high school, and teachers were becoming better qualified. College education was the domain of the elite and a minority of smart, hard-working poor kids. Changes were on the horizon, but the changes were so slow they could best be measured in decades and generations. Sadly, that horizon had moved farther away during the Depression.

With the extremely high basic literacy rate in this country today, it is hard to imagine what making a livelihood was like in those days for the illiterate. Nowadays, the only admitted illiterates anybody knows are very young children. In the 1930s, it was a sizable minority of adults.

"Well, it isn't like we're stupid or something! We are not! We got brains!" Polly was almost crying and almost screaming as she looked at Denny.

"I know that, Honey. We are just as smart as anybody else, but people can be so mean to us. They think they are so much better. It aint our fault. We just had bad luck." Denny knew that his words were useless. He could as easily been the one screaming, "We aint stupid." He felt the same way and had suffered in the same way. It was agony for people to know they were illiterate and could never become literate. They would always be walled off from what life could be for others, and the walling off was so unjust and permanent.

It took a week, but when they ran into Lucky again and he had a minute to talk, he asked how their driving lessons were going. This time Polly told the truth, or part of it. "Oh, we know how to drive a bit already, Lucky. We just don't have licenses."

"Well, good! Give me a short driving demonstration in the next couple days, an' then let's get you some driver's licenses. We try to do things legal when we can, an' we do need drivers."

Polly got that strange troubled look again, and so did Denny. Lucky remembered how they had blanched the first time he brought up the topic of driver's licenses. He knew that there was something behind it. His first thought was that these nice folks must have some kind of record with the law or something. He let the matter drop for the time being. He wanted to talk about it with his wife and maybe his mother.

That afternoon he had the occasion to talk to them together in his mother's *dukkerin' tan,* her fortune-telling tent. He mentioned how it seemed peculiar, how Polly and Denny were doing just fine with everything else, and how this part just didn't fit. A boss never knows the whole story behind people when they are hired.

Tillie and Camie both said they doubted that it was about the law. It must be something else. And it was really strange that they said they could already drive. The Brewers had particular insights into the possibility that the Dillons had never gone to school. After all, the Brewers had no formal schooling either.

"You *gin,*" said Tillie, "You know, once people grow up, they start thinking that they can never learn anything else. They just think that learning is for little kids in school. They get stuck. They don't want to be embarrassed or humiliated if they can't read. They hide it till they *murra,* till their dying day, any way they can. It is their big secret. They are all grown up. All they can see is the shame they would have to go through, sitting in some little school desk with babies an' reading *lils* for *bita chavies,* books for little kids. They can think like that."

"Yea, darling, I know what you mean. Their imagination just runs away with them," Lucky replied.

"So you two think it is a problem of reading. They don't know how to read?" Camie asked her son and daughter-in-law.

"*Ava, Dias,* Yes, Mama, I think that is it. I just wish we could find out. We don't want to insult them or anything. *Lesties* is *keker dinlos.* They're not fools. An' they are such good people. I am not sure that the jumping act has ever looked better," Lucky said.

"Honey, you leave it up to your mama an' me. I bet we can come up with a way to find out if it is reading or not, an' we won't insult them, as you say. We'll even see if Aunt Jenny or somebody can give them a start. Sometimes if a man or a woman gets a little start, then they really wanna go further on their own, with just a bit a' help at times when they need it," Tillie said to her husband but while looking at Camie, too.

"OK, darling, you two can do it if anybody can. What is really funny is that in a lot of places you can get a driver's license even if you can't read. 'Course you gotta be able to drive, an' you just memorize a few road signs. Some places make you do a test, too, but you take it the first time an' fail, an' you try to keep a copy, an' you get help from somebody, an' memorize where to check the answers, an' then you come back again an' take a new test. The guy might not even check the test paper," Lucky said.

"We don't like to do it, but there are towns where you can ask, an' they will give you a license if you *del* 'em *vonger,* give them money. That is all you need to do," Tillie said.

Tillie and Camie came up with an approach, one that wasn't entirely misleading or untrue. They told Polly and Denny that for GR to start scouting out for horses for them, there would have to be a simple agreement with the show, about how much would come out of their salary for how long to pay for the horses. They asked the two to come to Camie's *dukkerin tan* to discuss the deal the next afternoon.

When they came, Denny's first response was to say, "Oh, Ms. Camie, just a handshake is fine for us. We trust you. You have been so good to us. We don't need no fancy paperwork. Let's keep it simple."

"Well, son," Camie replied, "Unfortunately, for tax purposes an' whatnot, we have to do more paperwork nowadays. This is very simple, but we need you two to look it over an' see what you want to change."

"Oh, no, ma'am. It's fine with us. We don't like to do business like that. Why can't we just agree that you take what you need to out of our salary? Everybody knows that Amy Brewer is terrific with money an bookkeepin'. That is not a problem for us."

After a couple more times to-and-fro, they somewhat relented. Tillie pulled out a piece of paper that was an agreement. She handed it to them. They looked it over and nodded. They asked, "Can we just sign right here?"

"Well, Polly, Denny, we want to talk to you about something else. It is very serious. First I have to say that we love your work on the show with the jumpers an' everything, an' we hope you will stay with us for a long time. But we would like to help you with something, but only if you want us to," Tillie said in a business-like but gentle way.

"Well, what is that, Tillie?" Polly asked.

"I can start by telling you a little about one of the most intelligent people I ever knew," said Camie. "He was my dad's brother Ed. He knew all kinds of things, an' he could do all kinds of things. Everybody respected Uncle Ed. But he had one bad secret," Camie said.

"What was that?" Denny asked, intrigued by the story.

"Ed could not read, not at all," Camie replied. When she said that sentence, Denny and Polly changed their expression completely. Their faces dropped. They looked devastated.

"We know you can't read, an' there is no shame in that. You can be sure that we won't tell anybody. What goes on in this tent does not get talked about anyplace else," Tillie said.

"You see, when I handed that piece of paper with the contract on it, it was upside down. You both pretended to read it, but you could not. You were even going to sign what was really the top of the paper," she explained.

"You mean you are going to fire us because we can't read? That is not fair. We aint stupid! We are as smart as anybody else. It is just how we was brought up. This isn't fair!" Denny said, his voice going up and down. He wanted to scream, and at the same time he was ashamed.

"Oh, no! We know you are smart, very smart. We will not fire you. We want to keep you. An' you are right; it is not fair, an' it is not your fault. Uncle Ed was that way. He was so smart, but my grandfather an' grandmother, for some reason or another, never taught him reading an' numbers like they did their other children. It was not fair," Camie explained.

"Well, there is nothing we can do about it; so I guess we'd best just leave it like that. Let it be our secret. Nobody needs to know. We fake it all the time, every day," Polly replied.

"But there is something you can do about it. That is why we wanted to talk to you. We think that you are so smart that you could still learn numbers and reading. It just has to be all slow an' all confidential," Tillie said.

"Why, I never heard of such a thing! We aint kids, you know. We are adults. We can't sit down in a little chair with a picture book or something like children do. You should learn to read when you are a little kid, not as a grownup," Denny replied, sounding very defensive.

"Actually," Tillie continued. "We know of grownups who learned reading an' numbers, an' it was all kept quiet, completely quiet. They just worked real hard. They wanted things to be different for them. They learned. It made a new sort of life for them."

"We been doin' OK now for all this time. We just have to do like we been doin'," Denny said.

"Have you really been doin' OK? Have you ever worried about bein' taken advantage of? Have you ever thought you were shortchanged but had no way of knowing? Did you ever pretend you could read something an' had to make up a story when you couldn't?" Camie asked.

"Miss Camie, we have to do that kind a' thing every day. You have no idea how hard it is. You have to find people you think you can trust. That is why we like the Brewers. We don't think you are lyin' to us or shortchangin' us. We get a feelin' we can trust you," Polly said. Her eyes were getting moist. She was suffering. So was Denny.

Tillie continued, "We want to make you an offer. It is up to you. We think it will work. Here it is: tell us if you want to do some work with letters an' reading first, or if you want to start with some numbers, like counting money. Of course, you know some already. So you would have a fast start either way. Or you can do some letters an' some numbers at the same time. You can go as fast or as slow as you want. You can start or quit whenever you want. It is all up to you," Tillie explained.

"Well, how would it work, exactly? Who would be doin' it with us? Is there books or somethin'?" Denny asked.

Next Camie spoke, "Tillie can spend a little time with you most days, an' then you can work and look at it on your own, on little bits of paper or road maps or whatever. My grandson Gilly is really good at explaining things. You decide who you want to talk to or work with. You are in charge. It has to be really practical. There are no books yet.

"You can tell us if you want to work on road signs or prices in a store or counting money or reading billboard advertisements you see along the road. Oh, the words on the dashboard of a truck are important, an' what it says on an oilcan. You will be the boss.

"It all has to be casual an' quiet, completely quiet. We know how to keep our mouth shut. Nobody else on the show knows what is going on," Camie concluded.

Polly and Denny looked at each other, not knowing what to say next. Their minds were racing through too many thoughts. The idea of buying horses was not at the forefront now. They were fearful. They were hopeful, at least a little.

Tillie spoke next, "You two take some time to think about all this. You are fine folks, really good people, an' we want to do whatever you would like us to do. We hope you will try some of this out. But like you say, you are grownups. You know what you want to do. Just let us know what you think you want to try."

Tillie and Camie stood up, but standing up did not mean for Denny and Polly to leave the tent. It only meant that they were not going to try talking Denny and Polly into something they had not made their mind up about. Then there were handshakes, and then for the first time Polly hugged Tillie and Camie. It was awkward. They didn't know if it was OK to hug them, since they were Brewers and the bosses of the show, but Camie and Tillie hugged back warmly. Then they reached out their arms to Denny to hug him, too.

There was no contract signed for buying horses at the meeting, but the Dillons felt more secure than ever about their jobs. And something more important happened. The Dillons walked away with a chance for a different future. That night when they went to bed, they talked late into the wee hours. They did not sleep well. By dawn, they still had not made up their minds.

Two days later, Denny came to Tillie in the office and said, "We wanna get better at countin' money. That part is the worst. What can you do?"

"Here is a little bag of money. I am going to give it to you. You an' Polly count the money when you have a chance. Take your time. Count it a couple times. I always do. It is not a lot of money, mostly just ten or twelve coins. Then see if you can write the numbers down on the piece of paper in the bag. Try to make your numbers look like the numbers I have written on the paper there. There is a little pencil there, too. Just pass me the bag back in a couple days, an' I will check it out as soon as I have a chance. Yours is the only little Bull Durham tobacco bag with a red rubber band on the string. Does that seem a good way to start?" Tillie asked.

"Gee, we can try that. An' nobody needs to know. They will just think we are bringin' money into the office like anybody else. Maybe between the both of us, we can count it right," Denny replied.

The little Bull Durham tobacco bag with the red rubber band on the string went back and forth many times. Tillie made the amounts of money gradually more complicated with various mixtures of coins and small bills. Sometimes she sat down with them and watched them count and gave them encouragement.

Then she added a little list with the words "quarter," "dime," "nickel," and "penny," so that Polly and Denny would learn to read those words. She added the numbers one through ten so that they could write down how many coins of each kind there were, and the total value for each type of coin to add to a grand total.

It was quite a discovery for the Dillons to learn that it is better to count all the coins of each kind separately and then to add up the totals. They had just been adding randomly and making mistakes. They would add a nickel and a dime, and then a couple pennies and then another dime and a quarter, for example, making the arithmetic unnecessarily complicated. And they learned always to start counting with the five-dollar bills if there were any and then one-dollar bills. They were the important place to start.

This all took weeks. There were questions. There were errors. Yet there was progress.

One drizzly afternoon, Tillie surprised Polly. "Do you

think you could help on the pony ride for an hour or so before the matinee? We need help. You could collect the money an' make change. Our kids will get the town kids on an' off the ponies, but none of the bigger kids is there. It is better to have a bigger kid or an adult to handle the money."

"Oh, Ms. Brewer, gee, I suppose I could. You need help. But what if I have a problem?"

"Don't worry, Polly. Just say you need change or something, an' come on over to me at the ticket office. I can straighten it out. Don't worry," Tillie replied. "It is five cents a ride, so people usually pay with nickels, but you never can tell.

"Sometimes they give you pennies or dimes or dollars. Keep as many ones and fives as you can. Give back as many pennies and nickels in change as you can. Just give a couple ones back if you get a five. Then give them dimes or nickels with a few quarters. Get rid of the coins. That makes counting everything at the end of the day faster. You don't have ten pounds of coins."

"I wanna try. I won't make big mistakes. You are givin' me a chance to try, an' I have to take it. I'll do my best. Thank you, Ms. Brewer," Polly said as she took the pony ride change apron.

Within an hour, Polly was doing it like an old pro. Nobody could tell she was new, new on the pony ride and new as a change counter. Denny tried it a couple days later, and he had equal success. The pony ride work was an intense drill for their number skills. They got faster and more confident. The experience had carry-over to the rest of their life. They felt a thrill every time they paid for an item in a store and counted out the change they got back. It was a new freedom for them. Nobody could ever cheat them with money again.

While they were learning the numbers for handling money, they were learning to read their first fifty or so words. Tillie had started writing small words on slips of paper in the little Bull Durham tobacco bag. It was fun for the Dillons to learn that "OK" meant both OK and was the same as the two letters O and K. They learned to read the words for the numbers up to twenty, and then beyond twenty.

At Tillie's suggestion, they took Gilly into their confidence. He made a little list of words on road signs, like *stop, slow, curve, speed limit, school, town, right* and *left.* He let them ask about new words they wanted to add. *Welcome to Warrenton* was hard. Then they wanted a list of names of all the towns they had been in for the last two weeks. Gilly wrote up the list, but what he did next was not completely fair. He asked them to find the names of the towns on a road map.

It took a couple days, but they did it, and they began to sound out the names of other towns, and they got many of them right. Then they wanted to understand map reading, which interested them greatly. Nobody had ever really told them about the four directions, that the sun always comes up in the east and goes down in the west, and that the top of a map is always north. They got questions from other folks on the show about why they were spending so much time looking at maps. But they managed to handle the questions fine.

Denny and Polly were very amused when they learned about abbreviations and acronyms. They thought it was so funny that in reading there were all these rules, but then the rules could be broken at just about any time for any reason. For example, "St." meant "Saint" like in Saint Louis or Saint Paul, but it was just because people got lazy and left out three letters. They found it hilarious that "St." could also mean "Street," and yes, there was even a "St. Louis St." and then an "E. St. Louis St." And if "Mr." meant "mister," why didn't "Mrs." Mean "misters"? That would just be logical.

Because they were adults and highly motivated adults, they had a different point of view than children learning to read. They were not as ready to accept on faith what other adults told them. Were the rules really rules, or were they not really rules? They said that acronyms like MPH or RPM were not really logical, since unless you had memorized it, there was no way to know that MPH was "miles per hour" and RPM was "revolutions per minute." This meant that the rules were pretty weak. Then, for the first time in their lives, they learned what their own initials were, and they seemed rather proud of them. Denny liked that his initials could also stand for Donald Duck.

Their learning approach was not based on any theory of reading teaching. It was some combination of phonetics mixed with sight recognition. Denny was a little better at phonetics, and Polly was better at sight recognition. Mostly, though, the approach worked because Polly and Denny were highly motivated. They wanted to read. More than almost any-thing in their lives, they wanted to read. They actu-ally learned to read the names of eight makes of cars and trucks in one day. Aunt Jenny, who knew more about teaching than anybody on the show, made it a point to stick with the group of kids who came to her every day and to stay away from the Dillons. She knew how crucial it was for privacy to be maintained and for nobody ever to suspect that she was teaching them. But she did give Gilly and Tillie some coaching and suggestions on what to try with them, and she al-ways wanted to hear progress reports.

Counting and reading are easy skills compared to printing and writing. Denny and Polly hardly took a pencil in their hand except to write numbers till the season was over and they were where the show spent the winter. They had more time and privacy. They could read lots of words. Now they could pick some easy ones to try to put on paper. They wrote in a com-bination of printed letters and cursive. They didn't care. Nobody did.

Once in a while they might have thought that they were finished, that they knew how to count money and read signs and so on, and that was enough, all they needed. Then Gilly would give them a comic book, bringing them a new world. *Life* magazine came after that, and then *Saturday Evening Post*. The reading les-sons gradually became more like vocabulary lessons. By January they were reading real books, not long books, but not children's books. They read a romance novel once, and they could make out all but about twenty words in the whole book, but they did not like the story. Then they read a Western novel. They liked the story better, but they kept pointing out indications that the author really hadn't spent much time around horses.

On day Gilly got a copy of a blank one-page contract. He filled in the blanks with hypothetical words and numbers. He asked Poly and Denny to study the contract and tell him if they would sign it or ask for changes in it before signing it. The discussion this brought on was long and serious. The Dillons got to do something they had always wanted to do. They got to understand a contract and not just trust in the good heartedness of some boss. They could protect themselves. They had freedom.

One measure of their freedom was applying for their driver's licenses. They were bursting with pride when they could fill out the application form and take the written test. They got perfect scores on the test, and the clerk would have been suspicious, but he had them sit on different sides of the room. They could not cheat. The driving part of the test was easy. They passed that perfectly, too. They walked out of the county office with their first driver's licenses.

That March, Camie and Tillie asked them to meet again to go over a contract for GR to buy horses for them and for the cost of the horses to come out of their salaries over time. It was a real contract, the first one they could ever really understand. Just as a joke, Tillie handed it to them upside down. At first they looked shocked, but then they remembered, and Tillie, Camie, Denny and Polly howled with laughter.

Gradually, Denny and Polly got up to what would be called a middle school level of reading and math. They kept reading. They even got a used math book. They didn't care anymore what anybody said. They just wanted to learn, and they were not ashamed. They never did take a high school equivalency test. There were no such things in those days. But if they had, within two or three years, they would have passed easily.

When Denny and Polly had a son and a daughter, they were very careful to be sure they got good schooling. They taught them all about horses and riding, too, but they were damn sure they were going to be the last generation in the family with no formal schooling.

23. THE SUGARSTONES

Somewhere in the southern Great Plains in the late 1880s, the United States Cavalry murdered the grandfather of the circus performer known as Chief Red Hawk Sugarstone. The grandfather was captured in one of the last Native American uprisings. He was in a band of twenty-two Osage warriors who were armed mostly with bows and arrows and five ancient rifles for which they had little ammunition.

The Cavalry orders were to execute the captives, and the soldiers disarmed the Osages of their bows and arrows and rifles and tied their hands behind their backs. Some of the cavalrymen balked at executing them. To kill an enemy in battle was one thing. To shoot a bound captive at short range was another. But the reluctant men were under orders. They would be court martialed if they did not obey orders. The first nine captives were lined up and shot at a distance of twenty feet. Then the captain ordered the soldiers to stop shooting, saying that ammo should not be wasted on Indians, and that the rest were to be hanged. But first the shooting victims were searched for any silver ornamentation, which was to be handed in as government property. The soldiers were then allowed to take any pretty beadwork or nice leather they liked. They could keep it as souvenirs. They were ordered not to take scalps.

The next three hours were messy and chaotic. When the soldiers started carrying the corpses to a mass grave, they discovered that one of the captives who had been shot had survived. The bullet intended to kill went through the side of his face and out one side of his neck. He was still breathing, and his eyes were open, and he was watching what was going on around him.

There was some discussion about what should be done, and one of the soldiers pointed out that it would not be the "Christian" thing to do to bury him alive. Somebody commented that it didn't matter since he was just a heathen Indian and not a Christian anyway. The captain ordered the men to wait till he died before burying him or, if needed, to hang him or maybe just choke him.

Only two men in the platoon had been involved in hangings before. Some of the other men thought that victims just choked to death when hanged; therefore, what difference would it make if this Indian was just choked to death on the ground instead of taking all the time to hang him from a rope? The captain stood by while the experienced men explained that hanging was more than choking, that hanging was instant; it snapped the neck, and that there was not supposed

457

to be any doubt if the victim was dead or not.

On this prairie there was only one tree within a reasonable distance that would be suitable for hanging, except that the branches all pointed more skyward rather than parallel to the ground. One private was ordered to climb the tree and find the most suitable branch and drop a rope down from it. The rope he dropped down ended up being quite close to the trunk of the tree. Four more privates were assigned to pull on the rope to bend the branch down and out farther so that the hanging victims would swing free of the tree trunk.

One of the experienced men mentioned that there was a problem since they did not have a wagon or even a small buckboard to use as a sort of gallows, usually forcing the condemned men to stand in the back of the wagon with the noose on their neck and then pulling the wagon out from under them.

Some calculations would have to be done if the Indians were going to be put on the back of a horse and the horse led out from under them. One of the experienced men said he did not know if this would give the sudden jolt needed to break a neck or if, after all, there would be slow strangulation, something that could take considerable time.

The captain ordered one man to get on a horse with no saddle and hold onto the rope at about neck level. A second man was ordered to lead the horse out from under the man holding the rope. The man with the rope in his hands swung clear of the ground when the horse was pulled out from under him, but there was no more than a one-foot clearance between his army boots and the ground. Obviously, if the branch bent down too far or if the Indian being hanged was much heavier than the soldier who did the test, the feet would land on the ground and the hanging would not be successful. Since the remaining captives were all very lean, this did not seem like a major problem. Indeed, the Indians had been starving for many months, a major reason for the uprising.

Another topic that engendered considerable discussion was if they should remove any silver and souvenirs from the remaining captives before or after they were hanged. There was a consensus that the soldiers need not wait. It would be efficient to take what they wanted before the hangings so that they would only have to carry the corpses and throw them in the mass grave. The result was that two of the Indians who were wearing particularly nice beaded leggings and loincloths were left nearly naked before they were hanged.

It took two hours to hang the remaining thirteen captives, and a new branch had to be found twice as the old branches broke or bent down too far. The mass grave had to be expanded. The man who had survived being shot was finally killed by just having a saber run through him.

The Army does not have good records of these executions, beyond the number of Indians murdered. The month and date were not clear, and as far as the families of the survivors go, they did not use the European calendar anyway. The location of these murders was not recorded either. I could have been in the

Indian Territory, which was later to become Oklahoma, or it could have been in one of the surrounding states. Of course the Indians considered it all to be Indian Territory, and that is what the conflict was about.

Some of the soldiers were scarred for life by the executions they performed. It was something they could never talk about. Anything relating to controlling Indians and making the country safe for whites was considered a brave and patriotic thing to do. The soldiers' burden was that there is nothing very brave about killing bound captives.

Two people who remembered the season and the approximate location of the murders very well were the Chief Red Hawk's grandmother, who became a widow that day, and his great grandfather, who lost his son. The group of warriors who had left their village did not come back the evening of the day they left, nor the evening after. The old people and the women in the village knew what this meant. The older children understood, too. Two days later, three cavalry platoons showed up with several wagons. Their assignment was to clear everybody and everything out. They were to break up the village and haul the widows and orphans off in several different directions so they would not know one another's locations and could never unite again. The operation was to take one day. What could not be hauled away was to be put in heaps and burned. The village was never to exist again. The phrase "ethnic cleansing" was not used yet, but the policies implemented by the U.S. Government were certainly some variation of it.

An army scout who spoke some Osage served as translator. Cooking fires were to be extinguished and the teepees were to be taken down immediately. Only the old people and very young children could ride in a wagon. Mostly the wagons were to hold teepee poles, buffalo skins, and a few cooking pots.

When the wagons were being loaded, the soldiers routinely went around and pulled out some of the poles and buffalo skins. The mules pulling the wagons could not handle heavy loads. If a teepee usually required a dozen poles to erect and hold it up correctly, it would have to be put up with six. The remaining skins could barely cover the teepee poles; so there would be very few skins left to put on the ground in the teepee or to use to keep warm in winter.

Red Hawk's grandmother and five children along with his great grandfather were fortunate in that they managed to stay together. They were forced on a three-day march to a place that was barren and rocky with hardly any grass or any trees for firewood. There would be little game to hunt in such a place. The interpreter told them they would be getting a cow and three sacks of corn. The cow never came. When the corn came, it was not corn meal. It was not even kernels of corn. It was dried ears of corn, meaning most of the sacks were taken up with inedible corncobs. The cobs would be useless except for meager fuel to burn. The hard kernels would require many hours of pounding on rocks before the corn flour could be put in a cooking pot with water to make corn mush. They would have to live mostly on corn mush. They could make the mush only when they could find fuel to boil the pounded corn.

Three other Osage widows and their children were brought to this place, too. A fifth woman was brought with her children, but she was Otoe, not Osage. Nobody could explain why the army would bring an Otoe. She spoke none of the Osage language, and none of the Osage people spoke anything but a few words of Otoe.

Chief Red Hawk's father was the oldest son in his family. He had been named Bright Stone. Tradition would dictate that he try to assume some of the role of his murdered father in hunting for food. Bright Stone's grandfather, Old Hawk, was very wise, but he was too elderly, and Bright Stone's mother was busy with four younger children. Bright Stone was about fifteen, but he was short for his age, a fact that may have saved his life. If he had been taller, he might have been identified as a potential fighter and been put in a stockade or executed by the cavalry.

As the weather got colder, Old Hawk became more and more of a community leader, a tribal leader, and the women started calling him Chief Old Hawk, the first time the title had been used in the family. One of Chief Old Hawk's first suggestions was that the widows and children take down their five teepees and remake them into three. This was so that there would be enough poles and enough skins for each teepee to repel rain and wind correctly. There would be more buffalo skins to insulate the widows and children from the frozen ground and keep them warm in winter. Of course it meant that there would mostly be two widows with their sets of children per teepee.

Bright Stone's youngest brother died the first winter the surviving members of the family were in this place. His mother barely survived herself. There was a small wandering stream nearby, and it proved to be vital for more than water to drink. His grandfather Chief Old Hawk served as an oral library. He knew where edible bulbs and tubers could be found along the banks. He knew if leaves or roots had medicinal purposes. He could tell the children were there were shallows or eddies that would be best for finding small fish to catch in little woven nets. He taught Bright Stone how to make a flimsy but serviceable bow and arrow using the very unsatisfactory wood that could be found in the environs. If the little arrows were shot from a close range, they might kill a bird. And he taught the boy to make little snares to catch rabbits and muskrats, and how to place the snares on the probable paths of these animals, leave minimal human smell on them, and camouflage them from sight. It was crucial to check the snares often. Once an animal was caught, it might chew its foot off to escape, or some predator might take it. The catches were meager, but they helped survival. When spring finally came, the old man taught Bright Stone how to get eggs from the nests of pheasants and kill-deer, always leaving no scent and leaving one egg so the birds would come back and lay eggs again in the nests.

One day in late spring two whites came up riding on horses, and a third drove a small wagon. Every-one ran up hoping that they were bringing food. And they did offer a little bread. Then when the children were close, the white men started grabbing them, one in each hand, even dropping sacks over their heads, tying their hands and feet and putting them in the wagon. The mothers were screaming and swinging sticks at the whites, but the whites had clubs and wasted no time in clubbing back the women.

"No, don't take that little one. Leave her with the squaw. We don't want to be takin' care of any babies. We don't have time. An' we had two or three a' them little ones die on us anyway. Don't take none a' them big ones neither. It's useless. They already got too much pagan stuff in their blood. They are too old to change an' save. We have tried it. But I think these five or six we got tied up here in the wagon will be fine, an' we can come back in the fall an' get more," the lead white man said.

Of course none of this was understood by any of the families, and it wouldn't have mattered. One of the women used a sharp stick to try stabbing the horse that was pulling the wagon, and a club came crashing down on her head. She lay bleeding on the ground. Another of the women got down on her knees and wailed, hoping the white strangers would show mercy, but she was ignored.

The children were bound like bundles of firewood in the back of the wagon, and they bounced around painfully for several miles till there was a stream crossing. This was where the wagon stopped, and one child was taken out, or at least his head was held over the side of the wagon. One of the white men started cutting his hair off, first the braids, then just fists full of hair, and dropping it in the water. He kept cutting and cutting till there was almost no hair left. The boy tried to kick and bite, but he was slapped, and then the white man pulled out a knife, and the boy prepared to die. Instead, the knife was used to cut his worn leather clothes off him. The clothing was thrown up on the bank. Next the boy was taken to a deeper place in the stream, where he thought he would be drowned. But two of the white men merely dunked his body under the water and pulled him out, saying, "I baptize thee in the name of the Father and of the Son and of the Holy Ghost, Amen." The child had no idea what this meant. He was just trying to be a brave Osage boy.

The man who was driving the wagon got a bag out from under the seat and pulled clothes out of it, white children's clothes, and found pants and a shirt that would fit the wet child. The boy struggled, but the men were stronger, and they got the pants on him. They untied his hands but held them firmly till they got the shirt on before retying him.

This frightening process was repeated with each of the remaining five children. Before the wagon pulled away, one of the men gathered dry sticks and leaves and small pieces of wood in a pile and added all the children's leather clothing to it before setting it all on fire. There was a great deal of smoke, but the wood finally caught, and the leather burned with it.

It was nearly dark when the wagon stopped. The children were very sore and quite hungry. One had peed the clothes that had been put on her. They heard children's voices speaking a strange language, perhaps the white language. Some of those children carried them or dragged them to a place, and two older children came forward and spoke to them in the Osage tongue.

"Welcome Osage brothers and sisters to the Hadley Indian School. If you do what the white men tell you, they will not hurt you so much. They want you to worship the white god and speak the white language. You will learn white things here and become like a white. But we will help you. They are trying to do it to us, too. We can't speak much now because they might know that we are not telling you about prayers to the white god. Just do what we tell you. Pretend like you like it. Smile when they speak to you. Use the intelligence of an Osage child. You will not be hurt as much."

The children were taken to a place where there was food. Their hands and feet were untied. The other children prayed in the white way. There was food in front of them, but the other children were using funny little things like sticks to put the food in their mouths.

So began the white education of the abducted children. A white preacher and his two brothers came from back East with the mission of saving the souls of the Indians. They brought their wives with them. They got permission from local authorities to "get Indian children and save their souls and teach them to read the Bible."

The authorities said, "That sure sounds like a very fine idea. It could help make the country peaceful and save the lives of white people."

A piece of property with a little house and an old barn was purchased and a sign put up that said "Hadley Indian School, Reverend Wilbur Hadley, President." The old barn served as dormitory, schoolroom, refectory, and chapel. The three couples started with four little Indian orphans they got somehow. They increased enrollment in various ways, but one of the fastest ways was to visit the army post and get information about where the army had relocated groups of widows and orphans.

When Bright Stone got home from an unsuccessful hunting trip that sad day, he saw his mother sitting on the ground hunched over. Two of the other women were in the same position. His grandfather told him what had happened. Whites had carried off Bright Stone's brother and sister. Nobody knew where they were taken or what would become of them. He looked in his grandfather's sad eyes, and he knew that it was the truth. Four other children from other women had been taken, too.

"I just can live no more, my Son. I just can live no more," his mother said to him.

"Mother, you must live. Grandfather and I cannot live without you. And my little sister is still here, and she cannot live without you. You must live, Mother. Please live!" he replied.

Their lives would never be the same. They lived weeks and months of sadness. When the next winter came, Bright Stone's hunting trips had to increase, and he had to go farther and farther. Once, when he was looking in a new place for game or for anything to eat to take back to the survivors in his family, he saw a place where white people lived. He crawled up to it slowly to see better what was there, what he could steal. He saw that the people lived in one sort of place. It was wooden and did not look anything like a proper teepee. And he saw that there was another place with no people in it. His stomach was growling with hunger. He snuck up to that place with no people in it and found an opening in the wooden side where he could enter.

What he saw inside was amazing. There was dried grass everywhere, even piled high against the sides. There were animals he had never seen before. There were large birds just sitting peacefully. He grabbed one and cut its head of quickly and tied the feet to his belt. Then he found grain, and he filled a small bag he carried with it. There were two of the largest, tallest, fattest horses he had ever seen, not pretty colored ones like Indian horses, but meaty ones as big as a small buffalo. He decided to do a quick raid and steal one of the horses and run off with it before the white people came. He found a larger opening to push to get out of this place so that he could escape with the horse. He climbed up on some wooden things and got on the back of the horse. He grabbed the leather on its head and kicked it to make it run, but it would not move. He even screamed at it. It would not move. He tried harder and screamed more. He punched it with one of his little arrows. It did not move. Then a dog came barking, attracted by his screams at the horse. Soon there was a white man and a white woman looking at him in the barn. The woman held a large gun.

They just stared at him, and he was so surprised and frightened, he just stared back. He heard the woman speak.

"Will you look at that poor little thing! Why his arms an' legs are just like little sticks. That ragged deerskin he has hangin' over him, well, that couldn't keep a fire warm. Where do you suppose he came from, an' why did he come here?"

"Real strange," the man said. "Never saw nothin' like it. Why would they send a kid out to steal a horse? An' look. He killed one of our hens an' is trying to take off with it. He has no idea that Old Beulah has never been trained to ride. She just knows how to pull a plow or a wagon. She has no idea what that little ole thing is doin' up on her back, but she is a gentle ol' nag," the man said. Of course Bright Stone understood none of this. He could only try to imagine if they were going to shoot him or kill him with a club. His little arrows were useless on something as big as a human being. He was defenseless.

Then the woman smiled at him. "I bet you're hungry, honey. Why don't I get you a warm biscuit or two?"

"Course he don't understand you, sweetie, but why not try? If he is hungry enough, the boy might just come 'round a bit, settle down, be tamed," the man said.

The man smiled too, and Bright Stone was very confused. In his culture, if a thief was caught, he was usually killed. It was part of the code. The woman returned with something that smelled good. It was on a round stone of some kind. She held the stone up, and he did not know if she was going to throw the stone at him or what. Then the man took one of the things on the stone and put it in his mouth and started eating it. She smiled more and brought the things nearer to him. He was fearful, but his hunger overcame his fear. He took the thing on the stone and put it to his nose. It smelled wonderful. He put it in his mouth. The taste was wonderful. He ate it in no time, and the woman produced two more from some place in her clothes. He ate them both quickly.

Then the man took another one of the birds and cut its head off, and handed it to him, as a gift, smiling broadly. The woman also took something like a thick hide, but it was not a hide, and slowly came and put it on the back of the horse near him and smiled. He touched it. It was soft and warm. Against his better judgment, he pulled it up over his shoulders, and it felt like summer. The place where these people slept must be a very warm place.

The large dog was still watching him, and he could not get down and run away. He did not know what to do. These people were not like what white people were supposed to be like, not that he had ever seen any whites, at least not up close.

"You don't suppose he is one of those orphan kids the army relocated with those widows an' old folks up on Stone Ridge or around Stone Creek somewhere, the ones they needed to put somewhere after they wiped out all those renegades?" the man asked.

"Gee, you could be right. Where else could he come

from? He has a little bitty bow an' arrow, an' you can tell he has been walkin' forever. An' he acts like he aint eat in two days. I have an idea. Call the dog off, an' then pull old Beulah out. No, pull out Max first, an' get on him. Then untie old Beulah an' hand him the lead rope. Beulah will just follow Max anywhere Max goes. An' Max is broke to ride, an' she aint. The little tyke must be able to ride decent. They say Indian kids learn to ride before they can walk."

Then the woman continued," Anyway, I'll get you more food an' stuff. Maybe, just maybe, he will go on the horse with you to where he come from. His folks must need help. Well, he probably don't have a daddy anymore if his daddy was one of the bad ones that they had to kill. But he shouldn't starve because of that. Maybe he does have a mother."

In a few minutes, the man had a bag that the boy saw had been filled with flour and eggs and some kind of meat. The man had put on a big warm hat and another skin of some kind. He kept smiling a lot. He was on the other horse, and he pointed in different directions as he smiled.

Bright Stone could tell that the man meant, "Let's go." It was not clear where he wanted to go. The boy sat there, confused again. Then he decided there was only one place the man could mean to go. It was back where the teepees were. And this white man's horses, they were too slow and too stupid. Obviously, whites did not know how to train horses to be obedient, to run like the wind. What the boy did not know is that draft horses like these were bred to be slow, calm, and obedient in a different way, to pull heavy farm implements or heavy wagons long distances. Indian ponies were almost a different animal. Some Indian ponies had a hard time just walking. They wanted to run whenever there was a man on their back.

Bright Stone thought that if he were bigger, he would go with this man for a distance. When the man was not suspecting it, Bright Stone would trick him, take his gun, kill him, and take both horses and be a hero to his family. Yet there was something so good about this man plus the reality that the boy was not big enough. The best decision he could come up with was to go with the man, get the horses and food nearer where his mother was, and give himself more time to think.

They started out and rode on for about three or four miles, getting in the vicinity of the teepees. The man had kept smiling all along. He even started whistling in a way the boy had never heard before. It was all too much for a fifteen-year old to deal with. He decided when they got within screaming distance he would make a certain kind of cry that would alert the women and children in the teepees so they could run and hide. Old Hawk would know that Bright Stone was OK but that something different was happening.

When they arrived at the teepees, the man jumped from the horse and placed his gun flat on the ground to his left. Then in front of himself and the horse he put one of the big birds and a bag of grain. He stood calmly and smiled. Despite his young years, Bright Stone knew that this meant peace, but he stood at a distance from the man in case there was some trick involved. He had no idea what he would do if there were a trick, and he had already endangered everyone by revealing the location of the teepees. Finally, Old Hawk came out of a teepee and stood still. After a moment, he approached slowly, stopping ten feet from the man. The two stared at each other for what seemed like an eternity. The boy was counting on the wisdom of his grandfather to know what to do. They needed the food so badly. They had had awful experiences with whites. But now this white man came alone, with Bright Stone leading, and Bright Stone seemed just fine.

The white man took a knife from a holder on his belt and placed it on the ground with the chicken and sack of grain. He was adding to the gifts. Old Hawk read the white man's face and how his body moved. He was not braced for a fight. He was almost acting stupid. An arrow from a hidden archer could have pierced his heart at any moment, except that all the adult archers were gone now.

Old Hawk took another few steps forward and raised his hand. He was very cautious but also culturally embarrassed. He should have been able to put something on the ground as a gift, too. He could think of nothing at all that he had to give this man to reciprocate the peace and make it a temporary non-aggression agreement. Finally, he reached for the eagle feather in the back of his headband and put in on the ground. The white man smiled again and bowed slightly. Then he sat down on the ground, putting himself in a more vulnerable situation, indicating his trust.

At this point, Bright Stone felt free to talk. In as few

words as possible, he told his grandfather what had transpired. He knew the old man was listening with great interest, but it was not evident from his face. He sat down, too, and told Bright Stone to also. Of course Old Hawk wanted to look at the horses, the gun, the strange skins the white man was wearing, the big bird on the ground, everything!

The white man decided to speak. Even if the other two had no idea what he was saying, they could probably hear something from how he spoke. He spoke slowly and in a low tone for a few moments and bowed forward again. He took three biscuits from another bag he had and placed one in front of the old man and one in front of the boy. He started eating the third.

"This white man must be from a different tribe. He did not act at all like the ones with the brown horses who all dressed alike and shot at us. He doesn't even know about the war we had with them and how many of us were killed," the boy said to his grandfather.

Then the boy added that these things the white man put on the ground in front of us must be what white people eat a lot. He had already eaten three. The taste was strange but good. He picked up the biscuit in front of him and bit from it to show his grandfather that it was fine to eat. The old man picked up his biscuit and smelled it slowly, then took a small bite in his mouth.

The boy took the strange hide that the woman had put on his horse and that he had now covered himself with, the one that was so soft and warm. He held it out to his grandfather who touched it lightly. The feel was so different that the old man's look of stolid inexpression dropped briefly and surprise registered.

This encounter lasted more than an hour. There could be no verbal communication, but there was so much other communication. At one point, Old Hawk made a bird-like sound that told the women and children they could come out of hiding. They approached slowly, making no noise, taking in the man, the huge horses, and all that was on the ground, getting a good look at what they could not see well from their hiding places. Then they sat down.

Bright Stone's mother was a well disciplined woman, like all women of her group, but her heart was bursting, and as she saw the gentleness of this man, his kindness and his smiles, she dropped traditional protocol and made a series of movements and cries that were impossible to misunderstand.

The white man had already surmised that these women and children were the widows and orphans of Indian men whom the army had fought and killed, yet the woman's cries and motions went beyond that. Finally, through pantomime, he figured out that two of the woman's children were missing or had been killed. Then it became clear that three other women had also lost children. If the deaths had been from disease, the pantomime would have been different. In this case, she was asking him to do something. What could that be? Did she mean that the children got lost and she wanted to find them?

This cross-cultural exchange was the first of a long

series of meetings, a series that lasted years. The man, Ben Anderson, came weekly. After a few months, his wife Alice came along. She brought even more things to eat. What the children liked most was the sugar cubes.

Old Hawk could hardly ride a horse anymore, but in the spring Ben brought him and his grandson Bright Stone back on Beulah, and Old Hawk saw and learned many things for the first time in his long life. A sense of trust grew over the months, and after a year, an agreement was made for Bright Stone to come and do work for food. He also learned words in English. Early in the second year another agreement was reached. Ben brought a wagon, and the teepees were dismantled, loaded up, and brought to a much more hospitable location on the edge of the Andersons' hay field. The women loved this since it might hide them better from that other tribe of whites who steal children. Bright Stone had communicated the story to the Andersons about how his younger brother and sister were stolen. Ben and Alice could not believe the story, that any white people would do such a thing, but Bright Stone told it in the same way repeatedly.

That girl and boy, Bright Stone's brother and sister, suffered greatly at the Hadley Indian School. They lost weight and got sick. They cried themselves to sleep at night, though Indian children are taught not to cry from pain, at least physical pain. Some of the older kids comforted them as best they could. The girl and boy also learned the basics of reading and numbers, and they developed a growing English vocabulary. When they were caught speaking Osage with the other kids, they had to choose between being beaten with a switch in public or being locked in a closet with no food for a day. The children learned to say prayers and to sing hymns in English. They learned how to act in school. They put some weight back on.

But it seemed that the Hadleys underestimated whom they were dealing with. It happened one night when the Reverend and Mrs. Hadley had gone back to New Jersey to raise more funds for the Hadley Mission School, to tell the good folks around Camden how thirsty the little Indians were to learn English so they could read scripture, to understand Bible stories, to sing hymns in church, and how they pleaded to let their little brothers and sisters come to the school and be saved from pagan ways.

One night during this absence, when the other four Hadleys had retired to the house and when it was strictly forbidden for the children to talk or rise from their bunks, five of the older children came and woke all the others up. They told them in Osage, "You must put on all the clothes you have. You must not ask questions. If you have brothers or sisters here, you must stay in a group with them. Tonight we are all leaving. One of us will tell you what to do and where to crawl under the fence. We have killed the dogs. We have stolen bags of food. We will have to run as far as we can and then walk the rest of the night. We are going in five different directions so that they cannot round us up and punish us."

Indian children are taught to be obedient and to be silent. Besides, they had trust in the older children. The five groups were under the school fence and headed in different directions when a light started illuminating the night sky. Two big boys had stayed behind and set fire to bundles of straw and sticks that had been strategically placed under the sides of the house and in the barn where the children had slept. Flames were leaping high from both buildings.

The screams of the Hadleys could be heard through the night. They all escaped the fires, but their efforts to extinguish the flames were futile. The fires rapidly consumed the house and the barn. By dawn, nothing was left of the Hadley Indian School but ashes, and it would never rise again.

Groups of Indian children, dressed as whites and speaking understandable English, began showing up here and there across a large area. At first, it was all a mystery. Then the kids explained that their school had burned and they wanted to go back to their family. When they sang "That Old Rugged Cross" or "Amazing Grace," white families gave them food and shelter. Three brothers from the school were reported to make a living for several years as "The Indian Boys Trio." Local officials decided it was best for all concerned if somehow the kids could just be put back with their mothers. They were not a real danger. It took months to put the pieces together of where the widows and orphans had been relocated in different small batches after the old village had been destroyed. In the end, more than half of the children were reunited, and other widows adopted some of the rest. Of course, the children had changed. They had learned the white man's language and some of his ways. They could read and write to a degree. Some of them had taken the white man's god into their hearts.

Three of the nine children the Andersons crowded into a wagon were very disappointed when Ben and Alice brought them to the new settlement of teepees on the edge of the Anderson's hayfield, but six were beside themselves with joy. They were the six who had been abducted two and a half years before. Their mothers and siblings and Old Hawk were so happy that after a long period of tears, followed by still more tears, they all started to do the Osage joy dance, which was done when family members come back from a long trip. Alice and Ben were torn, so happy for the six who found their mothers; so sad for the three little ones would have to wait for another time.

Bringing home the abducted children forged a bond between the widows and the Andersons that could not have been stronger, at least between Indians and whites in those days. Their lives were now to be intertwined for the next few generations. Ben's sister Edith came from back East to be nearer her own children and grandchildren who had moved to some new towns not that far from the Andersons. Edith herself had never finished high school, but she had taught grade school in a one-room schoolhouse for many years. When she came, it was only natural that she would spend time with the Indian children. The idea evolved that a school for Indians was needed, a real school. They couldn't go to school with whites, but they did need to learn reading and writing.

The Andersons donated a half-acre piece of land near the road, and farmers and ranchers from all around and some people from the town gave money or time to put up a little schoolhouse, following Miss Edith's specifications. Then a little bunkhouse was needed for the Indian kids who lived too far away to walk home each day.

Bright Stone's oldest son was one of the first children to go all the way through Miss Edith's eight years of school, and he did very well at it. Bright Stone had married one of the girls he had grown up with in the small circle of teepees. The marriage had made both widows very happy, and Old Hawk, too. The son was born within a year. The parents thought he was such as nice baby, as nice as honey, and he was a heavy baby. They ended up giving him a traditional name that translates awkwardly from the Osage language.

The name was Sugarstone, and that became the family name, the surname in the Western sense, when Miss Edith said that all the children had to have two names, like white people. His parents did not understand this naming system, but eventually they agreed for their son to be Red Hawk, Red Hawk Sugarstone, and since his father had become chief upon the death of Old Hawk, Red Hawk could be a chief someday, too, though once again, the title *chief* is not really the same as in English. But Miss Edith reached the requirement of having two names on paper for all students in the little school. None of the Osage in that generation understood or liked the Christian names Miss Edith offered, such as Phillip or Mathew or Elizabeth or Sarah. Such names did not become common among the Osage for another generation or two.

Young Red Hawk was good in school, good with his

hands, good with animals, and a good rider. When one of Alice and Ben's sons visited and showed Red Hawk how to spin a rope, Red Hawk was captivated, practiced for hours, and after some months he invented new tricks of his own. The son offered the boy a job on his ranch. The boy accepted and within a year became a first-rate wrangler. One fall, there was a pow-wow about ten miles from the ranch, and Red Hawk was allowed to go. It was something he had never seen before. He even found some of his own tribe, and meeting other Osage brought a spirit to his heart that he had not known for a long time. Besides all the dances from Indians of various tribes, there was also a rope-spinning competition. Red Hawk joined in and won a small prize for third-place best roper. The rope-spinning competition was followed by an Australian whip-cracking exhibition, and Red Hawk could not take his eyes off it. He found the man with the whips after the show and asked him all kinds of questions. The man even let Red Hawk try out his whips. The man insisted that a good whip cracker had to know how to make his own whips, and he explained the basics.

That winter Red Hawk had to experiment and see if he could make some whips of his own. These whips were not like what the traditional cowboy uses on a cattle drive. Whips for a cattle drive were many feet long and completely flexible so they could be coiled up and hung on a saddle horn. But these had a long straight wooden handle that was covered by braided leather straps followed by a semi-flexible part of the whip then the longer very flexible section that tapered smaller and smaller as the leather straps became thinner. Finally, there was the last section, and that section had to be replaced periodically. It was a length of cord or coarse string braided together, ending in the "popper" that actually made the noise. The popper had to be just right for the noise to be right. If the whole whip was too long, the man using it could not get it all off the ground to make the pop. If it was too short, he could not get the maximum sound effect. It took a number of tries for Red Hawk to become skilled at popping the whips he made.

The next skill was hitting targets with the end of the whip. Could he move a pinecone across the ground about a foot each time he flicked it with the end of the whip? Could he pick off, one at a time, a dozen sticks he had poked into a barbed wire fence? Could he cut leaves off a tree, one at a time?

He was left handed, and his left arm was stronger and more accurate. It took lots of practice to develop good skills using a whip in each hand equally. He learned to alternate smoothly right-left-right-left in doing his tricks.

Red Hawk had learned that there was a circuit of powwows in several states. Some people followed the circuit and got to see a lot of the country. Some people even made a living at it, at least for part of the year, if they had a good enough act. He really liked ranch work, but he wanted to try the powwows, even though he had no idea how to get from one powwow to another. One spring, he bid farewell to the ranch owner, who was sorry to see him go and who offered him winter work whenever he wanted it.

Red Hawk proved himself to be a quick study again. He teamed up with some other Osage so he could get from one powwow to another. They had a lot of fun. He could do the traditional dances very well, and his roping and whip cracking skills kept improving. He even made money with the whips and ropes. It was a good way of life, one that he did not want to give up, and eventually, he didn't have to.

Another band of Osage showed up at one of the pow-wows. It included a wonderful girl who won lots of prizes for her traditional dancing. There was initially a competitive spirit between the girl and him, but it evolved into friendship and then into something more. When the season closed, he went to see her and her family. He had never seen so many Osage together in his life. He took new pride in who he was. He stayed for several weeks, and her father and mother said that they could marry. He would ask his family to come, and there would be a traditional Osage wedding, though a whole cow would be roasted instead of a buffalo. The buffalo had all been killed off.

The next year he and his wife, High Bird, were traveling on the powwow circuit in an old car when one day they saw the biggest tent in the world along the side of the road. They stopped and asked what it meant and why it was there. This was how they became introduced to the world of the circus. It took a little adjustment, but the two were happy to try this new world. They could come on as a two-person act with dances, ropes, and whips for this year, but the owners wanted a whole tribe of Indians for next year. The agreement was to settle on a "band" of twelve rather than a tribe. That is how Chief Red Hawk Sugarstone and his Band of Osage Indians became a leading attraction of Brewer Brothers World Famous Circus.

The act of authentic Indian dances required nothing new from the Sugarstones. They knew the dances. But their act did not begin with the dances. High Bird had a beautiful singing voice. Lucky Brewer would announce, "Now to introduce Chief Red Hawk Sugarstone and his Band of Osage Indians, it is our great pleasure to present to you Princess High Bird, who will sing one of America's all-time favorite songs, the famous, 'Indian Love Song: When I am Calling You.'" At this point High Bird, dressed in fringed white buckskin, would begin a slow march to the middle of the center ring singing *a cappella*, with the rest of the band following her single file and the drummer bringing up the rear. She always got a good round of applause and would smile modestly when she concluded.

Lucky Brewer had worked with Red Hawk to select and format the dances they would do. They came up with the hunting dance, the rain dance, the war dance, the dance of the broken heart, and the joy dance. Lucky had to work to come up with simple names for the dances, names that the audience would understand. The dances had to be shortened, with just samples given, since in village settings these dances usually continued for quite a long time, for as long as the dancers wanted to dance. Lucky had to introduce them and say a few words about them, so that the act moved along with rapid progression.

Most poignant to the audience was the dance of the broken heart. Lucky explained that it was a heart-breaking dance because it was done when warriors or hunters did not come home from their trip. No drums were played for this dance. Red Hawk's grandmother, old woman that she was, did most of this dance. The other members of the clan stood respectfully around the back of the ring. The grandmother put on leather sleeves with eagle feathers pointing out to the sides. She glided into the ring, arms extended, slowly and with dignity, making circles with a grace that belied her age. She was a bird high in the sky, looking for a lost mate. Then she would begin to wail in a low voice.

The right word for this type of wailing does not exist in English. It is not a European tradition, with the possible exception of something like the traditional keening done by the Irish. Her low wail would soon rise and crack as her body circled the ring like a lost spirit. The other clan members standing around the edge of the ring would begin to rotate slowly in place, shadowing her movements, lifting their arms slowly like birds gliding high in the sky. Then they would join her in the wailing, making a sad melody that filled the tent, alternating high pitches and low pitches, like nothing the white audience had ever heard before. Slowly, very slowly, the grandmother's circles would become smaller, and her body would cower lower and lower. After one high-pitched scream, she would collapse on the ground on her knees with her head on the ground, and the others would all flutter down on one knee with arms and heads down pointing in toward the fallen grandmother.

Only the least imaginative people in the audience could not understand this dance and the meaning of how it ended. The audience would fall completely silent. The old lady's dancing was so sincere that it was clearly more than a demonstration. It was remembering a man who never came home to her. She was honoring him day after day after all these years. At some performances, the silence from the audience was so long that Lucky had to intervene respectfully to say, "Ladies and gentlemen, may we please have a warm round of applause for this wonderful lady who has shown us how beautiful her culture is?"

As the applause mounted, the other dancers would surround the grandmother and lift her body from the ground and carry her at a slow dance step from the tent. Then they would reenter, and Lucky would announce the joy dance, the dance that was done to celebrate the return of warriors or hunters from their trips. The drum would play again and the band would then begin their most celebratory dance to end the exhibition of authentic Osage dances.

It is curious that in a span of fifty years, the 1880s to the 1930s, that Native Americans, as perceived by whites, changed from being mortal enemies who must be annihilated to featured entertainers offering a romantic reminder of how things were back in the "good old days." Native Americans would suffer prejudice for another century or more, but some of them would avoid assimilation, maintain their identity, and manage to survive as a small minority. Their survival was based on the strength they had through the family and the clan.

24. THE LAST PAYDAY

It was late in the circus season. The missed pay-days following the disastrous bank robbery way back in Choresville had been made up, though they were a little late. The Brewers did not owe any back salary. There was money enough to spend for good meals in the cookhouse. Every man and woman on the show had worked to bring in more cash. Even the children who were able to had chipped in their efforts.

They followed the plan outlined by Amy Brewer several weeks before with occasional updates. The pony ride and cotton candy opened at noon. There were flashy, visual attractions on the midway to drag people in from the highway and the town. The Sugarstones put up their teepees regularly. They even taught some of the other folks on the show how to help so it could be done in ten minutes. The teepees were the first attraction in sight every day. Poker did his stilt walk out front and waved to people in cars on the street. The circus sound truck was out early and often, making announcements about the show over the PA system. Performers took turns riding on the back of the sound truck, wearing their show wardrobe and waving to people. Pinky did his walk-around in town giving away balloons to kids with birthdays that month along with one free ticket each so that the kid's whole family would probably buy tickets and come to the show. As soon as the elephants had pulled up the tent, Uncle Harry took Dolly out front for various stunts, including the famous tug-a-war with members of the local sponsoring committee. Men took turns riding around on a horse as a cowboy. Most of them already wore blue jeans, boots, some sort of Western shirt, and a cowboy hat, so there was no need to change clothes. Later, Gilly was able to do some Roman riding on Chico and Two Bits to generate excitement. This preshow routine varied from town to town, but it was always done.

It had been discouraging at times. It had been hard to do. In some towns it did not work very well. It had been exhausting. But above all, it had been successful. The midway brought in more money, and more people bought tickets. Crowd size on average was forty to seventy-five people larger than before.

The additional income made a difference in the lives of the show folks. There was plenty of hay and grain for the animals and no worry about towns with no good grass on the lot. A gas tanker came and filled everybody up with a full tank. One show truck that had blown a gasket and been towed for three or four towns had now been repaired. There were smiles all around when for the first time Cookie and Slim served bacon at breakfast again, and more smiles when doughnuts showed up after lunchtime and pie after supper. Life was getting back to normal, or at least what passed for normal during the Great Depression.

There was barely a word of complaint from anyone about anything during the lean weeks and months after the show's financial crisis in Choresville. It was probably because everyday everybody got a clear view of how people in the towns and countryside were suffering. There were poor people along the side of the road who were not trying to hitch a ride. They were asking drivers to stop to give them food. There were closed farmhouses, closed gas stations, and closed stores. Circus people traveling from town to town got a better visual understanding of the Great Depression than almost anybody else. They preferred a hard job with long hours and tough conditions to no job at all.

All of the adult Brewers had spent some sleepless nights wondering if the show could turn around and get back on its feet again. When there were the first hopeful signs, they preferred not to believe them till there was more certainty. A delicate, short-term success was not enough. They wanted to be on solid ground. Solid ground came over time.

So a few weeks before the end of the season, the Brewers announced that there would be another meeting for everybody in the tent after the matinee show. As people came in to this meeting, they did not have the concerned looks they had had at the meeting weeks before. They had a look of curiosity and even some smiles. There were a couple washtubs of ice with bottled cold drinks chilled in them. People could choose Nehi Orange, Nehi Grape, or Nehi Cola. A couple kids were there with bottle openers to serve everybody quickly.

Woody, Amy, Lucky, and Tillie were seated on chairs in front of the section of the bleachers where they had been last time. GR and Camie were in the middle of the bleachers with some of the younger Brewer kids.

Woody stood up and began, "It is great to have another meeting like this, but it will be a shorter meeting, and it sure will be a happier meeting! Ladies and gentlemen, a little more than two months ago, we were meeting with you to lay out a plan to save the show. It was a hard plan, a tough plan, but you made it work.

"My wife an' I, my mother an' father, my brother an' his wife, all the Brewers, we want to thank you from the bottom of our hearts for making it work. We still have a circus! And we still have jobs! We trusted you, an' you trusted us. You have been terrific. You never gave up. You even gave us more good ideas. You worked your behinds off. We thank you now, an' we will be eternally grateful!

"As a small way of showing our gratitude, we want to pay you early this time instead of paying you late. We want to have one last payday today an' pay you your salary for the rest of the entire season. We trust you. You could just take the money an' leave us, but we trust you. We want to give you one week of bonus pay, too. An' at the very end of the season, if all goes well, we will give you that second week of bonus pay, but we won't call that a pay day. We will call it a bonus day. Again, we can't promise that yet; it will be if all goes well an' we have the money to pay a second bonus week's salary.

"Now you do not have to take all the money now. That will be up to you. You might not want to have that much cash in your possession yet. So you can just tell us what you want minus what we have counted out for you.

"And believe us, ladies an' gentlemen, we will not be putting any of the money in a bank, not the best bank in the country, not if it is Fort Knox itself!"

This brought a round of laughter.

"Now, we will not have payday in the usual way. Today it just might be a little faster. This time we want to pay you right here in the tent. Tillie, Amy, an' my mother will each be on a chair in one of the rings. They will have an empty chair beside them. So instead of everybody going to one place, we can do it three times as fast with three people giving out the money. One of the ladies will call your name. Go to her. Sit down. Get your money an' count it like usual. An' then come to me an' sign in the big book. It should go fast," Woody explained.

"An' Cookie and Slim have a little surprise for you for supper today. Cookie, would you like to tell the folks about it?"

Cookie shook his head no vigorously, overcome by an attack of shyness. Slim would not speak in Cookie's place.

"OK, I understand," continued Woody. "Their surprise is that the menu tonight is barbecued beef brisket with mashed potatoes, gravy, an' choice of other dishes. An' for dessert, there will be three kinds of pie, an' if you like, you can have all three, an' if you like, you can have "pie a la mode." That means pie with ice cream on it. Are there any objections to this?

"May we have a round of applause for Cookie an' Slim, please?" Everybody clapped and cheered for the lead cooks. Several men whistled.

"Thank you so much, folks, for all that you have done. An' we don't want to keep you any longer. So we will begin this payday now. We want Cookie an' Slim paid first so they can get back to the cookhouse an' get busy with supper. Cookie, please go to Amy in the first ring. Slim, please get your money from Tillie in the center ring. Jake, can you go to my mother in the third ring? Remember to come an' sign in the book with me when you get your cash. Thanks, folks. See you all at the cookhouse!" Woody concluded.

The show folks seated in the bleachers thinned out quickly as the women called out more names. The employees picked up and counted their money in one of the three rings and then came and signed with Woody in the big book.

Everybody took the full salary for the rest of the season as offered. They needed the money. They needed to buy things. They needed to get things fixed. They had been putting off what needed to be done. Pants had been patched till they couldn't be patched any more. Some got new shoes or had old ones repaired. Some got new tires to replace ones that had been patched over and over. Some started looking for a new set of clothes for their kids for the new school year. All of them stashed cash away to help them get through the long winter months off till the season of 1934 would open in May.

Aside from being very motivational for the staff, the offer of early pay had advantages for the Brewers, too. They did not have to keep such a huge sum of cash on hand. Bookkeeping was simplified. Almost all the money that came in for the rest of the season would be theirs. The Brewers also started putting money in a bag to make the second bonus week at the very end of the season.

Woody had had a startling sensation as he addressed the group that afternoon. He had to tell his family about it later that night after the evening show. He had a hard time of putting it into words, or putting his finger on it. "*Dadus, Dias, dovas* is *kushti fokie, dosta kushti*. Dad, Mama, they are good people, really great folks. There's *chichi*, nothing, they wouldn't do for us. There is real power when you stick together an' co-ordinate an' work hard. It gets results. It works. All the Brewers were listening to him except some of the younger kids. His wife Amy spoke first. "*Ava, mush, dova's tachi*. Yes, man, that is truth. I felt it, too. I wanted to *jawl* around *dellin'* 'em all *chums*, go around giving them all kisses."

GR and Camie looked their son in the eye and agreed. GR started, "Son, I have never seen anything like this season. You an' your brother an' your wives did fantastic work, an' you got the people to do it, too. It's wonderful."

Camie spoke next, "There was no way to tell if we were going to make it or if the show was going to fold. You just couldn't tell. Your dad an' I thought that if anybody could make it work, you an' your brother an' Tillie an' Amy could. It was *rinkna boudyin,* fine work!"

Without knowing it, all through the crisis, the Brewers had been using many management principles that would be written up in best-selling management books decades later. Unknowingly, they had been applying techniques such as quality management, team building, empowerment, and positive feedback.

But the Brewers didn't need an MBA to use those management principles. They managed by using common sense. They listened, they respected people, they built a common vision, they expressed appreciation and found ways to show it, they treated people fairly, they were down to earth and acted like peers instead of bosses. They built trust by trusting people.

They kept their circus on the road in a year when businesses were closing in almost every town they traveled through.

25. A RACE WITH A LOT RIDING ON IT

Gilly had gotten in his mind that since he would be finishing high school the next year, it was time for him to be more on his own, to start his own life, to get money together so that he could be more of his own man. He was not at all sure what his own life would be yet, but he knew that it would take money. So he needed to get money.

Two possibilities were foremost in his thoughts in the fall of 1933. One was to start college in a year. He didn't know what he would study, but it would take *vonger*. Yes, his family would help him, but he couldn't let them just pay his way, especially in these hard times when the show had such a tough season. If he studied science so maybe he would eventually be a veterinary, or if he studied accounting so that he could run a business better, like a circus or whatever, he would still need *vonger*.

He had talked to the school principal, who had been very helpful. Together they had laid out an estimated budget by the week and by the semester, taking into account if Gilly got some money for working at the college library or at the dairy farm of the agricultural school. Even if his mother and father could give him a hundred dollars, it would still be a challenge. He really didn't want to accept any money, except maybe a little for clothes or something.

The second possibility was to start his own bear act. There had never been a bear act in the Brewer family, but the show could obviously use one. And there were certain reasons why bears seemed like a pretty good idea. First of all, he could get some half-grown black bear cubs practically free. There was a little zoo called Story Book Park someplace around Chicago where they had shown that year, and this zoo always liked to have baby animals, little animals that fit into some children's nursery rhyme or story. In this case, they had bears so they could have a display on Goldilocks and the Three Bears with live bears in it. The problem was that the cubs grew fast, and every year they needed new little cubs, and they needed to get rid of the cubs that would be too large by the time the next summer came. There was no real problem with the displays on Peter Rabbit, Mother Goose, the Three Pigs, and Mary's Little Lamb. Those little animals could just be consumed, even as early as the employees' picnic at the end of each season. So the owners of Story Book Park were willing to give the bear cubs to a good home, whatever a good home for young bears might be.

Another attractive thing about bears was that, unlike lions, they were more omnivorous than carnivorous. They could happily and healthfully eat produce and oatmeal and even dog feed rather than expensive meat. They did not really live on a meat diet, at least the black bears at Story Book Park did not. They were not like polar bears. Another major advantage was that a bear act did not need a large steel arena like a lion or tiger act did. So there was less to buy, less to haul over the road, and less to put up and tear down with every performance. Bears could simply be trained to perform on a leash, usually with a muzzle.

Gilly had learned all this a few years back when Brewer Brothers Circus crossed paths with another show that had a bear act, and luckily there was a day off and the management and performers of one show could visit the others. Gene Cunio's Performing Bears were like nothing that Gilly had ever seen before. He spent hours with Gene and asked all kinds of questions. By this point, Gene was getting up in years and was happy to pass on what he knew to a show boy, a promising and interested show boy. Gilly already knew so much about animals, and the conversation was focused mostly on how bears were different. In respect to diet, they were more like monkeys or maybe even pigs. They would even happily munch on tender grass. Bears could easily learn to walk on their hind feet. They did it naturally when they wanted to see farther in the distance or if they were fighting. But Gene cautioned Gilly that it took time for bears to build up the muscles to go any distance on their hind feet. It was important to let them get used to it and not go very far. If they were made to go too far too soon, they could get sore and be turned off by the whole idea of walking on their hind feet. It was always good to leave the bear cages open when the bears were taken out and to throw a little treat inside, such as corn or stale bread. If a bear ever got loose, the first place he was likely to head to was his open cage.

Yet bears were similar to a lot of other animals. They liked routine. They would respond mostly to one or two people, and their reaction to strangers was not really predictable. A mildly irritating thing about having a bear act was that when some people saw the bears on leashes and being led by a man, they somehow thought that these bears had been "tamed," and they wanted to come up and pet the bears and even bring their children along.

Like other animals, bears have individual personalities. For example, most would eat citrus fruit, but some would never touch it. Some could learn a particular trick easily and enjoyably, but others could never get the idea, and it was better to give up. Some bears were relatively easy to train, and others were just not worth the time and effort. There was no point in trying with them.

Like some other show animals, a bear could take a disliking to an individual or group of individuals, and it could be hard to figure out why. Gene Cunio had a bear that did not like men in uniforms, and this made being near policemen or firemen awkward. Another bear did not like elephants and wanted to run away from them, even while the other bears barely noticed.

Gilly felt that if he could make a couple good-sized steel cages on wheels like Gene had and if he could pick up three or four cubs from Story Book Park, he could train his own bear act in six months or a year and start to be more on his own. But was that what he wanted to do, or did he want to go to college?

Either option would require some money. And a moneymaking opportunity arose that fall around Thanksgiving when all the *Romanichal* families gathered at Texarkana, a sort of annual conclave. It was at the old fairgrounds, and there were dozens and dozens of people there, not counting the little kids. This was the time of year to relax, reconnect, and have fun together. One of the things that everybody enjoyed most was riding horses. That fall, the Brewers had brought along some of their favorite horses, and Gilly had persuaded his folks to bring along Chico.

Somebody went into town to buy some horse feed in Texarkana, and the man at the feed store asked if they were going to enter any of their horses in the race at the fairgrounds. The man said that it was not just a little race around the track, which was only a quarter mile, but also off the track with another mile or more through woods and over creeks with some hurdles thrown in, up hill and down hill. The entry fee was five dollars, and the winner would get half the total pot, which would be fifty dollars if there were twenty horses racing. Second place got one quarter of the pot, third got ten bucks, and the rest went to the organizers, who were actually the owners of the feed store.

When this news got back to the *Romanichals* at the fairground, there was great interest. They all loved horseracing, and they felt that nobody could race horses better than *Romanichals*, nobody. Yes, there were some Indian boys who were good, very good, but not many *Gaudjas* could ride as well, and everybody knew it was not just a matter of how good a horse was but how good the rider was. Gilly really wanted to race Chico, but he knew there were risks. He could lose, and lose the five-dollar entry fee. Or the organizers could just run off with the money. The race could be rigged in various ways. There were so many ways to cheat at horse racing, but Gilly and his folks were familiar with just about all of them and knew how to prevent them.

One way to cheat was for riders who knew the cross-country course well to take some shortcut and then take the lead unnoticed. Or a malicious rider could cause an "accident" by forcing another horse and rider into a tree or a barbed-wire fence. Or somebody could hide in the bushes and come out and lower the hurdles the horses had to jump over for a certain rider and raise it for others. There were stories of some farmer siccing his pack of dogs on a particular horse. The ways of cheating were endless.

The *Romanichals* all knew that as outsiders, they would likely be the ones accused of cheating, and the local people would tend to take sides with their own friends and family. The only thing the *Romanichals* could do was to be very good racers and stay on guard. They also knew that the more witnesses there were, the harder it would be for cheating to go on. It was good for as many people as possible to show up as spectators at the start and finish and along the course, including the cross-country part.

The situation became more complicated when Rosie

Mae Stanley, one of the very best riders and racers among the *Romanichals*, said that she wanted to enter the race, too. Gilly had known Rosie Mae since they were small children, and their skills as a horseman and a horsewoman had grown at about the same pace over the years. The problem was that Rosie Mae's racing days might just about be over. In her earlier teens she had no problem putting a hat on her head with her hair pulled up underneath it, putting on baggy clothes, and acting the part of a boy jockey. Now it was not so easy. She was shapelier, and her figure was harder to hide. She now had long black braids that would be hard to cover up convincingly under almost any style of a hat a rider would wear.

But she was not ready to give up her jockey career quite so soon. After much discussion with family and girlfriends, she decided that this race would be worth cutting her braids for. She would even get a short haircut like a man. Her hair would grow back, but there might not be another time she could be in a race with all her family and other *Romanichals* around. It was too tempting.

Her brother told her that she had to be careful and walk like a boy and keep her voice low. She should just say as little as possible. He lent her his boots and gave her some lessons in acting boyish. As part of the ruse, they agreed she should cut herself on her face a little as if she cut herself shaving. A few dirt smudges on her face, as if she had not been very conscientious about washing, might help, too. Her sister pointed out that she had better cut her fingernails off and even chew on a couple. And she could chew tobacco or dip some snuff.

The transformation was suitably convincing, but Gilly hated to see it. First of all, he had long admired Rosie Mae, and more and more as she grew into her later teens, and this admiration was more for how womanly she was becoming. Her skills as a horse-woman were another issue. He had to admit that she could be a serious rival in the race. She had a good horse, a horse almost as good as Chico, and she could ride as well as any man, except, he hoped, himself.

It was only precedent and tradition that would keep a female from riding. There were no laws or regulations against it. People would have laughed and said that none were necessary. "Who ever heard of a girl jockey?" would be the common reaction. Yet there had been any number of women who had passed as male jockeys over the decades, and nobody had an idea how many. Racing was just another field where women who wanted to, and who could successfully disguise themselves, went into a man's world.

Everybody joined in the subterfuge for their two racers in one way or another. The whole camp of *Romanichals* got in on it. They decided that when they went over to the part of the fairgrounds where the racetrack was, they would not go as a group. They would not be seen as an identifiable block that might cause suspicion or animosity. They would go over in different groups at different times. Some would even arrive by car as if they were coming from town. And some would dress nicely and some poorly. The groups would not speak to one another at the race-track. And Rosie Mae and Gilly would act as if they did not know each other, either. Gilly would say he was from Shreveport, and she would say she was from Longview.

It was a clear Sunday morning when the crowd started coming, a morning when people should have been in church, and a few had gone to an early service, but horseracing was one of the Devil's temptations that otherwise virtuous people could succumb to. Twenty-three horses and riders showed up, so the pot to be won would be slightly larger than originally thought. Some riders rode their horse from home to the racetrack; others brought their horses in trucks or trailers so that the horses would not have used up any of their stamina.

Gilly and Rosie Mae were among those who had the advantage of training their horses three or four days in advance on the track and on what they thought would be the off-track, cross-country part of the course.

Some of the groups of *Romanichals* meandered out along the presumed cross-country part so that they would be around as observers who would help dissuade any of the riders from taking shortcuts, going around hurdles, or cheating in any other way.

That morning, the organizers and judges seemed to be taking their roles seriously. They at least looked honest. Somebody said that one of the judges was an actual judge from Texarkana, but Texarkana, Texas, not Texarkana, Arkansas, but that didn't matter. The fact that the whole race was in reality a betting event made the legal status dubious, but nobody was asking any questions.

The twenty-three riders rode up to the treasurer of the event to pay their fees. Most had five-dollar bills, so there was little counting involved. The treasurer would be the man who kept the kitty and disbursed the money to the winner and the riders who came in second and third, with the remainder going to the organizers. He was quite recognizable with his handlebar moustache and his boater straw hat – not a cowboy hat like many of the others had. Some people in the crowd knew him personally, but others would be keeping an eye on him. This was like a high-stakes poker game.

Each rider also had to go to the secretary. The secretary took down the name of the rider and his horse, where they were from, and the color and gender of the horse. (Fillies and mares could race despite the gender discrimination for riders.)

The judge reviewed the rules with riders, with the crowd being completely silent and listening in. There weren't many rules, and mostly everybody knew them already. The first and last parts of the race were laps around the quarter-mile track. The middle would be the cross-country part, marked by arrows that had been tacked up on trees and fence posts. Any rider who cheated in any way would be disqualified, with the judge determining what would be defined as cheating. Any rider who fell or dismounted from his horse would be disqualified. There was to be no remounting and continuing. Any rider who was disqualified for any reason would not get his entry fee back.

The riders lined up their mounts at the starting line, with the judge motioning to eleven of them that they would have to back up and form a second rank of starters a few feet behind the first. The track was wide enough for only a dozen horses to line up abreast.

Three of the horses kept jumping the gun and had to be pulled back. The judge warned the riders that if they could not control their horses, they would be disqualified. Finally, there was a pause with all the horses lined up and still, and the judge fired his pistol in the air.

In no time at all, the two ranks of horses melded into one mass, and then they started to string out around the quarter-mile track. Some of the riders were pacing their horses, holding them back a bit, for the harder part to come, and other riders were trying to take an early lead that they hoped to keep for the whole race. Rosie Mae and Gilly both found themselves about one-fourth of the way back in the pack, and that was a good place to be, far enough ahead but not too far ahead. And it would always be easier to pass by other horses in the cross-country part rather than on the track.

The horses were just warming up in this early part of the race on the track, but the crowd was cheering, and some people were excitedly calling out the names of riders and horses. The pack was strung out more and more as the first lap was completed and the horses needed to exit the track for the cross-country part. Two horses were just not trained well enough to obey their riders, and they stayed on the track to start a second lap despite how hard their riders were pulling on the reins to get them to take the exit. These horses had learned the "stay on the track" rule too well. One horse got turned around within fifty feet past the exit, but the other stubbornly refused for nearly a minute. Both lost valuable time. They were bringing up the rear.

Rosie Mae was now in about sixth place, and Gilly was ten feet behind her in seventh. In the cross-country stretch, racing across the creek involved more than just splashing water. There were muddy places in the crossing in which a horse could get bogged down. It was better to slow down and avoid risks. If a horse got suddenly stuck, the rider could go flying overhead and would be disqualified. But horses are racing animals, and it is hard for some of them to slow down and listen to a rider who is pulling on the reins.

As the pack crossed the creek, there were changes in position here and there. Riders who went ahead at full barrel passed some others. One rider went tumbling off into the water when his horse hit deep mud, and a rider following very closely behind him went down when his horse balked at crashing into the other horse. The two downed riders were nearly run over by four other horses before they could stumble to the side of the creek crossing. They were the first to be disqualified.

There were three hurdles in quick succession after the creek. Gilly and Rosie Mae were at an advantage here, since their horses were very experienced jumpers and quite undaunted. Not too far behind them, a horse went crashing through the hurdles and caused a backup while the hurdles were reset so that all the following horses made the required jump.

Another rider was disqualified when the cinch on his saddle either came loose or broke and he went off his horse with him still sitting on the saddle. This sort of accident was completely unnecessary. Horsemen who knew their craft would always have their tack in good shape. The fallen rider managed to pull himself and his saddle quickly out of the way of the horses coming behind him, but his horse stood dumbly in the way, and the other riders had to swerve around.

At this point, thanks to some very good jumping, Rosie Mae and Gilly were in fourth and fifth places, and at least one of the horses in front of them seemed to be really tiring. It was an interesting race. The rider let up a bit on that horse to give him a break, and the two *Romanichals* moved up to third and fourth. At a bend around some trees, Rosie Mae maneuvered up beside the rider in second place, and then Gilly saw something he had heard about but never seen. He could just make out that the second-place rider was beating Rosie Mae's hands with his quirt as she moved up beside him.

Most jockeys carried a quirt, the short stiff whip that was partly style but on occasion used to urge on a lagging horse. This jockey was striking Rosie Mae's hands viciously with his quirt to get her to pull back on the reins of her horse. She wasn't pulling back. She put her hands to her side while holding the reins securely. Then he started beating her legs, her horse's neck, her arms and stomach, anyplace he could land some blows. She grabbed a hank of mane and bent over to the far left side of her mount, clinging tightly with her legs and staying farther out of reach of that rider and his quirt. That helped, at least temporarily.

Gilly could see all this happening clearly enough that he could not doubt what was going on. He was enraged. He bent low over Chico's neck and egged him on a little faster to catch up with the other two riders not that far in front of him. There was a trap here. If he fought back to defend Rosie Mae, he could also be disqualified. If he didn't, she could be seriously injured. Chico caught up with the two, and now there were three riders tied for second place. They were not that far behind the first place rider.

They all came to an open place where there were people watching the race, and for the moment the rider who had been beating Rosie Mae stopped and pretended just to be riding his horse intently. Rosie Mae did have some possibility of getting him disqualified by simply showing the welts on her hands and arms and the spot that had started bleeding. But it might be discovered that she was a girl, and that would add a distracting layer of confusion to the situation. Also, she simply wanted to earn the money. At least for the moment, she would not fight back and run the risk of being disqualified, too. She would just try to run faster and outdistance him.

And Gilly wanted to win the money, and he did not want to be disqualified by fighting the other rider. Yet he did not want to see Rosie Mae beat up. She was a competitor, but she was also one of his kind, another *Romanichal*. And he knew that she would do anything to help him in such circumstances. Soon the trail was in a more wooded area again, and there were not any spectators, and the other rider started beating Rosie Mae's hands, even worse than before.

Gilly's mind was busy inventing ways to stop the cheating rider, but they all seemed to involve him cheating, too. He thought of bending over far to the left side of Chico and poking his own quirt between the running front legs of the cheater's horse. It would be somewhat like poking a stick into the spokes of a bicycle. This could distract the horse and make him slow down. Gilly was skilled enough to do such a maneuver, but it would also be cheating. Another idea was to take off his shirt and drop it around the head of the other horse, cutting off his vision. This would slow the horse down, if not stop him. But it was also cheating. And the horse might run into something, and Gilly had nothing against the horse.

The three riders were still neck-and-neck now. Second place in the race was still a three-way tie. The local rider turned and looked at Gilly as if to say, "Do you want some, too?"

In a flash, Gilly thought of an element of surprise that might make a difference, something he could do that could not be construed as cheating. He put his head as close as he could to the ear of the cheating rider. He took a big gulp of air, and with all his might he let out his best imitation of a war whoop that the Sugarstone Indians used in their act doing the war dance.

"Eeya-haja-oya!" he screamed at maximum volume. Screaming at another rider was not cheating. It could even be expected in horseraces.

The cheating rider jumped up in disbelieve, jerked on his reins, and turned his head to Gilly with a completely startled look on his face, one which said, "What on earth was that?"

He did not see the tree limb coming. It caught him on the left side of his head and knocked him from his horse to the ground. Rosie Mae and Gilly knew it was coming. Good riders did not ride without keeping a constant eye on potential dangers, high and low, especially racing cross-country. Both of them had seen the big, low branch through their peripheral vision. They had ducked and missed it.

A terrible thing about a rider hitting a large branch is the moment after the initial impact. It is the spring-back effect when the branch rebounds and throws the rider high into the air. In this case, the rider came down with a painful thud in a mud hole yards behind where he had hit the branch.

So Rosie Mae was now clearly in second place, and she even had a crack at first place. Gilly had pulled back to see what had happened to the rider who only seconds before had been cheating. That rider was now flat on the ground, motionless. It would only be seconds till other riders would come around the bend in the woods and be trampling him.

Gilly rode back to where the injured rider was lying, face down. He dismounted and used himself and Chico as a sort of shield to keep the other riders from trampling the downed man. He held his arms up to signal them away. He had no idea if his adversary was dead or alive, and for the moment he could not even check. He just had to keep the other riders from trampling the man on the ground.

Two other riders stopped and helped in diverting the other racers. Very shortly, it looked like all of them had passed, and there was no more danger of trampling. One of the riders who had stopped dismounted, automatically disqualifying himself. He and Gilly knelt down to examine the rider on the ground. They could see no blood, and they could tell he was breathing shallowly. They rolled him over. The other rider who had stopped dismounted, too, deciding he was now so far behind he could never win anyway, and he might as well lend a hand and be disqualified.

"Oh, no," he said. "It's Matt, Matt Harmon! What happened? His folks will be so scared!"

The two men who had been kneeling rose and looked at the third one. None of them spoke for a moment. They were all thinking what would be best to do.

Gilly spoke first, "My horse is the biggest. Let's see if you can get this guy up in the saddle in front of me, and I will hold him an' ride back to the grandstand as gentle as I can. One of you lead his horse, an' why don't one of you go back at a good clip an' tell everybody what happened an' get a doctor or something."

"Yea, that sounds good. If we laid him over his horse an' tied his hands an' feet to bring him back, everybody would think he was dead or something," one of the other men said.

"Frank, let's see if this guy can really hold Matt riding

on the saddle in front of him." It took a few minutes to get the unconscious rider up on Chico in front of Gilly, who put his arms around him to hold him in place. Gilly started Chico up at an easy pace, and it looked possible to hold the unconscious Matt Harmon in the saddle if the easy pace was maintained.

"OK, mister, it looks like you got him good in your arms. I'll stay with you in case there's any problem, an' I will lead his horse. Just follow me. There is a shortcut that will get us back to the grandstand pretty fast. Frank, why don't you run on back there now an' see if somebody can take off for Doc Reed?" the older of the two other men explained.

The shortcut got Gilly and the other two riders back in about five minutes. The other rider had alerted the crowd, and somebody was driving off to get Doc Reed from church. The crowd stood up as Gilly came into sight with Matt. Family and friends soon swamped the men and their horses. The grandstand emptied. Gilly had tried to rein Chico and their awkward cargo off the track to the infield. It was only natural not to set up an obstacle on a racetrack, but the crowd gathered too quickly around him. Matt was eased down off Chico and laid flat on the ground, in the race-track, in front of the grandstand.

Gilly had no way of knowing that only the first and second place horses had reached the finish line. The incident with Matt Harmon had slowed down every-body else. The other riders had not even gotten back for the final lap on the track after the cross-country part. All at once, the judges realized that a collision was about to happen, a collision of all the other racers with the crowd that had now blocked off the track.

The judges began blowing their whistles furiously, without much effect. The crowd was not moving from the track. They all wanted to see how Matt was doing. The judges ran up the track moving their arms up and down wildly, trying to signal the riders that they must stop and could not run through the crowd. Essentially, they called a halt to the race.

The confusion continued for many minutes. Some of the racers even wanted to enter the crowd to get a look at how badly the man was injured. This caused suspicion on the part of the remaining racers that some were trying to sneak through the crowd on their horses and end up at the finish line to come in third place and get some of the prize money.

Another wave of disorder came in when the Doc Reed arrived. Everybody wanted to hear what he would say about Matt Harmon, if he could be moved, how badly he was hurt, and if he would live or die.

Forty minutes later, the whole crowd was back in the grandstand, and the remaining riders were lined along the rail in a semblance of order. The judges had come up with a tactic to restore order by announcing that no awards would be made until everybody, man and beast, was back where they belonged. They pointedly ignored questions such as "Well, what's gonna be fair? Who won? Who gets how much money?"

When a degree of quiet descended on the racetrack, the judges announced that they would have a ten-minute private consultation, after which they would make the announcements. They also reminded the crowd that the decisions of the judges would be final. They asked the secretary and the treasurer to join them in the private consultation. It went on for fifteen minutes or more, and then the crowd started stamping their feet and clapping in unison to demand the result.

The private consultation was quite intense. Several solutions had to be immediately discarded. The judges could not ask for a re-race. The horses were too tired, and the first two riders had come in fair and square. They could not refund the entry fee to everybody, since again the first two riders had come in and clearly taken first and second place and were entitled to their share of the kitty.

The judge who was in reality also a legal judge came up with a phrase that saved the day. He said they could declare that the accident with Matt Harmon which had ended up blocking off the track and keeping most riders from finishing was indeed an "Act of God." This meant it was something that nobody had any control over. It was like a flood or a tornado. Nobody was at fault. If God did it, there was no arguing about it.

The judges had finally agreed to a decision that the first- and second-place winners would get their share of the prize money as announced at the start of the day. Then they said that the third-place money would be given to the Harmon family to help with the doctor bill. This was a wise decision, and it actually got a round of applause, since who could complain about money going to help the family of a boy who could have been killed?

"And so, ladies and gentlemen, coming in second and winning the second-place prize of $28.00, we have Mr. Willie Plunkett. Willie, please ride up and get your money."

Gilly's head snapped up in disbelief when the announcement was made. If Willie Plunkett had come in second, what had happened to Rosie Mae?

Willie was all smiles, and his friends and family clapped and whistled for him as he rode up and the cash was counted out to him. He waved it in the air and patted his horse's neck.

"And now, for the grand prize winner in first place, winning the first-place prize of $57.00, we have the man from over in Longview, Mr. Ricky Stanley!" the judge announced. Though his voice was hoarse, he did summon up enough volume and excitement for everybody in the crowd to hear what he said.

Gilly's momentary confusion ended when he realized that, of course, Rosie Mae could not register with the secretary as Rosie Mae Stanley. She just picked the name of Ricky, who was in reality one of her brothers. So Rosie Mae had, after all the pain in her hands from the beating they got, still managed to pass the first place rider, Willie Plunkett, and get the big prize. Well, good for her! Never doubt how well a Gypsy girl can ride when there is prize money involved.

Rosie Mae's family had already heard from her bits and pieces of what had happened, and the welts on her hands were evident, but she could not speak too much *Rumnis* with all the *Gaudjas shoonin',* with all the other people listening. So only a few major points came out. She could not talk much at all. She didn't want people to know that she was a Rosie Mae and not a Ricky. She just wanted that money!

But when the judges made the announcement, the *Romanichals* were forced to let down their guard for a bit and cheer for their winner. Some of the town people cheered, too, but none as loudly as the *Romanichals*.

Then the judge continued, "Ladies and gentlemen, we have a special announcement, please. Something unexpected has come up. We would like to ask Mr. Gilly Brewer to ride up here for a second. That's right. Gilly Brewer, please ride up here, son.

"Mr. Brewer, the family of Matt Harmon, the rider whose very life you may have saved this afternoon, the Harmon family wants to show their gratitude to you an' what you did in giving up your chance to win in the race to help their son Matt. Mr. Brewer, this is highly unusual, but they want to give you the money that the judges awarded to them to help their son. They say that what you did probably did more than anything to help their boy, and they want to thank you for it. So here is Mr. Wallace Harmon to pass you the money."

The loudest roar of the day went up from the crowd, both town people and *Romanichals*. Gilly had a hard time understanding what had happened. He sat there on his horse dumbstruck for a moment, but he had no choice but to go up to the judges. His father had taken

Chico's reins and was leading him anyway. When Gilly looked at Matt's father eye to eye, it was hard to believe that the man who could hand over money to him like this had a son who had so viciously cheated in the race. Gilly didn't know what to think. He just smiled back and said, "Thank you so much, sir. I appreciate it. An' I hope your boy gets all well soon."

Back at the other part of the fairgrounds, where all the families were camping, there was no end to the conversations and story telling that night. Nobody had ever seen a horse race like this one. Rosie Mae and Gilly shared equal but different spotlights. The crowd wanted to hear Rosie Mae's story and how awful that *Gaudja* boy had been to her. Then they wanted to hear how Gilly had brought the boy back out of the woods, literally. Then they wanted to hear Rosie Mae's story again and then Gilly's story.

Rosie Mae had some gold earrings and a necklace back on. The long braids she had cut off were now artfully twisted on top of her head with a bandana so that it was impossible to tell they were pinned on. Her mother and father had put salve and bandages on her hands and arms, but a pretty shawl over her shoulders mostly hid them anyway. She did not look at all like the boy jockey who had won the race.

She and Gilly sat side by side and listened to each other attentively, along with the crowd. Rosie Mae didn't know how Gilly had carried that boy on Chico back to the grandstand. And Gilly did not know how Rosie Mae had ridden so well to beat out Willie Plunkett, the second place rider, and win the purse. Willie had a good horse and was a good rider, but not as good as Rosie Mae, who could win even after she was beaten with a quirt. She was amazing. Gilly gave added details on how awful that Harmon boy was, how Rosie Mae rode over the side of her horse hanging by a hank of mane, and how that horrible boy just did not want to give up beating on Rosie Mae.

Then Rosie Mae's father sat down beside her, and her mother did, too. They looked at each other, and then her mother said, "Honey, you can tell everybody what you decided to do. We think it is a great idea. You go ahead, honey."

Rosie Mae turned to Gilly and spoke in a loud voice. The whole group became very silent. "Well, Gilly, I was *dosta hona*, really mad, when I heard you were gonna be in this race. Everybody *gins tutti* an' *tutti's grai*, we all know you an' your horse, Chico, are great. But I wanted to put in *mandi's pange lils*, my five dollars, an' see if I could at least come in second. There might not be another race for me like this one. It is getting too hard for me to pass as a boy.

"Gilly, you really helped me today. I didn't know if I could hang on much longer with that guy beatin' on my hands an' arms. I was *trashed*, really *trashed*, really afraid that I might fall off an' get hurt bad. Maybe I could not even finish the race. But you took care of that boy. You rode Chico right up beside us, an' you took care of him, practically *mourraed* him, killed him. You are so smart. You could have just gone right on past me an' come in second or even first. But you helped me today.

"So I have talked to my *dadus* an' *dias*, my folks, an'

they agree. They feel it is only right to do somethin' like those town people did. We're *dellin' tutti posh* of the *vonger*. We are givin' you half the prize money. It's $27.00."

Then Rosie Mae counted out the money to him and bent over and gave him a big kiss. The whole group hooted and clapped. Then a couple of the men yelled, "Now *dell laddie a choum!* Give her a kiss back!" Gilly was only happy to comply.

Of course there would be no end of gossip about Rosie Mae and Gilly, and they did not really mind. They took long rides together, including back to the spot on the cross-country part of the race where the incident had occurred, where the big tree limb hung down.

They danced together. People said they were a cute couple, but nobody knew if they were just good friends who both loved horses, or if they were just sweet on each other, or if they were headed for a life together. Rosie Mae and Gilly didn't know either.

Gilly had lost the race but ended up with a decent pot of money. He had a start on having a little account to make his own way to being independent. But would that way be as a *Romanichal* with a bear act? Or would that way be by going to college and going deeper into the *Gaudja* world? He had a little less than a year to decide.

26. A WORLD OF CHANGE

Gilly sat under the awning attached to his grandparents' trailer. Spring was in the air, and the show was gradually getting ready to leave and start the new season, the season of 1934. They were at the farm that the family had bought, with the two large barns, the big farmhouse, various outbuildings, and many acres of well-fenced land. This was the place that was becoming home to them, if Gypsies ever have a fixed home aside from the bosom of their family.

This winter had been different for Gilly, however. It was his final year of high school. He would soon finish his senior year; or rather he would just leave to go on the road, as he had done every school year of his life. He was graduating with honors though he would not be present for the graduation ceremony. And then he would not be in high school anymore.

His grandparents were sitting there under their trailer awning with him, and they had been talking about how last year had been a good season for the show, or at least how it started out good and then got awful with the robbery of the last bank in Choresville, and then how the show was gradually saved through everybody's hard work. Gilly appreciated having the attention of both of his grandparents, and he knew it would not last long till one of the other kids would come around or somebody with business would come by.

"Grandpa, Grandma, you have been through so much in your lives. You were even born in England and came over here as kids. How did you get through it? I don't know what to expect or what to do. I am gonna finish school this year. Then what should I expect?" Gilly looked into their eyes in a serious way, and they knew that he had had this on his mind, that he had been mulling it over, worrying about it.

"Well, Grandson, one thing you can be sure of, and that is that you will see a lot of change. We live in a world of change," Camie commented.

"What do you mean by that, Grandma?" Gilly asked.

"I mean that you should never expect things to stay the same as they are. Tomorrow is not gonna to be like yesterday, and the day after tomorrow is gonna be different again. It just won't stay the same. You can be sure of that," Camie explained.

"Yes, Grandson, you might even see more changes than we did," Grandpa GR added.

"More changes? That would be awful! How do you get through so much? Can you keep it from happenin'?"

Gilly asked.

"Why, hell, no! You usually can't keep it from happenin'. It just happens. You have to be as smart as you can an' work as hard as you can, an' that helps. You will find out. An' you have already seen some of it," GR continued.

"There are good changes an' bad changes, too. Some changes are just fine. I hope we have more changes with good medicine, for instance, an' cars, an' cook stoves. An' more an' more people have electricity nowadays. All that is good. Of course this Great Depression is just terrible, but we can all hope that one day it will end," Camie added.

"What was it like to leave England?" Gilly asked. He loved to hear them tell about the old days, in the United States or in England.

"Well, I was just a *bitta gara* then, not much older than your little brother Bart. In a way, it was just like movin' around, the way we always did, from place to place, but this time we were gonna go on a long boat ride, too. It would even be fun.

"We were so young, we thought it would all be a big adventure, an' then my father, your great grandfather, started sellin' our horses. I loved those *grais*, but they couldn't go on the boat with us all the way to America. I tried not to cry, but I have to tell you, I did cry," GR remarked, looking his grandson straight in the eye very seriously.

Each of his grandparents told a little of what it was like for their families to emigrate.

"An' I remember when my folks had to sell the wagons, too. An' they were the only *vordas* I had ever known. I even had little places where I hid things in them, secret places," Grandma Camie added.

"So we had to say goodbye to all that, an' goodbye to some of our family, too. They weren't all comin' over. But they promised us we would meet new family, family who were already over in America.

"I had to give away some of my dolls. I could only take two small ones. I sure cried," Camie added.

"An' we couldn't take our dogs either. Ole *Mullah* was my favorite. We called him that cause he looked white as a ghost. He used to sleep with me. Some of the family took them, an' we made them promise they would always take very good care of them," GR added.

"Oh, my gosh!" said Gilly. "That must have been really tough. There were so many changes."

"Well, those changes were just starting. The ride on the ship seemed to take forever, an' then New York was the biggest place you ever seen. There was nothing like it in England. The people talked different. An' the food was different. They drove on the right side of the road. The money was different. We were lost. An' we had no tents or *vordas* or *grais*. An' we had to change all our English *vonger* into American *vonger* so we could buy things an' eat," Camie added.

"We had letters from family in America, an' they said to get on a train in New York an' leave right away an' get out to where we could buy some horses an' tents an' wagons. It was rough going. We were on a train for two days, an' I never saw so many towns so fast in my life.

"It was in Tennessee someplace that we got off the train, an' do you know what? Within three days, we found some other English *Romanichals*, some Lovells an' Lees. They kinda saved our lives. We stayed with them for a couple months till we got set up an' could travel on our own again. We are still friends with them," GR said.

"Well, for us, it was a little different. We got on another boat right in New York an' went on down to Galveston. The letters had said that Texas was a good place to get horses an' wagons, an' there were a lot of *Romanichals* there in the winter. I liked Texas better than New York.

"That's where we got started. We stayed out at some friendly farmer's place till we could buy what we needed. He was an awful nice guy. His son still lives on that farm, an' the son is just as nice," Camie explained. "One evenin', we were sittin' on his back porch, an' my mama mentioned that she had 'the gift' an' she could tell fortunes. The farmer said he would like to try it. Then his wife wanted to try it. It went so well with them that next mornin' he gave daddy some canvas to paint a *dukkerin'* sign to hang out by their mailbox. It had a palm on it an' said, 'Madam Douana. Palmist. Personal Readings,' an' so on. Pretty soon, mama had a couple clients every day, an' that helped get us started," Grandma Camie explained.

"The first couple years were hard," Grandpa GR continued. "We couldn't find a circus we really wanted to join up with. We had to buy everything from scratch. It took a while to get some good racin' stock so we could go to racetracks an' fairs. We did a bit of everything, traded horses, sold stuff, whatever. The Wells family let us sell some of the baskets they wove. They were some of the best basket makers of all the *Romanichal* families. They gave them to us at a great price so we could make some *vonger* resellin'.

"My folks did some magic acts at schools an' so on, like they had done back in England. An' we trained some horses an' some ponies. Then we met up with a little circus owned by *Gaudja* folks, nice people. We worked on their show for practically nothin', just so we could see how the business worked over here. It was a pretty small show, but they did have three rings, an' they wanted us to fill in with different acts with horses and magic an' rope spinnin'. This was before there were any trucks, of course. Everything either went in a wagon or just walked over the road," GR said.

"You know your grandma and I met one fall in Texarkana, at the annual *Romanichal* families' get-together. She was only about fifteen, but when I laid eyes on her, I knew I wanted to know her better. Come to find out, our families must have come over on different boats the same year. An' our folks -- they were your great grandparents, Gilly --they knew each other from back in the Old Country. It wasn't for three more years at the Texarkana get-togethers that she would marry me, an' her folks would let her."

"Honey, that was such a happy time!" Grandma Camille broke in. "The wedding was so nice, an' everybody celebrated for two or three days. But the real good part was that I got to spend the rest of my life with your grandpa. I hope you can find a good *racklie* to *rummer* some day, Grandson. But take your time. Find the right girl before you go tyin' the knot," she smiled at him.

"Was it after you got married that you got a show like we have now?" Gilly asked.

"*Dawty, dawty,* Grandson. *Keker*. My, my no! It took years an' years. It was always a struggle. Your dad an' uncle helped so much as they were growin' up, an' then when they got married, your mama an' your aunt. I remember when we bought our very first little tent, big enough for just one ring. We were taking a chance, a big chance. We had only one tractor-truck, an' it had to go back an' forth every day to pull three semi-trailers over the road. We had to learn so much about trucks an' cars an' how to take care of them an' fix them. There wasn't that many mechanics around yet, an' a lot of them didn't know any more than we did.

"Oh, I remember what it was like learnin' to drive a truck. I learned to drive a truck before I did a car. If you can drive a truck, you can drive a car. Your great grandmother told me that if a girl can drive a team of horses, she can learn to drive a truck. It took me two days, going roun' an' roun' on that race track in Indianapolis, but I became a pretty good driver. Of course, they made us all learn to check the oil an' water an' even change a flat. Glad I learned how," Camie concluded.

Then GR chimed in, "We worked liked dogs to get that tent up and down. Even if you hire some *mushes* from the town to help, well those men don't know what to do till you tell 'em. You know how it is; you try to keep the good ones to go on with you to the next town. The bad ones, or weak ones or lazy ones, well, you know what I mean, Gilly. You have done it yourself. You just have to let 'em go, with no *chingerin'*, no fighting about it." GR explained. "You never want any beefs with the *gava fokie*, the town people. We worked till we dropped, but there was money to be made, an' over the years we built the show we have today."

"Honey, you know it has been twenty-five years since we started on our own, with our own show, changin' over completely to trucks from horse-pulled wagons, goin' from one ring to three rings, gettin' more horses and animals. Now we probably have too many horse acts. At first, the whole show was basically us, doin' our own acts. Little by little, we hired in some *Gaudjas* as performers, the best we could find. An' the midway in front of the bigtop grew, an' our season went from three or four months to six months. I get tired just thinkin' about it!" Camie exclaimed.

"You came along while we were doing all this, our first grandson. It was terrific. An' it seemed in no time at all you were walkin' around, learnin' everything, getting on a pony an' then on a horse. You were a natural! It just runs in our *Romanichal rat*, in our blood!"

"We had a fine season in 1929, a really good season.

Then that fall when the season was just over, the bottom fell out of everything. It was all on the radio. You sat around with us an' listened. People in the towns talked about it. People were jumping out of windows in New York when the big stock market crash happened.

"We would never put our money in stock markets or anything like that, so we were OK for the time bein'," GR explained.

"We had money to get through the winter, but, well, now we call it the Great Depression, an' we weren't sure if we should go out for the season of 1930. The *poura fokie* in the *gavs* barely had *hobin* to *haw*. Poor people in towns barely had food to eat. How could they come out an' pay money to see a circus? Nobody knew. We thought maybe we would just sit tight an' not go out with the show till it all blew over an' got better. Then they started saying that it wasn't gonna get better, not for a long time," he continued.

"Gilly, you were old enough to remember this time. You heard us talking at some of our meetings. It was very serious. The '30s weren't gonna be like the '20s. It was a brand new game. You remember a lot of this?" GR asked.

"*Ava*, Grandpa. Yes, I remember that it was scary, an' we used to listen on the radio, an' it was all bad news. The newsman kept sayin' how it was getting worse an' worse," Gilly said.

Then GR continued, "Finally, the people who worked for us were just beggin' us to go out so that they could make a livin'. They didn't have any work. An' really, we didn't have any other kind of work either. The show was our business.

"So finally we decided to do an experiment. We wouldn't spend any money sprucin' up for the new season, no new paint, no new trucks or canvas. We decided we would lower the prices because people just couldn't pay like they did before. An' we said it would all be an experiment that would last for a month. If we could cover expenses an' pay the folks an' clear a little money, we would stay on the road."

The story continued. Gilly liked it because he was old enough then to remember a lot of it. The one month experiment on the road became two months, and then two months became four. There were rough spots, like the string of towns where they had to lower the prices to half of what they usually charged, and that was from prices that were already lowered from the 1920s. But the tent stayed at least three quarters full, and they all decided it was better to have some people than no people. After all, they did buy some popcorn and cotton candy, so there was a little more money there, too.

When the show closed that season, everybody agreed that it was the worst season ever. 1929 had been very good, and 1930 was so bad they had to wonder all over again if there would be a next season. But there was, and it was a little better, better because the Brewers found even more ways to cut corners and because supplies were even cheaper to buy. The show was starting to look ragged, with things that needed painting and canvas that was ripped, but the town people did not expect much. Everything was clean, and what could be shined was shined, but peeling paint cannot be shined.

"An', Grandson," Camie continued, "like you know, things kept on like that, up and down, one thing an' another. An' that brings us up to just about today, more or less. You have seen it all yourself."

"Yes, Grandma, I did. But I was just learnin' to see it an' understand it like a grown person. I was a *chavie* then. Now I am older," Gilly said.

"So, Grandson, that brings us right to *duidivus*, to today, an' what we want to tell you is that things are never gonna stop changin', not in our lifetime an' not even in your lifetime. There are gonna be depressions an' wars an' other problems, an' good things, good changes, too. It will be up to you to work hard, be smart, an' grab ahold of the changes. Do your best to make them work for you, not work on you," GR said.

"You mean someday there might not be a Brewer Brothers Circus?" Gilly asked, with a grave look on his face.

"Nobody knows, Grandson. We hope it goes on for a long time. Maybe one day you will be havin' a talk like this with your own grandson. An' look at you. You are one of the wonderful changes in the family. You are the best Roman rider the family has ever had. You are the first one to go to school, an' you are just about to finish high school!" Camie exclaimed.

In this short conversation, it seemed Gilly had the rug pulled out from under him. It happens to every young person, sooner or later, and sometimes it is more gradual. For Gilly, the realization seemed sudden and definite. It was a painful fact about life that he had been ignoring.

In that moment he realized that the life, the family, the comfortable resting place that was so familiar to him so far, it was all going to fade and never be what he had grown up with. It might be chipped away, taken away, or blown away, and what the new wind might bring nobody could tell.

"*Nais tuk*," he mumbled to his grandparents. "Thanks a lot." And he wandered off toward the fence and put his arms up on it and looked out across the field. He stood there motionless for a long time. He felt lighter, because he knew he could do whatever he wanted to do. Yet he felt heavier, because the weight of responsibility, the weight of handling change, was coming down on his shoulders.

If there was one point in the conversation that seemed more important than any others it was the one about being ready for change and being smart and working to grab hold of what was coming up.

27. HAVE I BEEN ACCEPTED?

Gilly was practically haunting the mailbox for the last two weeks of April, 1934. It was the last two weeks before the show would open for the new season and the last two weeks he would be in high school. He had all his credits to get a diploma, and as usual, the plan was for him as well as his siblings and cousins to leave school a month early and be with the show when it opened May 1st. They had always got good grades, well above average, even though they were actually in school only seven or eight months a year, sometimes less. Pious arrangements were always worked out with teachers, assignments given, a few textbooks loaned, and so on. The assignments were hardly ever done, but no complaints were made. The kids had good grades and were consistently on the honor roll.

Gilly's case this year was different. He was getting a diploma, but with the help and guidance of Mr. Willis, the principal, he had filled out many forms and finally completed his application to Central State College and got it mailed in on time. Mr. Willis said that the college sent out notices in late April to students who were accepted and notices in early May to students who were rejected.

It was hard to be casual about the mail delivery each day. If he were rejected, he probably wouldn't even get the official letter until the show was out on the road. It might be weeks later when the bundle of mail got forwarded to General Delivery at the post office in some town they were showing. If he were accepted, the letter had better come this week. None of his family could understand what he was going through. None of them had ever had an experience like it. If he were accepted, would he go join the *Gaudja* world and be gone forever from what he knew and who he was? Sure, he had gone to school with *Gaudjas* and understood them well, but he had not become one of them, not yet.

On Thursday a letter came addressed to him with the return address of the college. There was only one sheet of paper in the envelope, and that was all it would take to say no. He sat there on the front porch with the letter, his hands shaking a little, his mouth dry, almost not wanting to know if he was in or out. Then he ran his index finger under the closure on the back of the envelope and tore it open. He pulled out the letter and unfolded it. He kept reading the introduction over and over, trying to be sure what it meant. Why did they have to take so long to get the point, the only thing that mattered? Was he in or out? Had he been accepted? This was not a time for formalities and verbosity.

Finally, he got to the third and fourth lines. There the words were clearly typed, "...please accept our sincere congratulations on being invited to join our long and proud tradition of scholarship and academic endeavor by becoming a member of this year's freshman class at Central State College." Did this really mean what it said? Was it contradicted somewhere else in the letter?

He read and reread. He parsed the sentences, looked for caveats and asterisks, tried to think of how a trick could be involved. It took ten minutes for him to be sure, for him to smile, to stand up, and to look for his parents.

"Mama, Dad, the letter came. They said 'yes;' I have been accepted! I can go. I am supposed to let them know if I am coming by May 1st," Gilly said.

His parents both spoke at once. They hugged him. They couldn't help but shower him with questions. They called over Grandpa GR and Grandma Camie and Aunt Tillie and Uncle Lucky. Woody couldn't help himself, "If any damn *Gaudja* thinks we aren't as good as them, well, here is the proof. Our son is definitely as good as any of 'em!" His chest was puffed out, and he was hugging Amy. Everybody was hugging everybody, even if it was far from clear what it all meant.

Gilly was happy to see them all so happy, and he felt a responsibility, even a burden, to prove that he could do it. Mr. Willis had said that there were cheap places to stay near the college. He could room with two or three other boys. There was a school cafeteria with three meals a day, and it was cheap. They would reduce the school costs if he took a part-time job at the library or the farm where the agricultural students and vets were trained. He said he would like to work at both places. He wanted to buy a few new clothes, and he would have to buy books. The college made students buy their own books. There was the money he had saved and the money from the horse race. He would save more that summer. He would have almost enough. And, yes, his parents could drive over and see the place with him.

"How do you know if you are going to like it, honey, if you don't at least try?" his mother asked. She was not pushing. She was just encouraging. His relatives were smiling at him, basically agreeing with his mother. It meant that the whole decision was up to him. They wanted him to try, but they would not say he had to.

"Oh, there is a bad thing, too. I really have to be there at the college right after Labor Day, Mr. Willis says. I couldn't work on the show in September an' October like I have always done. I would just have to get on a train or a bus an' leave. Is that OK?" he asked.

Of course the question was more than just about getting on a train or a bus in September.

His mother spoke first, "Gilly, we would be happy to take you to the train station in a carriage pulled by six white horses!"

With that remark, he looked around at his family, as if one more look would help him make the decision.

Somehow it did. They were beaming. He knew he would give Central State College a try.

He would embark on a long and change-filled life with episodes in the larger *Gaudja* world but with always a firm grounding in his own world. He would experience some of the saddest and most evil times in human history as wars spread across continents, but he would see marvelous advances that he could have never dreamed of in the spring of 1934. His life to date had equipped him very well to tackle it all, about as well equipped as a man his age could be. That rich, long, and fortunate life would take him all the way into the first years of the Twenty-First Century.

RUMNIS LANGUAGE GLOSSARY

This is a list of *Rumnis* words used in this work. *Rumnis* is the language spoken by some people of English Gypsy descent. Comprehensive dictionaries by linguists can be found online.

Rumnis is simple in many ways. It uses the same word order as English. For example, in Spanish the word order would be *casa blanca,* "house white," instead of "white house." But there are no such changes in word order in *Rumnis.*

Word endings are the same as in English, such as *s, ed, er,* and *ing.* So *cova,* thing, becomes *covas,* things. And *gin,* know, becomes *ginned,* knew.

The language does not use any sounds that are not in English.

It is spelled just as it sounds. There are no spelling rules since it is basically an unwritten language. Two speakers may write it slightly differently. Linguists have developed transcription systems for the language, but *Rumnis* speakers, in the rare instances in which they try to write the language, don't know of these systems.

On the other hand, the language is difficult because the vocabulary is not similar to any language most readers will know. That is because its distant roots are in ancient Sanskrit in India. Also, many words sound identical to English words, but the meaning is completely different. For example, *trash* means "frighten," and *drab* means "medicine."

Different families of *Romanichals* may use different pronunciations.

Rumnis as it is spoken by most English Gypsies nowadays is a much-simplified version of the language spoken generations ago, and much simpler than the varieties of the language spoken by Gypsies in other European countries.
As more and more English is mixed with *Rumnis,* it will probably fade and become a dead language in the coming generations.

Achitin' tan – stopping place

Adray – in

Ava – yes

Ava – come

Bawl – hair

Besh – sit

Bita – small, a small amount, baby

Bok – luck

Bootie – work

Bora – large, many, pregnant

Boutiker – store, shop

Brishnin – rain

Bukla – hungry

Bull – rear end, behind

Chavie – child

Chinger – argue, fight

Chawkas – shoes, boots

Chichi – none, nothing

Chore – steal

Coussie – drink, usually alcoholic beverages

Coussiefied – drunken

Chum – kiss

Corey – penis, common swear term

Cova – thing

Dadus – father

Danders -- teeth

Del – give

Diddikae – half Gypsy

Dias -- mother

Divia – crazy

Divus – day

Doi – there

Dorty – well, as an exclamation

Dosta – a lot, many

Dova – that, that one

Drab – drug, medicine

Drabermingra – pharmacist, doctor

Drum – road, street

Dui – two, too

Dui-pange – ten, literally "two fives"

Dukker – tell fortunes

Dukkermingra – fortuneteller

Gad – shirt

Gara – boy

Gav – town

Gaver – town person

Gaudja – non-Gypsy

Gin – know

Grai – horse

Hag – bother, pester

Hammiers – pants, trousers

Haw – eat

Heezes -- clothing

Hinger – feces, crap

Hingerker – toilet, bathroom

Hookabin – lie

Hobin – food

Hona – angry, mad

Hulivers – socks, stockings

Jawl – go

Jouval – woman

Jukel – dog

Kai – here

Kawla – black or black person

Kannie – bird or chicken

Kekker – no, not

Kekushtie – not good, opposite of Kushtie

Ker, Kera – house

Kill – butter

Kliven – close, lock up

Kushtie – good

Lay – down, as a direction

Lel – get, take

Lil – dollar, book, paper, document

Livnia – prostitute, common swear word

Lure – steal

Matchkra – cat

Maw – don't

Minge – vagina, common swear word

Moctar – box or container

Mourra – die, kill

Moutter – urinate

Moutterker -- bathroom

Mui – face, mouth

Mukeltie – dirty, filthy

Mullah – dead person, ghost

Mush – man

Mushker – cop, policeman

Nais tuk – thanks

Nock – nose

Nafla – sick

Ocher – burn

Pal or pral, brother

Pani – water

Pawnie – white, pale

Pay – drink

Pen – say

Pen or Phen – sister

Pooker – speak to

Posh – half

Povingra -- potato

Poura – poor, old

Racklie – girl

Radie – night

Rat – blood

Rawnie – lady

Rinknie – pretty, nice

Rokker – speak, speak a language

Romanichal – Gypsy

Rook – tree

Rummer -- marry

Rumnis – language of English Gypsies

Rye – gentleman

Shoon – listen, understand

Sootie – sleep

Sootiefied – sleepy

Stadie – hat

Sterobin – jail, prison

Tachie – truth

Tan – place, tent

Tatapanie – whiskey, literally "hot water"

Tav – smoke tobacco

Tikna – baby

Toug – trouble

Trash – frighten

Trin – three

Tud – milk

Valin – candle or light

Vasita – bad, dirty

Vater – look, be careful

Veshna – foreigner, or a Latino or Native American

Vonger – money

Vorda – wagon, car, truck

Woodrus – bed

Yarg – fire

Yock – eye

Yora - egg

Made in the USA
Las Vegas, NV
26 December 2020

14688144R30316